INTERME[DIATE]

Science

Michael Brimicombe, Roger Ellis,
Ken Gadd & Michael Reiss
Editor: Ken Gadd

Thomas Nelson and Sons Ltd
Nelson House Mayfield Road
Walton-on-Thames Surrey
KT12 5PL UK

Thomas Nelson Australia
102 Dodds Street
South Melbourne
Victoria 3205 Australia

Nelson Canada
1120 Birchmount Road
Scarborough Ontario
MIK 5G4 Canada

First published by Thomas Nelson and Sons Ltd 1995

I(T)P Thomas Nelson is an International Thomson Publishing Company

I(T)P is used under licence

ISBN 0-17-490002-3
NPN 9 8 7 6 5 4 3 2 1

Printed in Spain by Mateu Cromo, S.A. Pinto (Madrid)

The Intermediate GNVQ Science Team

The Editors and Authors

Ken Gadd is Assistant Principal at Yeovil College. He was also Chair of the GNVQ Science National Working Group and is a member of the NCVQ Science Advisory Committee. During a teaching career spanning over twenty years he has been extensively involved in resource development, having been co-ordinator of the Wessex A-level Modular Sciences scheme and President of the Education Division of the Royal Society of Chemistry.

Michael Brimicombe is Senior Teacher at Cedars Upper School, Leighton Buzzard. He is a Chief Examiner for Physics and Electronics at A-level and GCSE, and has written a number of key texts, including *Physics in Focus*, *Introducing Electronic Systems* and *Electronic Systems*.

Roger Ellis has been a member of the Science Team at Yeovil College for over twenty years, during which time he has taught a wide variety of courses. He has contributed to the Wessex A-level Biology syllabus and wrote support material for the modules.

Michael Reiss is Senior Lecturer in Biology at Homerton College, Cambridge. He taught in schools and colleges before moving into Higher Education, and has written or contributed to a number of leading texts, including *Biology: Principles and Processes* and *Advanced Practical Biology*. He is a Vice-President of the Institute of Biology and a Chief Examiner and Moderator.

The Advisers

John Avison
David Billings
Neville Reed
Mary Jones
David Varnish
Doug Wilford

Safety Adviser

Peter Borrows

Acknowledgements

Photographs

The publishers and authors are grateful to the following for permission to reproduce photographs:

0.1a Science Photo Library/Will and Demi Macintyre
0.1b Science Photo Library/James King-Holmes
0.1c Science Photo Library/Adam Hart-Davis
0.1d Trip/T. Fisher
0.2 Science Photo Library/US Department of Energy
0.4 Stuart Boreham
0.6 Trip/Helene Rogers
0.17 Science Photo Library/James King-Holmes
0.18 Alan Thomas
0.20 Alan Thomas
0.22 Alan Thomas
0.26 Alan Thomas
0.28 Alan Thomas
0.29a Alan Thomas
0.29b Alan Thomas
0.32 Environmental Picture Library
0.33a Alan Thomas
0.33b Alan Thomas
1.0.1 Greg Evans
1.0.2a Alan Thomas
1.0.2b Britstock/IFA
1.1.1a Science Photo Library/US Department of Energy
1.1.1b Science Photo Library/St Bartholomew's Hospital
1.1.1c Science Photo Library/D. Parker
1.1.1d Holt/Nigel Cattlin
1.1.2a Geoscience/Dr B. Booth
1.1.2b Oxford Scientific Films/Tim Shepherd
1.1.3 Life File/J. Griffin
1.1.4a Geoscience Features
1.1.4b Biophoto Associates
1.1.5 Science Photo Library
1.1.6 CP Pharmaceuticals
1.1.7 National Forensic Science Service
1.1.8 Britstock/IFA/Weststock
1.1.9a Science Photo Library
1.1.9b Science Photo Library
1.1.10 Science Photo Library
1.1.11 Science Photo Library
1.1.12 Science Photo Library
1.1.13 Stuart Boreham
1.1.14 Trip/G Hopkinson
1.1.15 Trip/Richard Drury
1.1.16 Trip/G Hopkinson
1.1.17 Britstock/IFA
1.2.1a Environmental Picture Library
1.2.1b Science Photo Library/Bob Edwards
1.2.2 Science Photo Library
2.0.1 Oxford Scientific Films/Geoff Kidd
2.0.2 Science Photo Library
2.1.1 Science Photo Library/Hank Morgan
2.1.2 Holt
2.1.3 Trip
2.1.4 Science Photo Library/Geoff Tomkinson
2.1.6 Oxford Scientific Films/G. MacLean
2.1.7 Gene Cox
2.1.8 Britstock/IFA
2.1.9 National Rivers Authority
2.1.11 Oxford Scientific Films/Okapia
2.1.13 Stuart Boreham
2.1.14 Oxford Scientific Films
2.1.16 Oxford Scientific Films/London Scientific Films
2.1.18 Oxford Scientific Films/Martin Chillmaid
2.1.19 Science Photo Library/John Durham
2.1.21 Science Photo Library/Martin Dorrn
2.1.23 Oxford Scientific Films/Terry Heathcote
2.1.24 Oxford Scientific Films/Mike Birkhead
2.1.25 Stuart Boreham
2.1.27 Science Photo Library/Dr J. Burgess
2.1.29 Oxford Scientific Films/G. MacLean
2.1. Case Study 1 Countryside Restoration Trust
2.2.1 Stuart Boreham
2.2.2 Britstock/IFA/C.L.Schmitt
2.2.3 Stuart Boreham
2.2.4 Stuart Boreham
2.2.5a–cStuart Boreham
2.2.5d Leslie Garland
2.2.6 Science Photo Library/David Guyon/BOC Group
2.2.7 Science Photo Library
2.2.17 Alan Thomas
2.2.19 Britstock/IFA/Eric Bach
2.2.21 Alan Thomas
2.2.24 Lotus plc
2.2 Case Study 1 Oxford Scientific Films/Ronald Toms
2.2 Case Study 2 Stuart Boreham
2.2 Case Study 3 Life File/John Woodhouse
2.2 Case Study 4 Stuart Boreham
2.3.1 Science Photo Library
2.3.2 Andy Ross
2.3.3 Andy Ross
2.3.4 Alan Thomas
2.3.5 Stuart Boreham
2.3.6 Stuart Boreham
2.3.7 Alan Thomas
2.3.9 Alan Thomas
2.3.10 Alan Thomas
2.3.11 Alan Thomas
2.3.12a Alan Thomas
2.3.12b Alan Thomas
2.3.13 Science Photo Library
2.3.14 Alan Thomas
2.3.15 Alan Thomas
2.3 Case Study 1 Science Photo Library
3.0.1 Stuart Boreham
3.0.2 Science Photo Library
3.1.1 Oxford Scientific Films/M. Wendler
3.1.2 Geoscience Features/W. Hughes
3.1.3 Life File/Lionel Moss
3.1.6 Oxford Scientific Films
3.1.7 Life File/Angela Maynard
3.1.8 Science Photo Library/Andrew Syred
3.1.10 Oxford Scientific Films/Richard Davies
3.1.12 Oxford Scientific Films/Geoff Kidd
3.1.13 J. Allan Cash
3.1.17 Oxford Scientific Films/John Paling
3.1.18 Rex Features/Tim Rooke
3.1.19 Science Photo Library/Dick Luria
3.1.20 Life File/John Cox
3.1 Case Study 1 Science Photo Library
3.1 Case Study 4 Holt
3.2.1 Stuart Boreham
3.2.2 Science Photo Library/NASA
3.2.3 Science Photo Library
3.2.4 Alan Thomas
3.2.5 Alan Thomas
3.2.7 Alan Thomas
3.2.8a Alan Thomas
3.2.8b Alan Thomas
3.2.10 Alan Thomas
3.2.11 Alan Thomas
3.2.12 Alan Thomas
3.2.13 Alan Thomas
3.2.15 Alan Thomas
3.2.17 Alan Thomas
3.2.21 Jerry Mason
3.2.26a Alan Thomas
3.2.26b Alan Thomas
3.2.27 Shades Photography
3.2 Case Study 1 Stuart Boreham
3.3.1 Science Photo Library
3.3.2 Rex Features
3.3.4 Alan Thomas
3.3.5 Alan Thomas
3.3.6 Science Photo Library
3.3.7 Life File/Cliff Threadgold
3.3.8 Alan Thomas
3.3.9 Alan Thomas
3.3.19 Stuart Boreham
3.3.24 Alan Thomas
3.3.27 Stuart Boreham
3.3.29 Alan Thomas
3.3.30 Alan Thomas
3.3 Case Study 1 Trip
4.0.1 Sporting Pictures
4.0.2 Britstock/IFA
4.1.2 Allsport/Simon Brut
4.1.4 Barnaby's Picture Library
4.1.5 Andy Ross
4.1.6 Allsport/Chris Cole
4.1.8 Life File/Mike Maidment
4.1.9 Robert Harding
4.1.14 Sally and Richard Greenhill
4.1.15 Sally and Richard Greenhill
4.1.16 Andy Ross
4.1.18 Allsport
4.1.20 Science Photo Library/Will McIntyre
4.1.21 Allsport
4.2.2 Trip/Helene Rogers
4.2.3 Mirror Syndicate International
4.2.5 Stuart Boreham
4.2.6 Oxford Scientific Films/O. Newman
4.2.7 Science Photo Library
4.2.8 Alan Thomas
4.2.9 British Petroleum
4.2.12 Alan Thomas
4.2.13 Stuart Boreham
4.2.14 Ford Motors
4.2.15 Alan Thomas
4.2.23 Science Photo Library
4.2.26 Science Photo Library
4.2 Case Study 2 Science Photo Library
4.3.1 Alan Thomas
4.3.5 Britstock/IFA
4.3.16 Stuart Boreham
4.3.19 Stuart Boreham
4.3.27a Stuart Boreham
4.3.27b Stuart Boreham
4.3.27c Stuart Boreham
4.3 Case Study 1 Alan Thomas

The publishers and authors are grateful for permission to base the following illustrations in this book on previously published sources:

Figures 2.1. 15 (page 67) 3.1.4 (page 124), Figure 3.1.11 (page 126), Figure 3.1.15 (page 129) and Figure 3.1.16, (page 129) are based on Figures 8.3, 13.4, 15.3, 11.2 and 10.4 respectively of Adams, C. R., Bamford, K. M. and Early, M. P. (1993). *Principles of Horticulture, 2nd edn*, Butterworth Heinemann.
Figure 2.1.28 is based on Figure 13.12 of Chapman, J. L. and Reiss, M. J. (1992). *Ecology: Principles and Applications*, Cambridge University Press.
Figure 3.1.5 (page 124) is based on Figures 8 and 16 of Boatfield, G. (1983). *Farm Crops*, Farming Press Books.
Figure 4.1.1, (page 186) is based on Figure 18.3 of Lachman, S. and Jenner, J. R. (1994). *Soft Tissue Injuries in Sport*, 2nd edn, Blackwell Scientific Publications.
Figure 4.1.10, (page 192) is based on Figure 1 page 109 of Wright, D. (1989). *Human Biology*, Heinemann.
Figures 4.1.12 and 4.1.13, page 193, are based on Figures 8.33 and 8.34 of National Coaching Foundation (1986) *NCF Coaching Handbook no. 3: Physiology and Performance*
Figure 4.1.19, page197 is based on Fig 11(d) page 212 of Mackean, D. (1988) *Human Life*, John Murray.

The authors and publishers are grateful to the following for permission to reproduce printed material:
The Guardian, for the article 'Heart Disease Toll Worst But Falling' on page 29;
Mr Robin Page of The Countryside Restoration Trust, for the article 'An Astonishing Year' from issue 2 of the Countryside Restoration Trust newsletter *Acorn*, on page 74–75;
Dr D. G. Smith, Department of Biology, University College London, for an article from *Molecular Cell Biology at University College London* on page 32;
NovoNordisk AS, for an article from issue 4 of the magazine *Biotimes*, on page 36;
Bayer Group, for an article taken from the Bayer Group magazine *Research*, on page 33;
The National Back Pain Association, for material from the leaflet *Self-care for Back Pain Sufferers*, on page 198.

Contents

How to use this book

To do any work successfully you need the right tools. This book provides the ones you need for GNVQ Intermediate Science. To get your GNVQ you will need to:

- show through your **coursework** that you have met the requirements of the qualification
- pass **tests** for the mandatory units.

In this book you will find information about the knowledge, skills and understanding needed to tackle both coursework and tests. You may need more specialised books or information from other sources if you are undertaking a more complex piece of work.

The structure of the book

Unit 0 covers methods and ideas which you will use often. These are general and do not relate to particular GNVQ Intermediate units.

Units 1–4 in this book link directly with the mandatory science units 1–4. Each begins with an introduction which:

- describes the area of scientific work upon which the unit is based
- gives the titles of elements in the unit
- outlines what you need to do to achieve each element.

Essential facts and ideas are found in **Focus** boxes in the margin. This introduction is followed by methods and ideas relevant to the unit.

These summaries in the margin enable you to move through a section quickly. You can turn to the main text if you want more information. The text also contains **figures** and **tables** which, together with the boxed summaries, may be useful for revision as well as for coursework.

Towards the end of each unit are **assignments** and **case studies**. These give you the opportunity to collect evidence for your portfolio. For the assignments, the parts of the Intermediate GNVQ specifications covered are indicated.

At the end of each element there are **questions**. Together, the questions at the end of each element can be used as a **pre-test check**. Try to answer these a week or two before the unit test. Check your answers against those provided. The correct answers will provide a revision aid for the test.

FOCUS

Electricity can be used to move people and objects. It allows people to communicate over long distances. Electrical devices can monitor situations and warn us when things go wrong. They can make measurements for us. They can automatically control processes for us.

A typical ***Focus*** *box.*

Finding information in the book

There are three ways in this book in which you might find the information you need:

- using the contents list at the front
- reading the index at the back
- 'pressing' the appropriate button from another section.

Buttons in the outer margin direct you to relevant sections. They are a cross-referencing system which allows you to find the information you need quickly. When you do look something up, don't forget to mark your place in the book so that you can get back to it!

Buttons look like this:

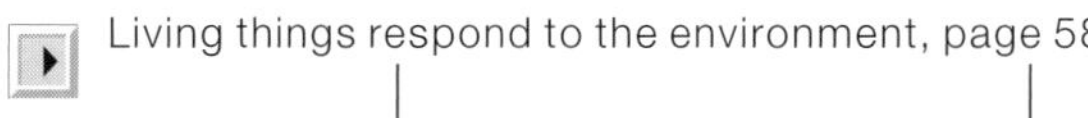

heading to look for in the text **page to turn to for further information**

Throughout the book, words in **bold** type direct you to Focus boxes in the margin. Focus boxes provide summaries of the information you will need in order to pass unit tests. Other words, which need emphasis, are in *italic*.

Safety

Note to students

Safety legislation makes all employers and educational establishments legally responsible for providing you, other workers and visitors with a safe working environment. You must also be given training and information on safe working practice. There must be a written health and safety policy and the means to carry it out.

You are legally obliged to take reasonable care and to protect your own and other's safety. This includes knowing how to use and using the appropriate safety equipment and knowing and applying safety rules in each work area you use. You must:

- know what to do in an emergency such as a fire
- carry out risk assessments for practical activities, especially those that you design yourself
- know the risks and safety measures that must be taken before you start
- make sure your supervisor checks your risk assessment before you start.

Note to supervisors

When practical *instructions* have been given, we have attempted to indicate hazardous substances and operations by using standard symbols and appropriate precautions. Nevertheless, you should be aware of your obligations under the Health and Safety at Work Act, the Control of Substances Hazardous to Health (COSHH) Regulations and the Management of Health and Safety at Work Regulations. In this respect you should follow the requirements of your employers at all times.

In developing assignments, students should be encouraged to carry out their own risk assessments, i.e. they should identify hazards and suitable ways of reducing the risks from them. However, they must be checked by the supervisors.

The supervisors should be familiar and up-to-date with current advice from professional bodies.

Introduction

Intermediate GNVQ Science

What do scientists 'do'?

Intermediate GNVQ Science is about what scientists do. Their work falls into three broad categories. Scientists:

- *characterise* things (e.g. investigate the world around us, both living and non-living, and analyse substances)
- *obtain or make things* (e.g. grow plants, make chemicals and make electronic devices)
- *monitor and control change* (e.g. the human body during different types of activity, chemical reactions, and mechanical or optical devices).

Essential to all of this work is the ability to carry out scientific tasks, either using standard methods or by adapting these methods to suit a particular situation.

The structure of the qualification

Science units

Intermediate GNVQ Science is divided into units, each based on a particular area of 'what scientists do'. Information needed for the four **mandatory** units is provided in this book. However, many of the methods and ideas will also be useful when you tackle your two **optional** units.

Each unit consists of three elements. The titles of the elements tell you what you must do to achieve the unit. In turn, each element consists of:

- **performance criteria:** a checklist of things you need to do to show that you can meet the requirements of the element
- **range:** the particular situations in which the performance criteria are to be met.

> FOCUS
>
> **Intermediate GNVQ Science consists of:**
> - **4 mandatory units**
> - **2 optional units**
> - **3 core skill units.**

Core skills

There are three core skill units that you must gain:

- application of number
- communication
- information technology.

They should be achieved within the science activities that you undertake. The requirements of these units are laid out in the same way as the science units, with elements, performance criteria and range. There are five levels of core skills. For Intermediate GNVQ, you must achieve at least level 2.

> FOCUS
>
> **You will find that words in the performance criteria are explained in the range. For example,**
>
> **Performance criterion: '*device* is assembled, observing safe practice'.**
>
> **Range: '*Device:* electrical, electronic'.**

FOCUS

Core skill units:
- **application of number**
- **Communication**
- **Information technology.**

However, you should strive to get higher levels. This extra achievement will be recognised on your certificate. It is worth working for.

Application of number involves gathering and working on data, solving problems (for example, using graphs and equations), interpreting and presenting data (for example, using symbols and diagrams). The nature of science means that you will have many opportunities to show your ability in this core skill.

Communication involves writing about science (using suitable illustrations such as diagrams and tables) and talking about science (using suitable visual aids such as posters or overhead projector transparencies). Of course, some people know more about science than others and so you need to be able to communicate with people with different experiences and areas of knowledge.

Information technology involves word processing and using databases and spreadsheets. It is an invaluable aid to storing and communicating scientific data and ideas. You will have many opportunities to show that you can retrieve information from databases, word-process scientific reports and use spreadsheets to handle data.

Assessment

There are two parts to the assessment:

- your *portfolio of evidence*. This is a collection of your coursework. It should contain evidence that you have carried out work to:
  - meet the requirements of elements through the related performance criteria and range (and so achieve the units)
  - meet the requirements of the core skill units
  - show that you are worthy of a merit or distinction grade
- *unit tests*. These are designed to allow you to show that you have covered all aspects of the mandatory units. If you do not pass a test you may take it again. Optional units do not have tests.

FOCUS

You should have access to the full specifications for science and core skill units, as well as the grading criteria for merit and distinction.

The activities designed by your school or college will have opportunities to meet these requirements built into them. However, an important aim of a GNVQ programme is that you begin to identify opportunities to gather evidence yourself. This may be, for example:

- extension work you have suggested to a given activity
- experience gained on a work placement
- extra core skills you have used in an activity because of the way you chose to do it
- an activity that you designed and carried out.

It is important that you understand the GNVQ specifications and are able to recognise that you collected relevant evidence. This can be presented to your teacher or lecturer and you can 'claim' the appropriate part of the GNVQ. You are taking control of your own programme.

Meeting performance criteria

Put simply, your portfolio must show that you have met all the performance criteria for each element. You must show that the *breadth of the range* has been covered. This means showing that you understand the key features of each *range category* within a *range dimension*. Finally, for each element you must show that you have looked in *depth* at those aspects of range which are the focus of the particular assignments you are tackling.

This probably sounds very complicated! An example will help you understand the process. Consider the following performance criterion and related range:

You need to show that you understand how these purposes (aid recovery

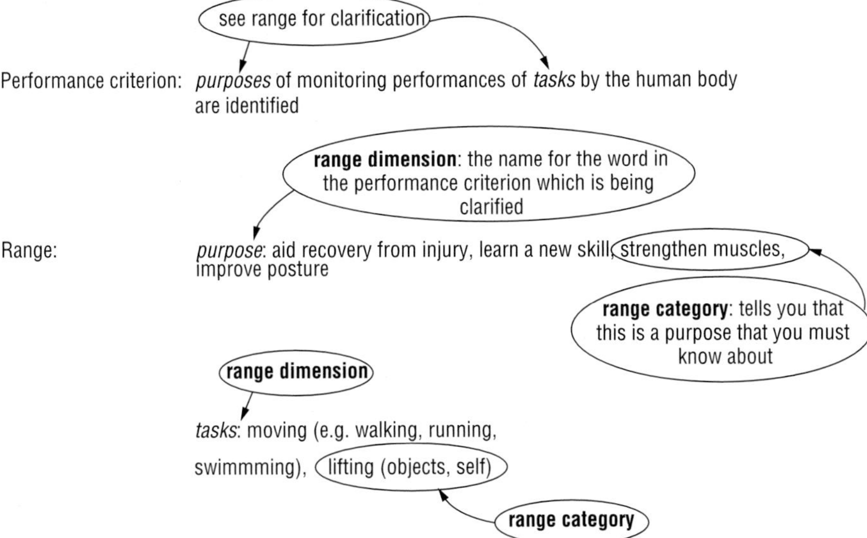

from injury, learn a new skill, strengthen muscles, improve posture) relate to monitoring the performance of tasks (moving, e.g. walking, running, swimming, lifting e.g. objects, self). However, you would not be expected to monitor the performance of all these tasks. For example, one assignment might focus on monitoring a person's increasing muscle strength by monitoring their ability to lift heavy objects.

Evidence indicators

Each element has *evidence indicators*, showing the minimum amount of work you need to do. However, they are not prescriptive. Other types of evidence may be presented provided they are comparable in *coverage* (performance criteria and range) and *sufficiency* (number of activities). For example, consider these evidence indicators:

Alternative types of evidence might be a poster or a talk accompanied

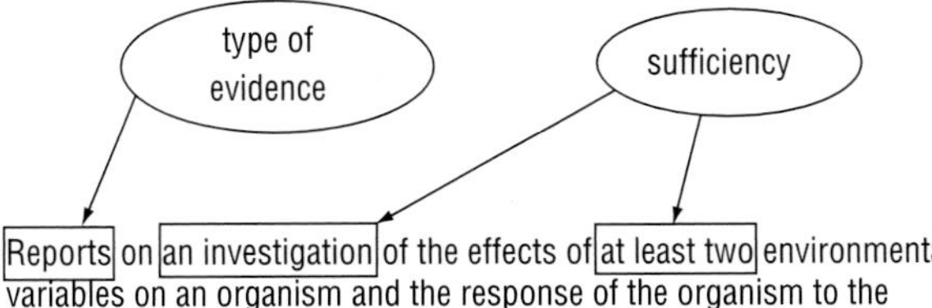

by visual aids. It is always helpful to look at the core skill specifications because the form of the evidence can often be tailored to meet core skill requirements as well.

Whatever the form, at least two environmental variables must have been investigated. Between them, the investigations must show that performance criteria and range have been covered to the same extent as the evidence indicators given in the specifications.

FOCUS

Grading themes:
- **planning**
- **information-seeking and information-handling**
- **evaluation**
- **quality of outcomes.**

Grading

Individual units are not graded. Instead you will be awarded a grade for the whole qualification. At least one third of your evidence must meet the grading criteria for merit or the criteria for distinction. You will need to show that you can tackle activities using the knowledge, skills and understanding associated with Intermediate GNVQ Science. The grading criteria also reflect the increasing responsibility that you are expected to take for the work you do. These are just the skills that employers are looking for.

There are four grading themes:

Planning

1 drawing up plans of action
2 monitoring courses of action

Information-seeking and information-handling

3 identifying information needs
4 identifying and using sources to obtain information

Evaluation

5 evaluating outcomes and justifying approaches

Quality of outcomes

6 synthesis of knowledge, skills and understanding
7 command of scientific language.

Grading criteria reward independent work – your ability to make many of the decisions about what to do and how to do it.

Building up your GNVQ portfolio

Knowledge, skills and understanding

Your GNVQ programme will consist of various activities, such as lectures, discussions, experimental work, problem-solving exercises, debates, presentations, discussions, information searches (library and electronic) and so on. You will be given increasing responsibility for your work.

The activities you undertake will have been designed to allow you to meet the requirements of elements and so achieve units. Your record of these activities will form the main part of your portfolio. You may be able to add relevant evidence from other sources such as work placements. To do this you will need a 'toolkit' of methods and the skills to use them, together with the underpinning knowledge and understanding, to apply to the problem at hand. You will be able to use a method most effectively if you understand how it works.

Activities: tasks and assignments

In this section you will see how activities are designed so that you have opportunities to meet:

- requirements of the science units
- requirements of the core skill units
- grading criteria.

Understanding this will help you to devise extensions to activities or even initiate your own investigations and projects. It is likely that you will build up to this by tackling activities of increasing complexity and taking increasing responsibility for your own work. Let's see what this might mean.

It is helpful to think of activities as either **tasks** or **assignments**. For the purposes of your GNVQ Intermediate Science and of this book, these are described as follows:

A **task** is a structured activity which allows you to collect evidence for science and core skill units. It is often a short piece of work which allows some or all of the performance criteria for one or more elements to be met. You are usually given precise instructions and there is little or no opportunity to meet the first five grading criteria relating to planning, information-seeking and information-handling, and evaluation. However, you can show 'quality of outcome'.

You may be given the opportunity to carry out extension work of your own design. In this way, the task may develop into an assignment.

An **assignment** is a more open-ended activity which allows you to collect evidence for science and core skill units. It also allows some or all of the grading criteria to be met. Assignments are not equally demanding. They may vary from *straightforward*, consisting of a number of discrete tasks, to *complex*, where the tasks involved are interrelated. Complexity will also increase depending on the extent of planning and information use carried out. You will need to demonstrate a thorough grasp of the underlying knowledge, skills and understanding to meet the fourth grading theme.

This may be a little confusing, and some people may use the terms activity, task and assignment in different ways. Perhaps the important message is that some things you do will give you the chance to meet performance criteria and range requirements. However, you will not be able to show the skills associated with grading. On the other hand, some things will give you the opportunity to do both. For convenience, we are calling these tasks and assignments respectively.

One example of a task (*The quantitative analysis of vinegar*) and one example of an assignment (*An investigation of limescale removers*) will illustrate the idea.

FOCUS

Tasks have precise instructions which you follow. No planning or finding and using information is needed.
Assignments require you to take more control. They can be broken down into tasks but you will need to:

- **plan the approach and monitor how things are going**
- **find and use information relevant to the problem**
- **evaluate how things went and justify your approach**
- **bring together the relevant knowledge, skills and understanding.**

Task

THE QUANTITATIVE ANALYSIS OF VINEGAR

Setting the scene

Fish and chips without vinegar just wouldn't be the same. The sharp or sour taste of many foods is due to the presence of organic acids such as ethanoic acid (in vinegar), citric acid (in citrus fruits) and lactic acid (in sour milk).

The concentration of the ethanoic acid in vinegar is usually about 4% w/v, in other words about 4 g in 100 cm^3 of solution. You can buy various types of vinegar in the supermarket or food store. It is straightforward to find the ethanoic acid content in different brand-named vinegars.

The task

Your task is to determine the concentration of ethanoic acid in vinegar.

Eye protection must be worn.

IRRITANT
sodium hydroxide

TOXIC

HIGHLY FLAMMABLE
phenolphthalein indicator solution

Requirements

0.100 mol dm^{-3} sodium hydroxide solution phenolphthalein indicator solution
50 cm^3 burette, stand and white tile
20 cm^3 pipette
10 cm^3 pipette
safety filler
100 cm^3 volumetric flask
250 cm3 conical flask
sample of vinegar to be analysed

Method

1 Use a pipette and safety filler to transfer 10.0 cm^3 vinegar into a 100 cm^3 volumetric flask. Make the solution up to 100 cm^3 with distilled water.
2 Place the 0.100 mol dm^{-3} sodium hydroxide in the burette.
3 Pipette 20 cm^3 of the diluted vinegar solution into a conical flask and add 2–3 drops of phenolphthalein.
4 Titrate against the sodium hydroxide solution to a permanent pink colour.
5 Repeat the titration several times.
Record your results and calculate the average titration.

Calculations

Use the following formula to calculate the concentration of ethanoic acid in the sample of vinegar you analysed:

Concentration of CH_3COOH (w/v) = $0.3 \times V_b$ %

where V_b cm^3 = the average titration of 0.100 mol dm^{-3} sodium hydroxide

Questions

1 Why is vinegar a mixture?
2 Although vinegar is a mixture, a single sample only is taken for analysis. Why is this sufficient for the purpose?
3 Why is the sample of vinegar diluted before analysis?
4 Write a balanced equation for the reaction between ethanoic acid, CH_3COOH, and sodium hydroxide, NaOH.

Opportunity to collect evidence

In completing this task you will have the opportunity to meet the following requirements for Intermediate GNVQ Science:

Element 2.3

Determine the composition of substances

PCs 1, 2, 3

Range:

sample:	single
substance:	compounds (acids), mixtures (aqueous solutions)
prepared:	converted to required form
analysis:	quantitative analysis (acid-base titration)

The instructions are precise. Safety warnings are given. There is a clear link between the task and the performance criteria and associated range. You would be able to gather evidence for your portfolio. Since no planning, information finding and use, or evaluation is involved, you would not be able to show that you are worthy of a merit or distinction in these grading themes. The following assignment, however, has these opportunities built into it.

Assignment

AN INVESTIGATION OF LIMESCALE REMOVERS

Setting the scene

If you live in a hard water area, you will be familiar with the problem of kettles and similar appliances scaling up (or furring). The scale is sometimes called limescale and is, in fact, the chemical substance calcium carbonate, $CaCO_3$.

Products which remove limescale can be bought in the supermarket under a variety of brand names. They are acidic solutions which react with the calcium carbonate, dissolving it. The acid commonly used is methanoic acid. The following information was taken from the label of a commercially available product.

CORROSIVE methanoic acid

Removes limescale in less than 20 minutes.

Furgon ultrafast formula dissolves limescale from all types of kettles, steam irons and coffee makers, leaving them shiny clean and working more efficiently.

Use dose markings on side of bottle to help you use just the right amount.

Kettles

1 Half fill with water, boil and then unplug.
2 Add 4 doses (200 ml) of Furgon
3 Leave for 20 minutes or until fizzing has stopped.
4 Empty the kettle, rinse twice and then refill, boil and empty.
5 Heavy scale may require a second application.

Steam irons

1 Heat on medium setting, then unplug.
2 Add 1 dose (50 ml) of Furgon to 150 ml cold water in a jug.
3 Pour into unplugged iron and set control to 'steam' position.
4 Gently shake iron over the sink until the solution starts to drain through the steam holes. Use spray button to pump through briefly.
5 Rinse thoroughly with cold water. Clean soleplate and ensure iron is dry.

Coffee-makers

1 Put 500 ml water into the reservoir and add 2 doses (100 ml) of Furgon
2 Switch on for 1 minute.
3 Switch off and leave for 4 minutes.
4 Switch on and allow reservoir to empty into jug, then discard the jug contents.
5 Rinse machine through twice with clean water.

Caution: Do not use on enamelled, marble or alabaster surfaces. Do not allow to come in contact with any other cleaners. Wipe off spillages with a wet cloth. Keep out of reach of children. In case of contact with eyes or cuts wash thoroughly with cold water.

Use monthly to prevent limescale build-up, prolonging the life of your appliance and saving energy.

Eye protection must be worn

The assignment

You should work on this assignment in a team of three. Read through what is required and decide how your group will divide the work between its members.

SAFETY: *Before you carry out any practical activity, the hazards and suitable precautions must be identified. Check your plans with your supervisor before carrying out any practical work.*

1 Find out how limescale builds up in a kettle. Each member of the group should write a brief account, using balanced chemical equations to represent any reactions involved.

2 (a) Plan and carry out tests to show that limescale is calcium carbonate.
(b) Plan and carry out tests to check that the limescale remover is acidic and see if it contains chloride or sulphate ions (which you would expect if it consisted of hydrochloric acid or sulphuric acid).
Each member of the group should carry out their own analysis.
Results should be recorded in a suitable form.

3 You will be provided with a bottle of the limescale remover whose label is reproduced above.
(a) Determine the quantity of methanoic acid in one dose.
(b) How much limescale could be dissolved by one dose of the limescale remover?
(c) Calculate the concentration of methanoic acid that the manufacturers recommend to clean (i) kettles (ii) steam irons and (iii) coffee-makers.
Each member of the group should carry out their own analysis.
Remember to check your plans with your supervisor before carrying out any practical work. Results should be recorded in a suitable form.

4 'Removes limescale in less than 20 minutes.' Plan and carry out a series of experiments to find out how the rate of reaction between limescale and the descaler depends on:
(a) how finely the limescale is divided
(b) the temperature of the acid
(c) the concentration of acid.
Your group will need to divide up this work. You should produce a plan and discuss this with your supervisor before starting any practical work. In your report, make it clear which work you actually carried out and which results were obtained by other members of the group. The report should also contain an explanation of your observations.

5 Identify the safety precautions that the manufacturers recommend and explain why they are necessary.
Each member of the group should produce their own summary chart.

6 'Use monthly to prevent limescale build-up, prolonging the life of your appliance and saving energy.' Energy is required to heat the water in a kettle. The time it takes for a quantity of water to boil is a measure of the energy required. The longer a supply of energy is needed, the greater the energy consumption. Why does preventing limescale build-up save energy? Plan and carry out experiments to

check this claim. How much money can be saved by using a kettle which is not scaled up? How does this compare with the cost of keeping it free of scale?

Your group should produce a plan and discuss it with your supervisor before starting any practical work. You may decide that each member of the group will carry out different experiments and compare results. If so, make it clear in your report which work you actually carried out and which results were obtained by other members of the group.

Presenting your assignment

Your written report will consist of several parts:

- action plan, together with a record of any modifications made during the course of the work
- reports on each of the parts described above
- an overall conclusion to the investigation
- a bibliography.

At the end of the five week period there will be an open evening. The outcome of your group's investigation will be on display to staff, parents and other students. You will be allocated a display area consisting of bench space with a notice board behind. Your display might contain laboratory reports, apparatus used for certain parts of the work, posters to highlight important techniques or key conclusions from the investigation. You will be on hand during the evening to explain more fully what you did and to answer questions.

Additional information

You will have access to *procedures* for:

- Qualitative chemical test, page 104
- Carrying out an acid-base titration, page 107
- Measuring the volume of gas given off during a reaction, page 207
- Measuring the loss in mass of a reaction mixture, page 208.

In each case, look through the unit specifications and list the aspects of range which you have covered in completing this work.

Grading

This assignment gives you ample opportunity to meet merit or distinction criteria. All four themes are covered:

- Planning
- Information seeking and information handling
- Evaluation
- Quality of outcomes.

You will need help with some of the science in this assignment, so don't be afraid to ask.

Read through the grading criteria carefully and make sure you know what must be done to gain evidence that you are worthy of a merit or distinction.

Opportunity to collect evidence
In completing this assignment you will have the opportunity to meet the following requirements for Intermediate GNVQ Science:

Science units
Unit 1:
Element 1.3, PCs 1, 2, 3, 4
Unit 2:
Element 2.2, PCs 1, 2, 3
Element 2.3, PCs 1, 2, 3
Unit 4:
Element 4.2, PCs 1, 2, 3, 4, 5, 6

Core skill units

Application of Number:
Element 2.2

Communication:
Element 2.2, 2.3, 2.4

This is a complex assignment. Don't panic! You would undertake it towards the end of your course, after you had developed the relevant skills and knowledge to tackle it. Assignments of this kind are a major source of evidence for the award of a merit or distinction grade.

Let's see how you would be able to show that you are worthy of a distinction.

Criterion 1: Drawing up plans of action.
Together with other members of your group, you have a great deal to plan. You will need to work out what needs doing and how long it will take. Your action plan will prioritise tasks and put them in a logical order. How you tackle one task may affect when and how you can work on other parts of the assignment. The laboratory will only be available at certain times. Some parts of the work must be divided amongst the team. You need time to write up the assignment. There is much to think about!

Criterion 2: Monitoring course of action.
Five weeks is a long time. There is a lot to do and you may decide to change your plans depending on how things unfold. An analysis may have to be repeated and this may have a knock-on effect on your other plans. The resources you need for a particular task may not be available. Therefore, you need to review your action plan regularly and be prepared to modify it if necessary.

Criterion 3: Identifying information needs.
You will need various pieces of information in order to tackle the assignment, for example suitable practical techniques and relevant scientific ideas. When planning your work, all your information needs must be identified.

Criterion 4: Identifying and using sources to obtain information.
Where can the required information be found? Sources (e.g. text books, data book) need to be identified. You must justify your selection in terms of its suitability for providing the relevant information.

Criterion 5: Evaluating outcomes and justifying approaches.
Your overall conclusion to the investigation should justify the approach you took. Its advantages and disadvantages compared with alternative approaches should be discussed. You should also comment on how you might do things differently if you tackled the investigation again.

Criterion 6: Synthesis.
Throughout the investigation you must show a grasp of the relevant scientific knowledge, skills and understanding. You can show this by explaining decisions taken. For example, 'This experimental procedure was chosen because...'. Your planning, data handling and the conclusions you draw will reflect your grasp of the subject matter.

Criterion 7: Command of 'language'.
Finally, you will need to show that you can use scientific words, symbols (including hazard symbols) and other conventions accurately and appropriately.

Good luck with your studies and enjoy your Intermediate GNVQ Science course.

0 The basic toolkit

Figure 0.1 All scientists use the same basic ideas and techniques. They use the same basic toolkit in their work.

Working safely

Scientific work is potentially dangerous, yet accidents amongst scientists are rare. It is also important that they avoid the risk of diseases that can come from long-term exposure to hazardous substances. Scientists have to learn how to work safely. This is so essential that it forms the first part of your toolkit.

In your work, you need to pay special attention to safety issues. Scientific work brings you into contact with both hazards and risks. What is the difference between them? An example will help to illustrate. Concentrated sulphuric acid is a *hazard*. It is extremely corrosive. This means that it will destroy living tissue. However, the *risk* that it presents in a stoppered bottle, clearly labelled with a hazard warning symbol, is considerably less than if it is in an open, unlabelled beaker on the bench of a busy laboratory!

Hazards and risks

It is important that you learn how to work safely by:

- identifying **hazards**
- taking the correct measures to reduce **risks** to acceptable levels.

An essential first step before doing any practical work is to carry out a *risk assessment*. Often this will have already been done for you.

Even though you will usually be given practical instructions which include safety precautions, it is important to double check. You must take account of the particular conditions in which you are working.

You should always check with your supervisor before you start any practical work.

FOCUS

A hazard is something that is potentially harmful. A risk is how likely it is that harm will occur in a given situation.

Figure 0.2 Hazards must be recognised before risks can be assessed. The radiation scientists are wearing protective clothing. Early investigators were unaware that radioactivity was a hazard and did not realise the risk of handling radioactive materials. Many died of cancer, including the famous French scientist, Madame Curie. Now people are aware of the risk, and radiation hazards are clearly labelled.

IRRITANT chemical

HARMFUL chemical

WARNING

TOXIC

OXIDISING

Electrical hazard

CORROSIVE chemical

FLAMMABLE chemical

BIOHAZARD

Figure 0.3 These hazard warning symbols help to alert you to possible risks in your work. Before starting work you should find out what safety measures are necessary and what to do in the case of spillage or an accident. Discuss with others the kind of things that could produce each of the hazards shown. What precautions and measures could you take to reduce risks to an acceptable level for each kind of hazard?

Procedure

Carrying out a risk assessment

1. Identify the substances and equipment required and their use.
2. Identify hazards associated with the substances and equipment.
3. Identify how you and others may be exposed to risk, including accidents that might occur.
4. Determine methods to reduce risks to acceptable levels. You should consider:
   - changing to an alternative, possibly smaller scale, procedure
   - using protective equipment or control measures (such as heat-resistant gloves, a safety screen, eye protection or a fume cupboard)
   - Being ready to deal with possible accidents, for example to mop up spills or to provide first aid. The safe disposal of wastes must be organised.
5. Inform everyone involved about the risks.
6. Apply laboratory rules.
7. Ensure that everyone knows the correct action to take in the case of fire.

Note. *If risk cannot be reduced to acceptable levels, the activity must not be carried out.*

Electrical hazard

Figure 0.4 *Electricity is an everyday hazard, but imagine life without it! It only represents an unacceptable risk when used carelessly. In five minutes list all the ways that you can think of in which different electrical appliances can be dangerous. For each idea, suggest what the dangerous consequences could be and how the risk of them occurring can be increased or decreased.*

Table 0.1 Useful sources of information for risk assessments

These include:
CLEAPSS Hazcards (new edition free to members, 1995)
CLEAPSS Laboratory Handbook (updated, 1995)
The Merck Index
Chemical manufacturers and suppliers catalogues and data sheets
Hazardous chemicals: a manual for schools and colleges (SSERC, 1979)
Topics in Safety (ASE, 1988)
Microbiology: an HMI guide for schools and Further Education (HMSO, 1990)
Safeguards in the school laboratory (ASE, 1988 under revision 1995)
Preparing COSHH Risk Assessments for Project Work in Schools (SSERC, 1991)
Safety in Biological Fieldwork: guidance notes for codes of practice, ed. D Nichols (IOB, 1990)
Safety in Outdoor Education (HMSO, 1989)

Symbols and standards

Products can be awarded kite marks (British) or CE (European) marks if they meet certain minimum standards. A CE mark indicates that a product meets certain essential requirements of the EU's New Approach Directives (NAD). It is intended to be easily recognisable throughout the EU and to give users confidence in the equipment. Unmarked equipment may not meet safety requirements and will need checking and testing before use. As these standards are minimum requirements only, it is important to remember that they do not indicate safety in all conditions of use.

Figure 0.5 British and European Standards ensure that certain minimum safety requirements are met. Equipment that can pose a hazard but does not have either of these marks should be rigorously tested before use.

Table 0.2 Common accidents and precautions

Common accidents	Precautions
Heating Naked flames, hot objects and liquids, heating elements and ovens can cause burns, scalds or fire.	
• long hair or unsuitable clothing ignites in a Bunsen flame • flammable liquids (e.g. ethanol) catch fire • boiling liquid spurts out of a heated test-tube • fingers are burnt lifting a hot trlpod after a Bunsen is switched off	• treat all heating operations with caution • use correct procedures for heating flammable liquids and heating with a Bunsen burner (see fig 0.6) • tie back long hair • ties and scarves should not be allowed to dangle • appropriate protective clothing should be worn
Using glassware Glass is fragile and breaks to give razor sharp fragments. It may shatter and scatter fragments if dropped, heated incorrectly or cooled from hot suddenly. Vessels under pressure or vacuum may burst or implode.	
• test tubes or thermometers roll or are knocked off the bench • soda glass test tube cracks when heated • hot test tube shatters when rinsed with cold water • glass tubing breaks when being pushed into a rubber bung and lacerates palm or wrist • glass splinters cut fingers when picked up • test tube or specimen tube breaks when bung is inserted	• always wear eye protection if there is any risk of glass breaking • place apparatus on a firm surface and away from the edge • avoid clutter and crowding • never hold bottles by the neck or attempt to force tight stoppers in or out • use borosilicate glass vessels, such as Pyrex, of the correct size and type when heating • do not attempt to push thermometers or glass tubing into bungs or to remove them

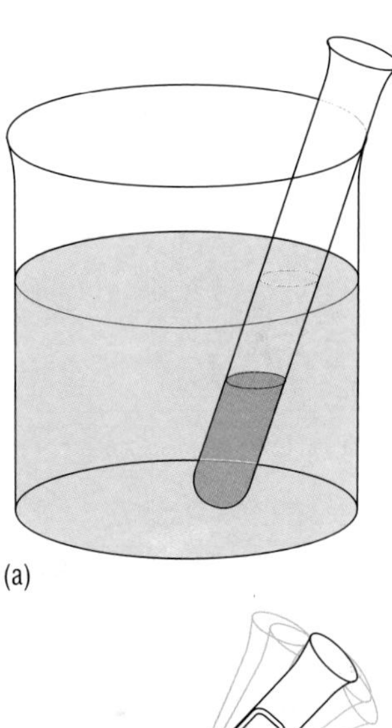

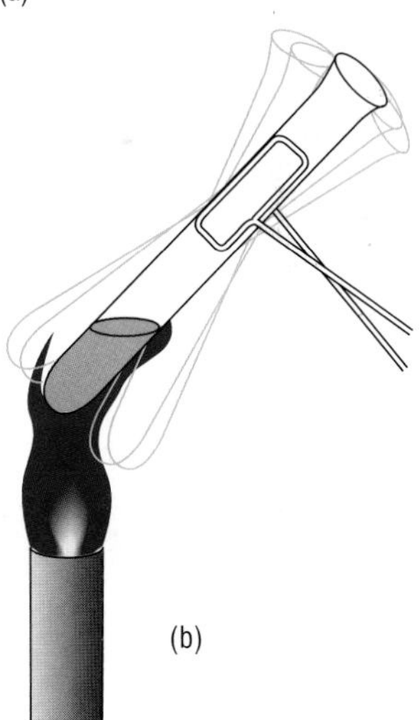

Figure 0.6 *(a) Flammable liquids with low boiling points should be heated in a boiling tube, no more than one-fifth full, placed in a beaker of hot water. (b) Non-flammable material shold be heated gently in a Pyrex boiling tube, over a blue Bunsen flame. The tube should again be no more than one-fifth full, tilted so that the tube-holder is to one side of the flame and the mouth of the tube is pointing away from anybody nearby. The tube should be shaken gently.*

Figure 0.7 Safety posters are useful reminders.

Using electrical equipment

Shock and fire are the two main risks from the use of electricity.

- electric shock from incorrect wiring (e.g. earth cable not connected, or is too short in a plug so it has pulled off and made contact with the live terminal making the apparatus live)
- wet hands or apparatus conduct electricity giving a shock
- trailing leads are caught so that apparatus is pulled off the bench

- avoid water: do not handle equipment or switches with damp or wet hands, or if standing on a wet floor; keep electrical apparatus away from sinks or areas where spillages may occur
- no trailing leads
- avoid using extension leads
- use less than 20 volts for open terminals (60V may be fatal)
- know how to isolate the supply (labs should have isolating switches)
- make a visual check for faults such as broken plugs, frayed or cracked leads, visible inner insulation, loose or damaged casings
- regular checks by competent person keeping written record

Protective Clothing

Skin can be damaged by contact with a range of materials encountered in laboratories, or chemicals may be absorbed through it. Eyes are especially vulnerable to permanent damage.

- irritant or corrosive chemicals are splashed onto the skin causing rashes or burns
- corrosive liquids are split on the feet causing burns
- heated glassware shaters causing eye injuries
- chemicals spurt out of heated test-tubes

- use protective clothing
- wear a buttoned-up lab coat
- wear shoes that protect your feet (not open-toed)
- wear gloves if hazardous chemicals could be touched
- use eye or face protection (i.e. goggles, safety spectacles or a mask) if any operation hazardous to eyes is being carried out in the lab

Safe working in the laboratory

You will carry out much of your scientific work in a laboratory. Laboratories contain more hazards than the average household (there are exceptions!). However, you are more likely to suffer an injury at home. This is because you anticipate greater potential risks in the laboratory and, therefore, take steps to reduce them.

You can only keep risks to a minimum if you ~~are care~~ful. You must make safe working practice a habit. This means:

- making yourself aware of the meanings of hazard warning symbols
- learning which precautions need to be taken with each hazard
- taking hazard warnings seriously and never taking risks
- treating all chemicals as potentially dangerous
- knowing correct procedures to follow in case of accident:
  - how to summon expert help, such as a first aider, if necessary
  - how to mop up a spillage safely (chemicals and micro-organisms)

– how to dispose of wastes safely
– how to dispose of broken glass safely.

Remember that these are guidelines only. You must be alert to the hazards and risks of each specific situation that you work in. *Again, always check with your supervisor before you start, especially if you have made your own plans.*

Table 0.3 Safe Procedures

Follow the correct procedures
Using correct procedures for common operations is one of the most effective ways in which you can reduce risk to yourself and to others.

- use the minimum amounts of materials that you can
- make sure that all containers are labelled correctly, including hazard warning symbols
- use safety filters for pipetting
- smell gases with extreme caution, using the correct procedure (see Figure 0.8)
- use a fume cupboard if the risk assessment requires it (e.g. working with toxic gases)
- use a safety screeen if there is any risk of apparatus shattering
- check procedures for spillages in advance (chemicals and micro-organisms)
- use correct lifing procedure for heavy objects, keeping your back straight
- clean/clear up at the end of a session
- dispose of all waste materials safely

Emergencies:

- know what to do in advance
- know locations of: fire alarm, fire assembly point; isolation switches and valves for gas and electricity; telephone; eye washing station or bottle; trained first aider; first aid kit
- get first aid training

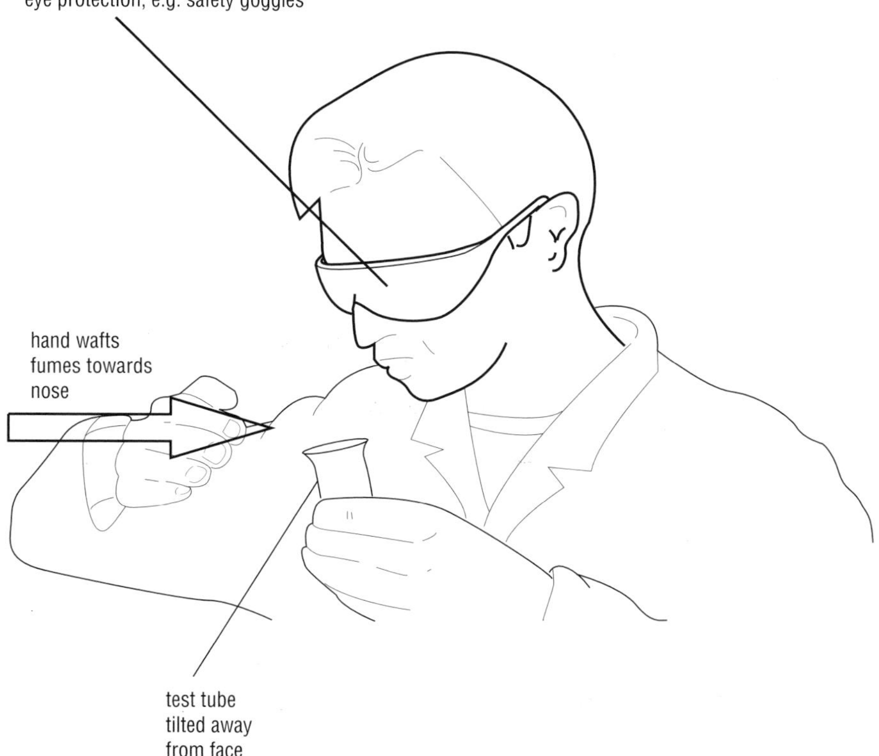

Figure 0.8 *Safe procedure for smelling gases.*

Describing and naming

Scientists share a common language and common ideas. This is essential if science is to be truly international. For scientists all around the world to be able to exchange their knowledge, they must be able to describe and name things using the same systems. Internationally accepted methods must be used to name chemicals and living things. Everyone must agree on the units to use when making measurements.

Living and non-living

Things can be *classified* (grouped together) as being either *living* (e.g. animals and plants) or *non-living* (e.g. rocks and minerals).

The earth and its atmosphere provides all the materials from which living things (also called *organisms*) are made. Life is the result of a well co-ordinated and complicated series of chemical processes. Therefore, the basic rules that apply to non-living systems also apply to living ones. However, to be alive, an organism must show a number of characteristic properties. This is discussed in detail in Unit 2.

Elements

Elements are the simplest substances from which all materials, living or non-living, are made. They cannot be broken down into simpler chemical substances. About 90 elements occur naturally (usually in chemical combination with one another). About 20 more have been made by scientists.

Each element is given a name and a symbol. Each has its own characteristic properties, both physical (e.g. melting point, boiling point, density, conductivity) and chemical (e.g. reactions with water, oxygen, acids and other chemicals).

Elements are often classified as *metals* (e.g. aluminium, copper, sodium, iron) or *non-metals* (e.g. hydrogen, oxygen, carbon, chlorine). They are made up of *atoms*.

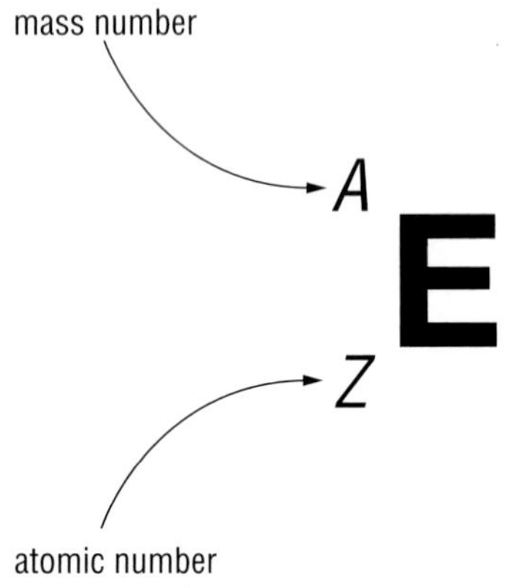

mass number

$^{A}_{Z}\mathrm{E}$

atomic number

Figure 0.9 Giving information about an element.

Atoms and elements

Atoms are tiny. If you drew a line 1 metre long, 6 000 000 000 (6 billion) atoms could be lined up end to end. Each atom has a central nucleus in which positively charged *protons* and neutral *neutrons* can be found. Around this nucleus is a space in which negatively charged *electrons* are found. All atoms of a particular element have the same number of protons in their nuclei as one another. This is called the element's *atomic number* (given the symbol Z). It characterises the element.

The sum of the numbers of protons and neutrons in the nucleus of an atom is called the *mass number* (given the symbol A).

Table 0.4 Particles that make up atoms (called sub-atomic particles)

Particle	Where it is found	Mass	Charge
Proton	nucleus	1	+1
Neutron	nucleus	1	0
Electron	region of space outside the nucleus	$\frac{1}{1850}$	–1

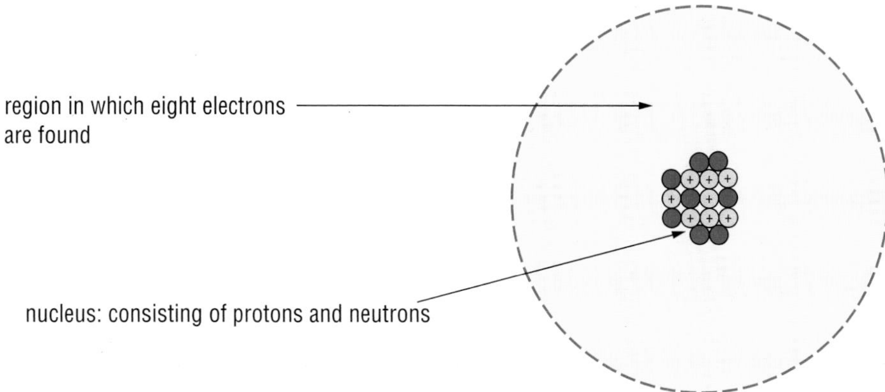

Figure 0.10 *Representing the structure of an oxygen atom. To get an idea of relative size, if the nucleus were the size of a table tennis ball, the electrons would be a region about the size of Wembley Stadium.*

Atoms carry no overall charge. The number of protons and the number of electrons present are equal. For a particular element, these numbers are always the same. The chemical properties of an element are determined by the number of electrons in its atoms.

Isotopes

The number of neutrons can differ from one atom to another of the same element (though within a small range). For example, carbon can exist as $^{12}_{6}C$ (called carbon-12) and as $^{14}_{6}C$ (called carbon-14). $^{12}_{6}C$ has 6 protons (which makes it carbon!) and 6 neutrons. $^{14}_{6}C$ has 6 protons and 8 neutrons. The mass number of carbon-12 is 12, and of carbon-14 is 14.

Atoms of the same element but with different numbers of neutrons are called *isotopes*.

The atoms of isotopes with a relatively large number of neutrons can become unstable. They may break up to emit *radio emissions*.

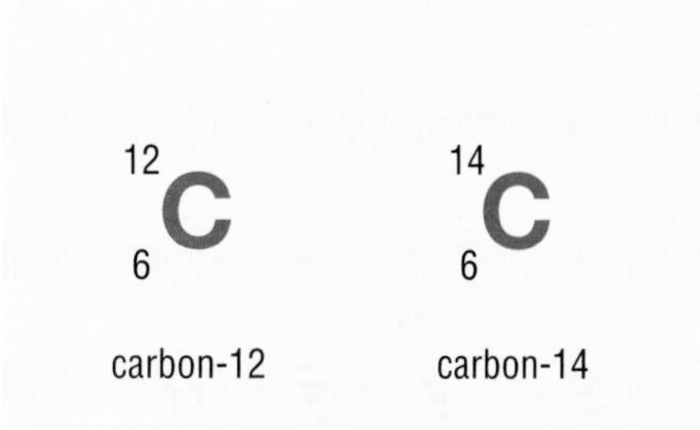

Figure 0.11 *Shorthand for the isotopes of carbon. How many more neutrons are there in an atom of carbon-14 than in an atom of carbon-12?*

The Periodic Table

A useful way of arranging the elements according to their physical and chemical properties is the Periodic Table (see Figure 0.12 overleaf). Elements with similar properties are placed below one another in a column. This is called a *group*. The horizontal rows are called *periods*. The Periodic Table is one of science's great success stories, summarising patterns and relationships in a simple form.

Elements in Group VIII are called the *noble gases*. They are remarkably inert. This is due to the arrangement of their electrons. Other elements tend to undergo reactions in which they either transfer or share electrons in order to get the same number and arrangement of electrons as is found in one of the noble gases.

Compounds and mixtures

Elements combine to form *chemical compounds*. Together, these substances make up all of our world – living and non-living.

Compounds can be broken down into the elements from which they are made, though not always easily. To obtain elements from a compound, chemical bonds must be broken. Compounds have different properties from their elements. For example, common salt, which is used on food, is sodium chloride. It is a white, crystalline solid which dissolves in water. It is made from sodium (a soft, shiny metal that reacts violently with water) and chlorine (an extremely poisonous yellow-green gas). The properties of these elements are very different from those of the compound they form.

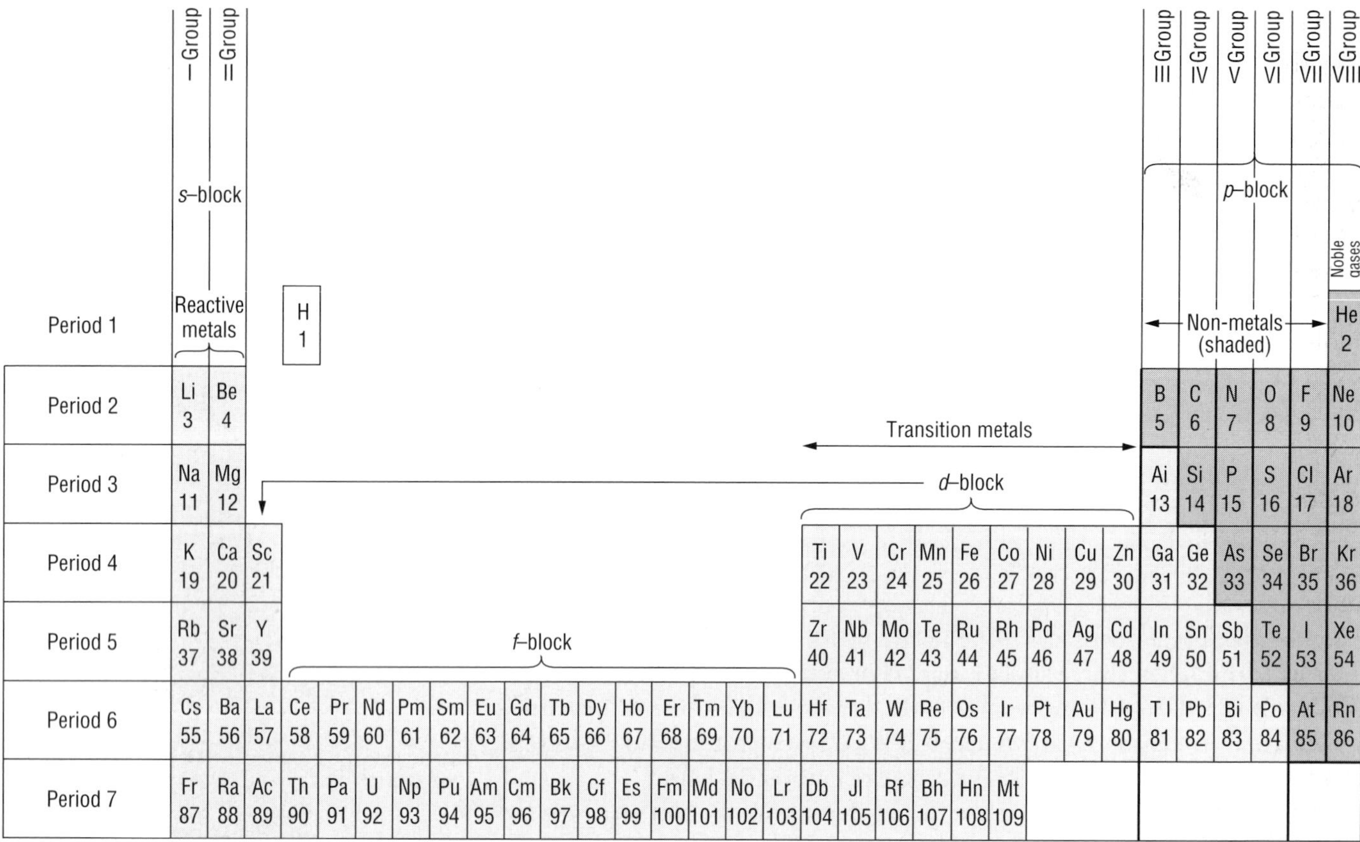

Figure 0.12 *The Periodic Table. The elements are arranged in order of increasing atomic number. As you move left to right across a period there is a tendency to change from metals to non-metals. A period ends when the next element has similar properties to those of the other Group I elements.*

Mixtures can be made up of two or more pure chemical substances (elements or compounds). The properties of a mixture are the same as those of its components. Mixtures can generally be separated by physical means such as filtration, crystallisation or distillation.

Structures of elements and compounds

Chemical substances have molecular or giant structures.

Molecular structures

Most elements and compounds which are gases or liquids at room temperature exist as *molecules*. They have *molecular structures*. Most substances which have low melting points are also molecular. In a molecule, atoms are held together by strong chemical bonds called *covalent bonds*. Electrons are shared between atoms. The mutual attraction of the atoms' nuclei (which are positively charged) for shared electrons (which are negatively charged) holds the atoms together. The bonding between one molecule and another is weak.

Examples of elements with molecular structures, and their chemical formulae, are:

hydrogen, H_2
oxygen, O_2
chlorine, Cl_2
sulphur, S_8

The subscript tells you how many atoms are bonded together in a molecule. So, there are two atoms of chlorine in a chlorine molecule, Cl_2.

Many compounds have molecular structures. Again the atoms are held together by covalent bonds. Examples of compounds with molecular structures, and their *chemical formulae*, are:

carbon dioxide, CO_2
ammonia, NH_3
water, H_2O
ethanol (often simply called alcohol), C_2H_5OH
sucrose (common sugar), $C_{12}H_{22}O_{11}$

The subscripts tell you how many atoms of each type are present in the molecule. If there is no subscript it means that there is just one atom. For example, a molecule of ammonia, NH_3, consists of 1 nitrogen atom and 3 hydrogen atoms. A molecule of sucrose, $C_{12}H_{22}O_{11}$, consists of 12 carbon atoms, 22 hydrogen atoms and 11 oxygen atoms.

Giant structures

Elements and compounds with high melting points have giant structures. A *giant structure* is one in which atoms are chemically bonded to one another in an enormous network. They have no definite finished size – you can keep adding more atoms or ions to them.

Metals are giant structures with the atoms held together by *metallic bonds*. They can be thought of as positive ions (atoms which have lost one or more of their electrons) in a sea of electrons. The chemical formula is simply the symbol for the element, e.g. copper, Cu; iron, Fe; calcium, Ca.

Many compounds have properties which can only be explained if they are made up of ions. Electrons are transferred from one atom to another. Atoms losing electrons form positive ions (*cations*). Atoms gaining electrons form negative ions (*anions*). Ions of opposite charge are held together by *ionic bonds* (sometimes called *electrovalent* bonds). These are usually compounds formed between metals (which form the cations) and non-metals (which form the anions). Examples of simple ionic compounds, and their chemical formulae, are:

sodium chloride, NaCl — calcium chloride, $CaCl_2$
magnesium oxide, MgO — aluminium oxide, Al_2O_3

The subscripts tell you the ratio of atoms of each type that are present. For example, magnesium oxide, MgO, has magnesium and oxygen atoms in a ratio of 1:1. In aluminium oxide, Al_2O_3, the ratio of aluminium atoms to oxygen atoms is 2:3.

Some elements and compounds have atoms held together by covalent bonds in a giant structure. For example, carbon and silicon(IV) oxide.

Salts are examples of ionic compounds. However, the anions are often

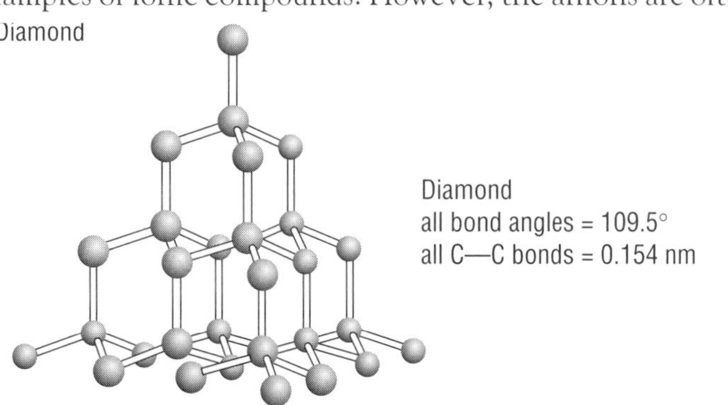

Figure 0.15 *Diamond is a natural form of carbon. The carbon atoms are arranged in a giant lattice, with covalent bonds binding the atoms to one another.*

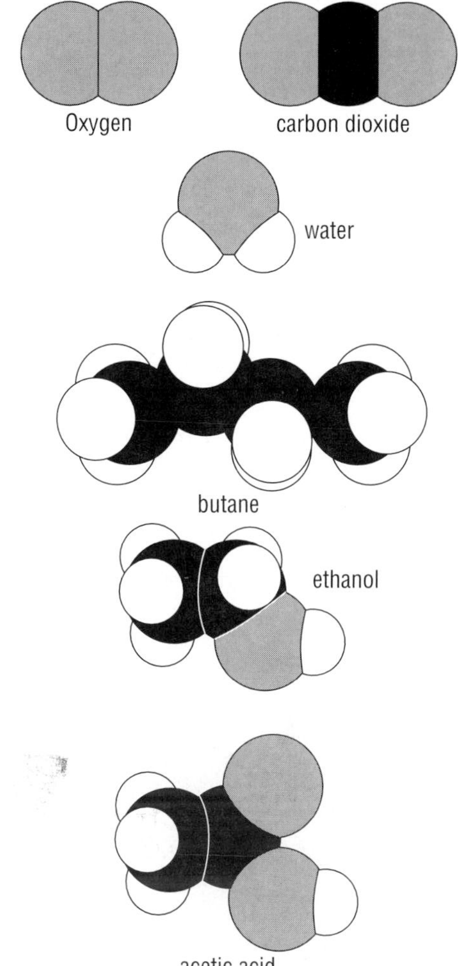

Figure 0.13 *Molecules are clusters of atoms held together by covalent bonds. They have definite shapes.*

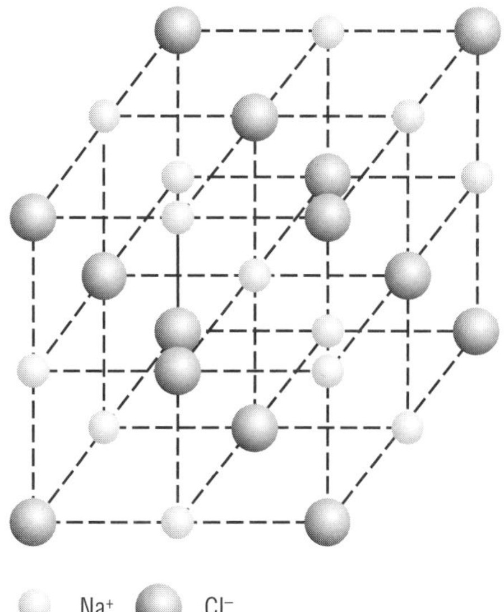

Figure 0.14 *Sodium chloride has a giant structure. Sodium ions (Na^+) and chloride ions (Cl^-) are arranged in a giant, regular lattice.*

clusters of atoms held together by covalent bonds but with an overall negative charge. For example: nitrate, NO_3^-, carbonate, CO_3^{2-}; sulphate, SO_4^{2-}. Here are some examples of such salts and their chemical formula:

sodium nitrate, $NaNO_3$
sodium sulphate, Na_2SO_4
magnesium nitrate, $Mg(NO_3)_2$

Again, the subscripts tell you the ratio of atoms of each type that are present. Anything in brackets must be multiplied by the subscript just after them. For example, magnesium nitrate, $Mg(NO_3)_2$, has magnesium, nitrogen and oxygen atoms in the ratio 1:2:6.

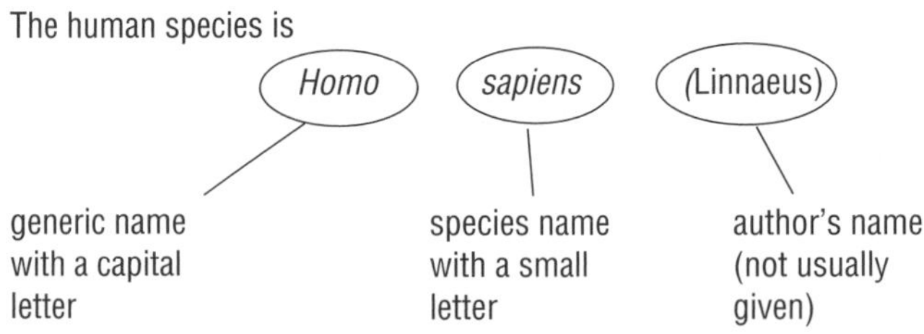

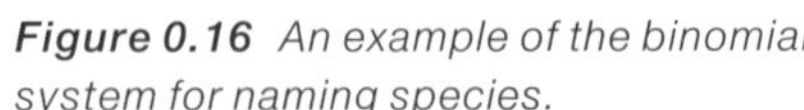
Figure 0.16 *An example of the binomial system for naming species.*

Naming living things

Species represent the level at which organisms are able to reproduce to give new organisms similar to themselves. It is important that scientists can use a universal label for every species that they can all recognise. The Linnaean Society in London has the responsibility for naming every new species as it is discovered. A *binomial system*, that is, a double name, is used (see Figure 0.16).

The generic name is like your surname. It can be shared with other closely related species. *Homo erectus* and *Homo habilis* are names given to species in the fossil record thought to be human ancestors.

A genus is ,therefore, a group of closely related species. Closely related genera can be grouped together in a family. There are millions of known species, so a large number of groupings is used to classify living things. Above family is order, then class, then phylum and finally kingdom.

Figure 0.17 *An example of* Homo sapiens.

You belong to:

kingdom: Animalia
phylum: Chordata
class: Mammalia
order: Primata
family: Hominidae
genus: *Homo*
species: *Homo sapiens*

The other five kingdoms are viruses, prokaryotes (bacteria), protoctists (simple organisms, mainly unicellular), plants and fungi.

Measurement and observation

Scientists need data if they are to be able to make sense of the world around them. They must be able to measure and observe.

Units for measurement

The universally adopted system of units for the measurement of physical quantities is the SI system (short for Système International d'Unites). The seven base units are shown in Table 0.5.

Table 0.5 The seven base units

Measured quantity	Name of SI unit	Symbol
Length	metre	m
Mass	kilogram	kg
Amount of substance	mole	mol
Time	second	s
Electric current	ampere	A
Temperature	kelvin	K
Luminous intensity	candela	cd

All other units of measurement can be derived by combining the appropriate base units. Some important ones are shown in Table 0.6.

Table 0.6 Common derived SI units

Quantity	Unit	Symbol	Base SI units
Velocity	–	–	$m\ s^{-1}$
Acceleration	–	–	$m\ s^{-2}$
Force	newton	N	$kg\ m\ s^{-2}$
Energy	joule	J	$kg\ m^2\ s^{-2}$
Power	watt	W	$kg\ m^2\ s^{-3}$
Area	–	–	m^2
Volume	–	–	m^3
Density	–	–	$kg\ m^{-3}$
Pressure	pascal	Pa	$kg\ m^{-1}\ s^{-2}$
Concentration	–	–	$mol\ m^{-3}$
Electrical potential difference	volt	V	$m^2\ kg\ A^{-1}\ s^{-3}$
Electrical resistance	ohm	Ω	$m^2\ kg\ A^{-2}\ s^{-3}$

The mole: the scientist's counting unit

You cannot count individual atoms, ions or molecules: they are too small! As a scientist you determine *quantities* of chemicals, by mass or volume.

Scientists can determine *relative atomic masses*, A_r. That means, we know how much one atom weighs compared with another one. The smallest atom is hydrogen. It has a relative atomic mass of 1 (A_r[H] = 1).

A carbon atom has 12 times the mass of a hydrogen atom. Therefore, A_r[C] = 12. Similarly, a magnesium atom has 24 times the mass of a hydrogen atom (twice the mass of a carbon atom). Therefore, A_r[Mg] = 24.

We say that 1 g of hydrogen contains 1 mole of atoms. Similarly, 12 g of carbon and 24 g of magnesium both contain 1 mole of atoms.

The *mole* is the scientist's counting unit. Scientists talk about moles of substances in the same way that people talk about a dozen eggs or a ream of paper.

Figure 0.18 *12 g of carbon and 48 g titanium. The two samples contain the same number of atoms as one another. This is because titanium atoms (A_r[Ti] = 48) have four times the mass of carbon atoms (A_r[C] = 12). What mass of carbon would contain the same number of atoms as 12 g titanium?*

Table 0.7 Relative atomic masses of some elements

Element	Symbol	Relative atomic mass
Calcium	Ca	40.1
Carbon	C	12.0
Chlorine	Cl	35.5
Copper	Cu	63.5
Hydrogen	H	1.0
Iron	Fe	55.8
Magnesium	Mg	54.9
Nitrogen	N	14.0
Oxygen	O	16.0
Phosphorus	P	31.0
Potassium	K	39.0
Sodium	Na	23.0
Sulphur	S	32.1
Titanium	Ti	47.9
Zinc	Zn	65.4

This is a key idea. It means that we can measure out equal numbers of atoms of different elements. Indeed, we can measure them out in any proportions that we wish.

So how many atoms are present? 1 g of hydrogen contain 6×10^{23} atoms. This is called *Avogadro's number*.

One mole of anything contains 6×10^{23} of that particular thing. We can talk about a mole of atoms, a mole of molecules, a mole of ions, a mole of a chemical compound – even a mole of moles! In each case we mean 6×10^{23} entities.

The mass of one mole of a substance is called the *molar mass*, M (units: *g mol*$^{-1}$).

For a compound, the molar mass is found by adding up the relative atomic masses of the elements present. For example, zinc oxide, ZnO

$A_r[Zn] = 65.4$, $A_r[O] = 16.0$

Therefore, $M[ZnO] = 65.4 + 16.0 = 81.4 \text{ g mol}^{-1}$

calcium carbonate, $CaCO_3$

$A_r[Ca] = 40.1$, $A_r[C] = 12.0$, $A_r[O] = 16.0$

Therefore, $M[CaCO_3] = 40.1 + 12.0 + (3 \times 16.0) = 100.1 \text{ g mol}^{-1}$

To convert masses (m) into numbers of moles (n), and *vice versa*, use the formula:

$$\text{number of moles} = \frac{\text{actual mass}}{\text{molar mass}}$$

$$n = m/M$$

rearranging this formula

mass of substance = number of moles × molar mass

$m = nM$

Here are two examples:

(a) How many moles of sodium chloride, NaCl, are there in 5.85 g of the compound?

$A_r[Na] = 23.0$, $A_r[Cl] = 35.5$

Therefore, M[NaCl] = 23.0 + 35.5 = 58.5 g mol^{-1}
so, number of moles of sodium chloride = 5.85/58.5 = 0.1

(b) What is the mass of 4 moles of water, H_2O?

$A_r[H] = 1$, $A_r[O] = 16$

Therefore, $M[H_2O] = (2 \times 1) + 16 = 18$ g mol^{-1}
so, mass of 4 mol $H_2O = 4 \times 18 = 72$ g

Choosing the correct tools

Choosing a ruler to measure length or an electronic balance to measure mass is not quite as simple as it may seem!

Accuracy and precision in measuring length

A ruler may measure to 1 cm. Another may measure to 1 mm. It depends on the divisions marked on the rulers. This allows you to choose the precision you need. You can measure to the nearest 0.5 mm if you choose the ruler with the smaller divisions. This may seem the best choice, but what if you are measuring the length of the laboratory?

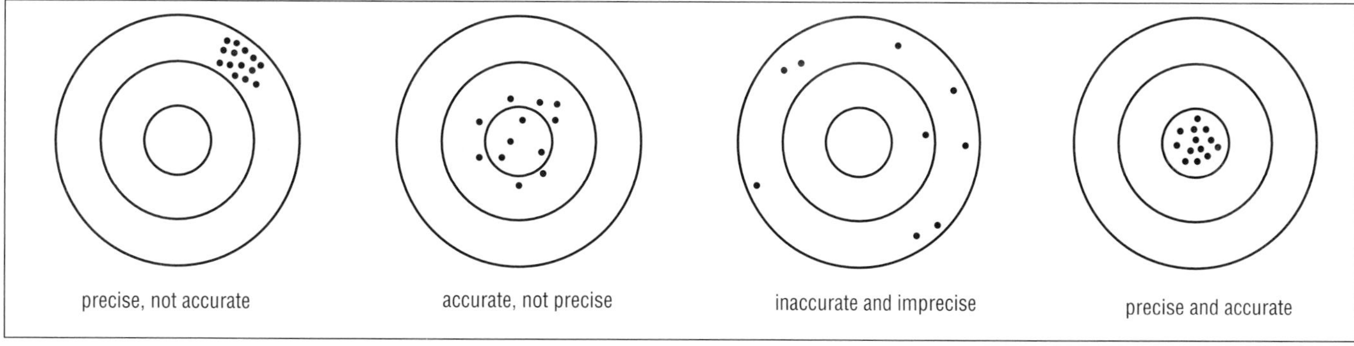

Figure 0.19 *Accuracy and precision.*

Whatever quantity you are measuring, you will need to decide:

- if the precision of an instrument is good enough for your purposes
- if you need to use the instrument to the limit of its precision.

Precision is reflected in the values that you record. You should always decide how many 'figures' or 'decimal places' to measure to. For example, which of these do you think would be appropriate?

Height of person: 1 m, 1.8 m, 1.84 m, 1.843 m?
Length of central heating radiator: 90 cm, 93 cm, 92.6 cm, 92.64 cm?

Multiplying values together compounds errors in measurements. Imagine you want to calculate the area of the radiator. The calculated value for the area will be less accurate than the lengths to which the sides were measured.

Measuring length with greater precision

Using a ruler will never give great precision because of the thickness of the lines. A steel ruler with narrow etched lines would help, but scientists can use more precise instruments. Vernier callipers and the micrometer screw gauge can measure to the nearest 0.1 mm and 0.01 mm respectively.

Requirements

- ❐ Vernier callipers
- ❐ Object to be measured

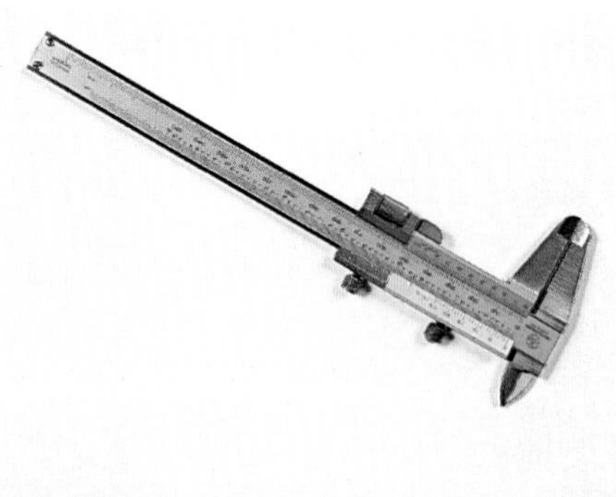

Figure 0.20 *Use Vernier callipers to measure to the nearest 0.1 mm, using a Vernier scale.*

Procedure

Using Vernier callipers

1 Grip the object with the jaws firmly but lightly to avoid distortion (note: two types are available, depending on whether internal or external dimensions are required).

2 The numbers on the fixed scale are centimetres, these are divided into millimetres; read off the number of centimetres and millimetres to the left of the first division of the moving scale.

3 The moving scale has 10 divisions in the space of 9 mm of the fixed scale; use it to measure to the nearest 0.1 mm by finding the line on the moving scale most closely in line with a line on the fixed scale.

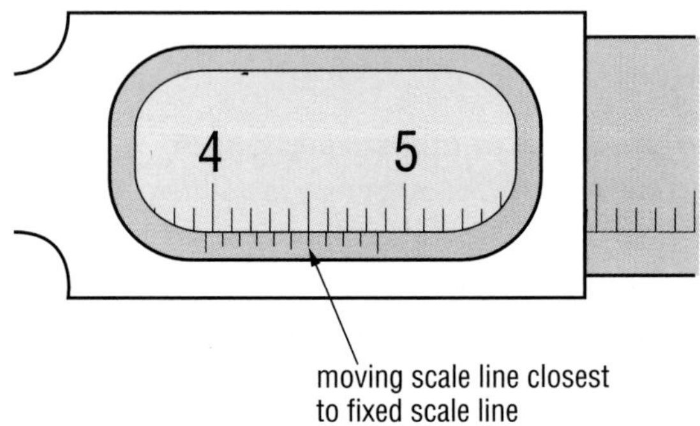

Figure 0.21 *Reading = 3.9 + 0.06 = 3.96 cm.*

Requirements

- ❐ Micrometer screw gauge
- ❐ Object to be measured

Figure 0.22 *Use a micrometer to measure to the nearest 0.01 mm.*

Procedure

Using a micrometer screw gauge

1 Clamp the object, a ratchet prevents over-tightening.

2 The numbers on the scale are millimetres, read the number to the left of the moving scale.

3 Use the numbers on the moving scale to find the measurement to 0.1 mm.

4 The small divisions form a Vernier scale with the line of the fixed scale. Count the number of small divisions from the 0.1 mm value to this line.

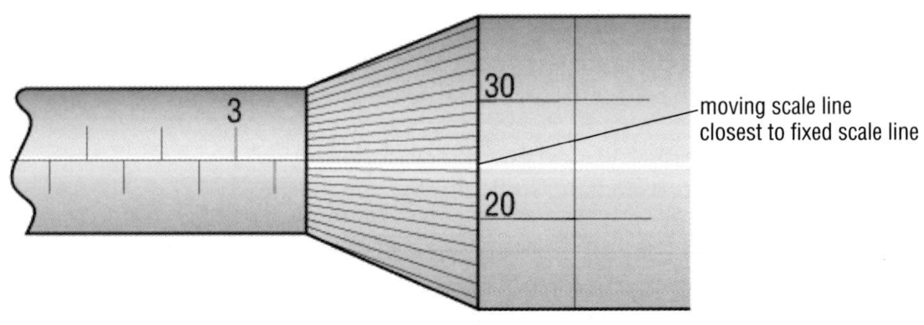

Figure 0.23 *Reading = 3.5 + 0.26 = 3.76 mm.*

It is possible to go one step further. A microscope gives even greater precision when measuring very small objects. There is a measuring scale in the eye piece, called an eye piece graticule. This has to be calibrated by using a very accurate measuring scale on a microscope slide.

Calculating surface areas

The surface area of a simple regular shape can be found by measuring its external dimensions (see Figure 0.25).

Shape		Perimeter	Area
Square	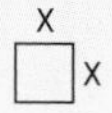	4x	x^2
Rectangle	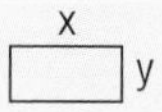	2(x+y)	xy
Right-angle triangle	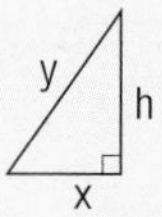	x + y + h	$\frac{1}{2}$hx
Any triangle	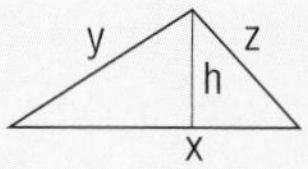	x + y + z	$\frac{1}{2}$hx

Figure 0.24 *Calculating the perimeters and areas of simple regular shapes.*

When irregular shapes are involved, the area can be estimated by tracing the outline of an object onto graph paper. All the squares covered by half or more are counted.

Two-dimensional objects can also be photocopied or traced. The paper is then cut out and weighed. Paper from the same stock, or even from the same piece, is cut out to a known area and weighed for comparison.

Measuring volume

Volumes of simple regular solids can also be found by measurement of their dimensions (see Figure 0.24). The volume of an irregular solid, if not too large, can be found by displacement of a liquid. Displacement cans can be used. The overflow can be collected and its volume measured (see Figure 0.26).

Shape		Surface area	Volume
Cube	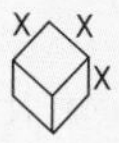	$6x^2$	x^3
Cuboid	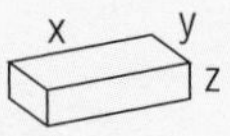	2xy + 2xz+ 2yz	xyz
Sphere		$4\pi r^2$	$\frac{4\pi r^3}{3}$
Cylinder	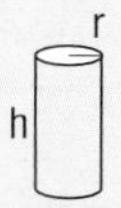	$2(\pi rh + \pi r^2)$	πr^2h

Figure 0.25 *Calculating the volumes and surface areas of simple regular solids.*

Volumes of liquids can be measured in various ways. You must decide how precise you need to be. Generally, precision depends on the diameter of the glassware where the graduation marks are found. The smaller the diameter, the greater the precision (see Figure 0.27). For example, a 50 cm^3 burette can measure to the nearest 0.1 cm^3 (precision ±0.05 cm^3).

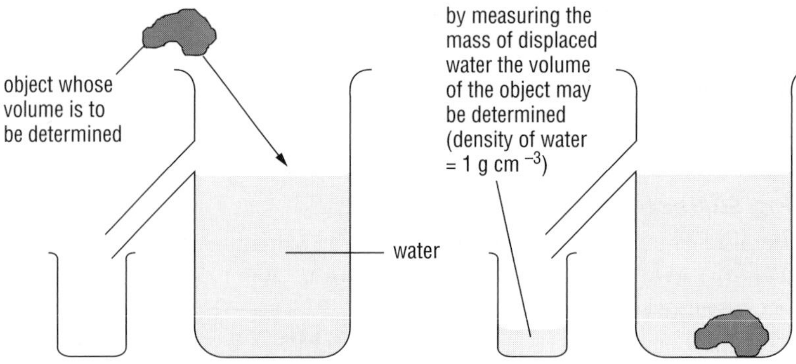

Figure 0.26 *Using a displacement can.*

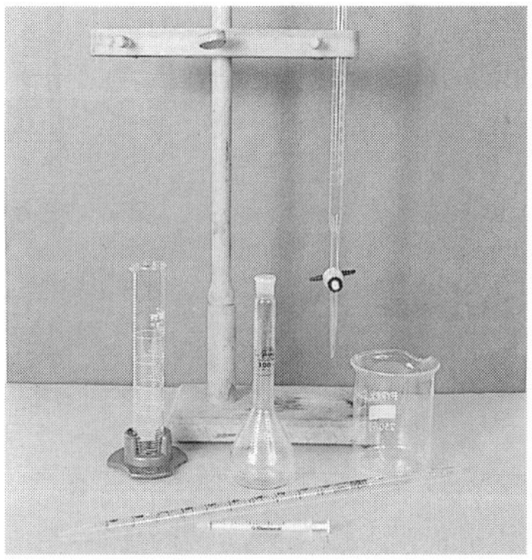

Figure 0.27 *Accuracy and precision increase from beaker to measuring cylinder to volumetric flask to burette to pipette to micro-syringe.*
Note. *Beakers should only be used for very approximate measurements. Measuring cylinders are better for approximate measurements. Get to know what different volumes look like. About what sizes are 1 cm^3, 5 cm^3, 10 cm^3, 50 cm^3, 100 cm^3 and 1 dm^3? Sketch apparatus of these sizes to scale on a piece of paper, then check your estimates.*

To read volumes accurately, make sure that the apparatus is vertical and that your eye is level with the graduated mark on the scale. Read to the bottom of the meniscus (see Figure 0.28).

Volumes of gases can be found by collecting them by displacing water from a graduated vessel such as a burette (if the gases are not too soluble) or by using a gas syringe.

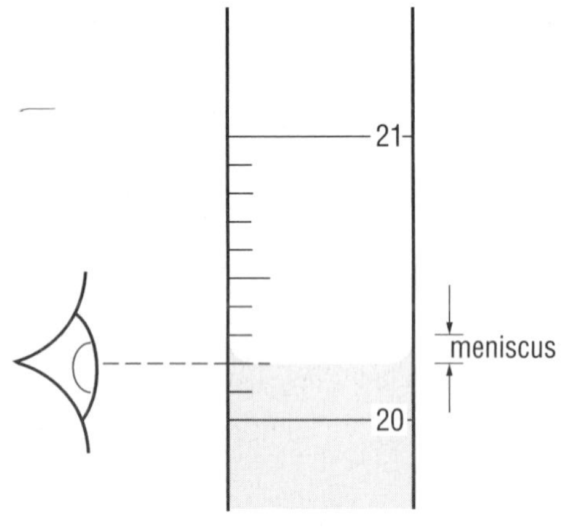

Figure 0.28 *Reading a volume accurately. Get your eye level with the bottom of the meniscus.*

Measuring mass

An electronic balance can be used to find masses of objects quickly and easily. However, there are certain important considerations that you need to take into account. As for length and volume, you need to decide on the precision you require.

Figure 0.29 *Using an electronic balance.*

Procedure

Using an electronic balance

1 Check balance is level (use spirit level bubble if present and adjust feet).
2 Check surface is firm and avoid leaning on the bench (balances are sensitive to small movements).
3 Use a draught screen for balances which read to ±0.01 g or ±0.001 g.
4 Use a weighing boat or other suitable container such as a weighing bottle for liquids.
5 Pre-weigh or use tare if available.
6 Remove container from balance to add solids or liquids (this helps to prevent spillage on the balance).
7 Use a spatula to transfer solids. If spillage does occur, clean up immediately.
8 Weigh to the required precision.
9 If the material is to be transferred to another vessel, do so and weigh the container again. Work out the exact mass transferred by the difference between weighings in 8 and 9.

Requirements

- ❒ Electronic balance
- ❒ Draught screen
- ❒ Weighing boat or bottle

Measuring temperature

Temperature changes can be measured in a variety of different ways. You need to take into account a number of different factors including:

- precision
- range
- accessibility.

Choose the range carefully, as exceeding the maximum on the scale will cause the bulb to burst. Increasing the range will reduce the precision, see Figure 0.30.

Mercury thermometers are in common use, but should be treated with care as glass is fragile and mercury vapour is toxic (poisonous). A mercury thermometer may withdraw a significant amount of heat from a small sample. Alcohol thermometers can be used to measure lower temperatures.

Thermistors can be used in temperature probes. The electrical resistance varies with temperature. This can be converted to a scale on a meter. Probes can be placed in a wide variety of inaccessible places, such as in opaque objects where glass thermometers cannot be read. They also have the advantage of being usable with data loggers. Temperature change over a period of time can be recorded and plotted using these devices.

Ovens and water baths are thermostatically controlled devices which can be used to control temperature. These should be checked to make sure that they are accurate enough for your work.

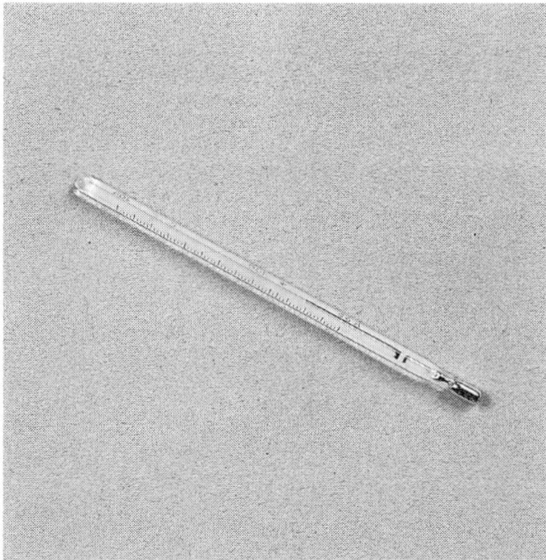

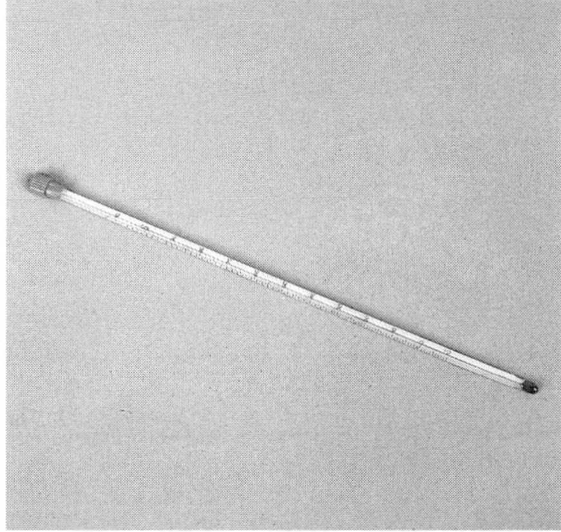

Figure 0.30 *A clinical thermometer needs to give high precision over a low range. A wider range makes a thermometer more versatile but less precise. What are the limitations of a clinical thermometer?*

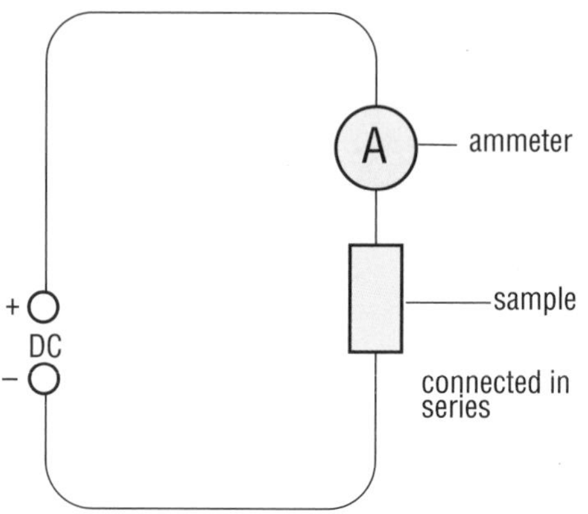

Figure 0.31 Measuring current using an ammeter.

Measuring current

An ammeter is connected in series with the sample through which the current to be measured is flowing (see Figure 0.31).

Measuring voltage

A voltmeter is connected in parallel with the sample across which the potential difference is being measured (see Figure 0.32).

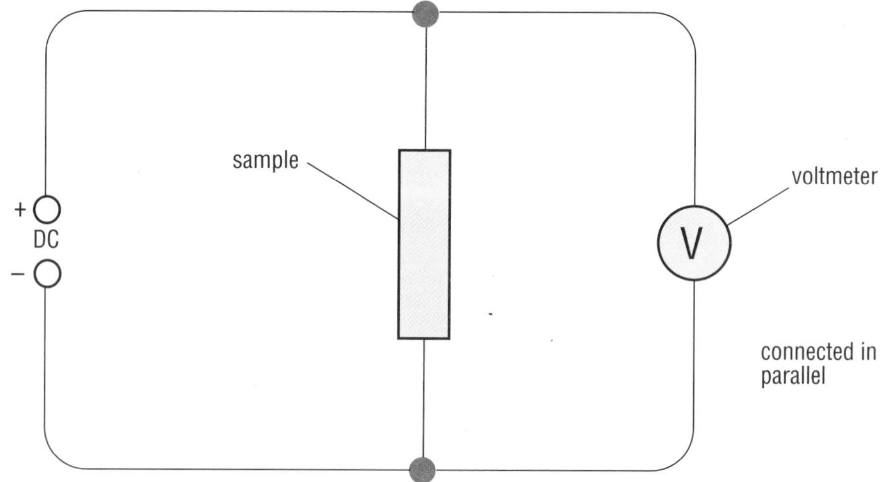

Figure 0.32 Measuring voltage using a voltmeter.

Sensory probes and data loggers

There is now a wide range of electronic devices which can be used to monitor changes and collect data automatically. (The use of temperature probes has been mentioned). Such devices can be used in the field as well as in the laboratory.

Data can be collected by a recording device, the data logger. It can be transferred later to a data handling program in a computer. This is especially useful if you want to:

- collect large numbers of measurements in a short time (faster than you could take readings)
- monitor continuously over a long period (such as changes over a 24 hour period). Table 0.8 gives some examples.

Figure 0.33 This environmental scientist is using probes to monitor the conditions (temperature and dissolved oxygen) of the river.

Table 0.8 Some useful sensory devices

Sensor	Useful applications
Temperature (Thermistor)	Temperature changes inside and outside differently insulated rooms over the course of a day
pH	pH changes in a culture of microbes over a week
Oxygen	oxygen concentration of a pond over 24 hours
Light	two sensors can be used to detect velocity: an object cuts off light from lamps as it passes
Movement	stretching of a wire under tension, movement of a spirometer

Note on using meters

Digital meters give you a readout in figures to appropriate precision for that instrument. Analogue meters have a needle over a scale sub-divided by lines. This presents you with two problems:

- the needle and scale need to be lined up by looking at them from directly in front. If a mirror is present on the scale the image of the pointer should be hidden exactly behind the pointer itself (see Figure 0.34)
- it may be possible to sub-divide a scale in 'your mind's eye'. The scale should indicate the precision of the instrument, so it is advisable not to go below the nearest half unit in taking readings.

Figure 0.34 *Inaccurate reading of an analogue meter. Correct reading = 5.0 volts; inaccurate reading (when viewed from side) = 4.8 volts.*

Using a microscope

Many things of interest to the scientist cannot be seen with the naked eye: the microscope can often help. Figure 0.34 shows the main parts of a light microscope. The sharpness of the image is limited by the nature of light. Electrons can be used to give more detailed images by using an electron microscope.

Procedure

Using a light microscope

Requirements

- ❐ Light microscope
- ❐ Microscope slides with specimens
- ❐ Cover slips
- ❐ Pencil or mounted needle

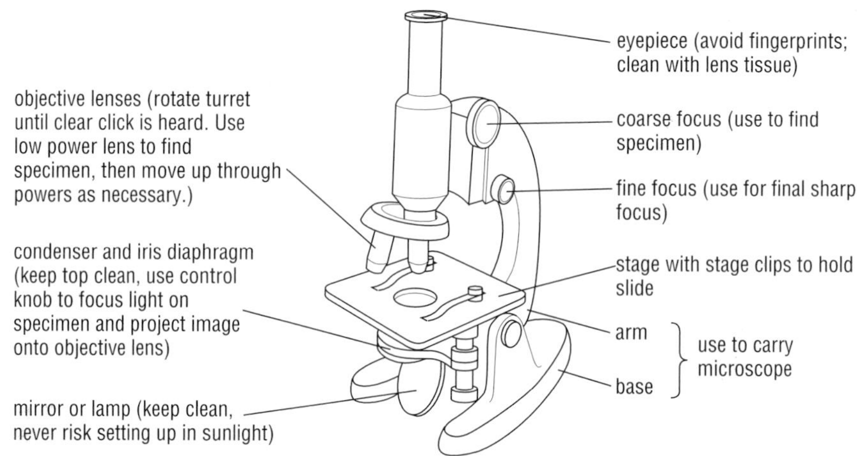

Figure 0.35 *The light microscope.*

1 Set the microscope up firmly on a bench in a position out of direct sunlight, where you can be comfortable.
2 Select low power (shortest objective lens; magnification is eyepiece power x objective power).
3 Clip slide to stage, positioning it so that the specimen is in the light from the condenser (use a cover slip for temporary slides).
4 Focus with coarse then fine focus knobs.
5 If specimen cannot be found:
   - focus on edge of cover slip and then search for specimen
   - try next power if the specimen is very small.
6 Close the iris diaphragm, then open to point at which the illumination is high enough to see the object clearly but is not too bright (comfort level).
7 Focus the condenser by placing a pencil or mounted needle tip on the light source and focusing until the specimen and point are in focus together.
8 If necessary use the iris diaphragm to adjust the light intensity
9 Use fine focus when moving to higher powers. Take care: high power objectives can break slides and the lenses can be damaged. If there is difficulty focusing using high power, watch the objective and move it close to the slide. Then attempt to focus by moving the slide away from the lens.
10 Readjust the illumination using the iris diaphragm; it will normally need to be opened a little more when using high power.
11 If lenses appear dirty, check by rotating the eyepiece. If the dirt moves, clean the eyepiece. If it remains stationary, check the objective and condenser lenses. Use *lens tissues* only; ordinary tissues scratch lenses.
12 When finished, remove the slide, return to the low power objective and check the microscope is clean and dry.
Report any faults to your supervisor.

Specimens must be thin enough for light to pass through. Sectioning is a specialist technique for making thin slices a single cell thick. Specimens that are small enough or thin enough can be mounted for inspection under a cover slip in a drop of liquid on a microscope slide. Specimens that are too large can also be macerated (broken up chemically or by needles) or squashed by pressing down on the cover slip (if soft enough).

Procedure

Making a temporary slide

Requirements
- ❒ Microscope slides
- ❒ Cover slips
- ❒ Mounted needle
- ❒ Specimen for mounting
- ❒ Suitable stain
- ❒ Teat pipette
- ❒ Small piece of filter paper

1 Place specimen on slide.
2 If it is in a liquid use only one small drop. If it is dry add one small drop of water or a suitable stain (chosen to suit the specimen).
3 Using a mounted needle, small spatula or other suitable implement, gradually lower a cover slip at an angle over the specimen. This pushes air bubbles out of the side as the cover slip is lowered.

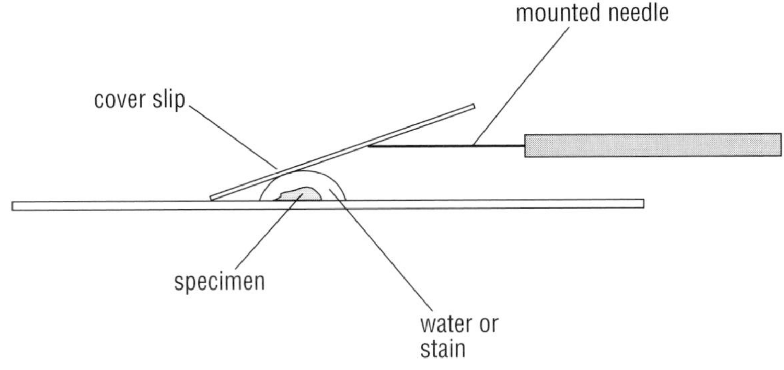

Figure 0.35 Making a temporary slide.

4 Remove any excess liquid with a tissue and view using the microscope.
5 If the specimen is mounted in stain the stain should normally be diluted first, as otherwise it will be too dark. Stain can also be added by irrigation (see Figure 0.36).

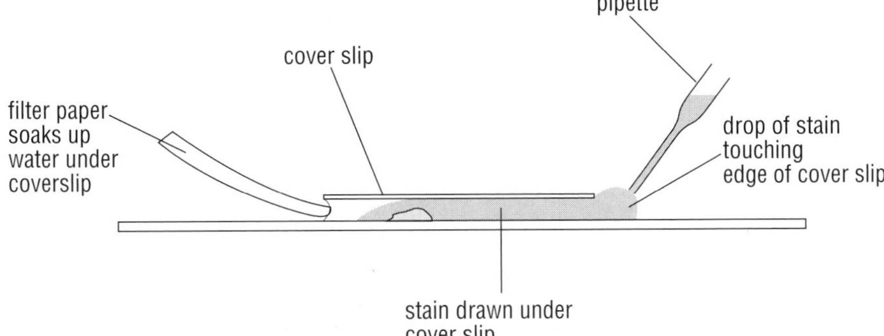

Figure 0.36 Irrigating a temporary slide. with a stain.

A drop of stain is placed on the slide next to the cover slip. A piece of filter paper is used on the opposite side to remove the water under the cover slip. Stain is drawn under and the specimen is stained.

1 Working on scientific tasks

Scientists are employed in a variety of services and industries. Many are employed in health-related activities. Others are employed in agriculture, engineering, chemical and pharmaceutical industries. In all these fields, scientists use their knowledge, skills, understanding and imagination to solve problems.

For example, scientists analyse substances to find out what they are and what they might be used for. Others are involved in making useful products or in monitoring and controlling change. Often this is within the three traditional areas of science: biology, chemistry and physics. However, the boundaries between these are becoming increasingly blurred. An effective scientific team uses expertise from a variety of backgrounds.

Figure 1.0.1 *Teams draw upon the expertise of all their members to solve scientific problems.*

Scientists work in the laboratory, the field and other environments. No matter where they work, scientists need to be able to use standard procedures, adapt them when necessary to meet particular needs and make best use of the time and resources available to them.

Above all, scientists must go about their business with due regard for the safety of themselves and others. They must be aware of the hazards and take the appropriate precautions.

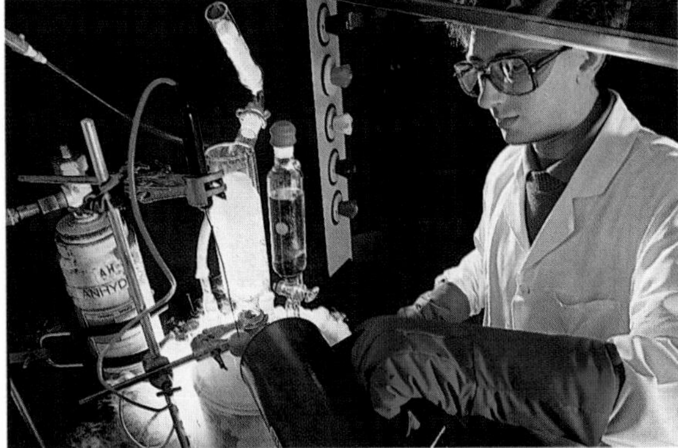

Figure 1.0.2 *Whether working in the laboratory or in the field, scientists must take all possible precautions to minimise risk.*

The Elements

Element 1.1 Examine science-based employment

You will need to show that you can:

- describe how science is used in services and industries
- describe work practices and identify how commercial factors and safety regulations affect them
- identify symbols for safety, explain their purpose and identify how the risks can be reduced.

Examine science-based employment, page 26

Working safely, page 2

Element 1.2 Carry out scientific tasks using standard procedures

You will need to show that you can:

- identify the resources needed
- use a standard procedure safely
- collect, process and display data
- compare the results with data from secondary sources
- draw valid conclusions.

Carry out scientific tasks using standard procedures, page 41

Element 1.3 Carry out scientific tasks by adapting procedures

You will need to show that you can:

- describe why a procedure needs to be adapted
- adapt the procedure and use it safely
- describe the effects of the adaptions made.

Carry out scientific tasks by adapting procedures, page 50

Examine science-based employment

You will need to show that you can:

- describe how science is used in services and industries
- describe work practices and identify how commercial factors and safety regulations affect them
- identify symbols for safety, explain their putpose and identify how the risks can be reduced.

What is science-based employment?

The simple answer to this question is 'Any job that uses science'. Of course, this raises the question, 'What is science?'.

Some people think that science progresses logically through careful experimentation. Others think that luck plays a major part, and there are plenty of examples of fortuitous discovery. Most people, however, do agree about the general nature of science and so you can often recognise if an occupation is science-based or not.

Many services and industries use science. Table 1.1.1 indicates some of these. In some occupations, although people do not use science all the time, they need to use scientific ideas to be able to do their jobs properly. Many people are more effective if they are able to use scientific knowledge in their work.

Table 1.1. Science-based employment

Laboratories are used by:	Science is used by:
biotechnology companies	agricultural/horticultural/forestry/ fishery workers
breweries	behavioural scientists
chemical companies	biologists
clinics	chemistry/gas/petroleum workers
colleges	chemists
dental services	chiropodists
environmental health departments	dentists
engineering companies	doctors
(e.g. mechanical, electrical)	engineers (all types)
food manufacturers/processors	food processing workers
forestry	geologists
hospitals	laboratory technicians
manufacturing companies	managers
pharmaceutical companies	marketing managers
research bodies	meteorologists
schools	midwives
universities	nurses
water authorities	occupational therapists
production/works maintenance	opticians
	pharmacists
	physicists
	physiologists
	physiotherapists
	psychiatrists
	radiographers
	science teachers
	speech therapists

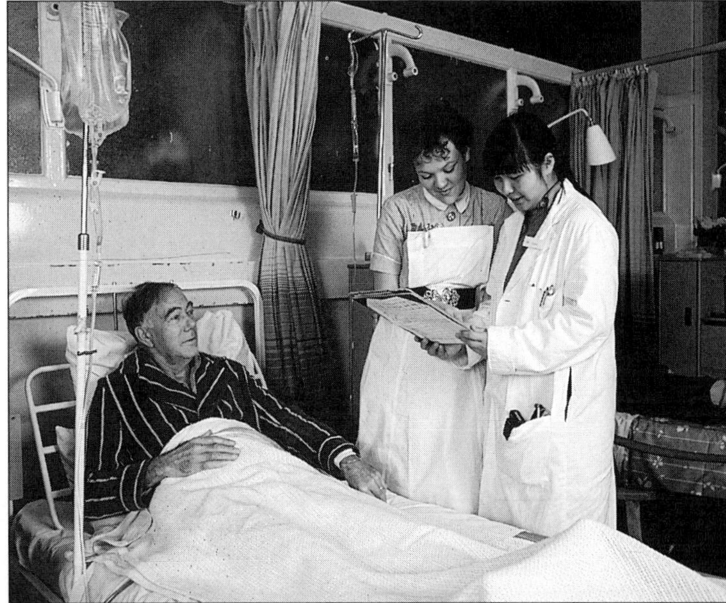

Figure 1.1.1 *All these people use science in their jobs.*

The ways science is used

Scientific work provides information that allows important decisions to be made in a rational and logical way. There are many ways in which scientific information is used.

Supporting education

The National Health Service has improved the health and quality of life of the nation. This success depends not just on treating people when they are ill: it is more effective to **educate** people to try and prevent disease in the first place. In addition, it is also cheaper.

Politicians need facts and figures to help them make decisions. For example, the decision to spend money on public works to provide clean drinking water and safe sewage disposal helped enormously to improve

> **FOCUS**
> **Science is used in:**
> - **industry and services – research, analysis, development**
> - **the health service – diagnosis, treatment therapy, monitoring.**

> **FOCUS**
> **Information and ideas discovered by scientists can be used to support education.**

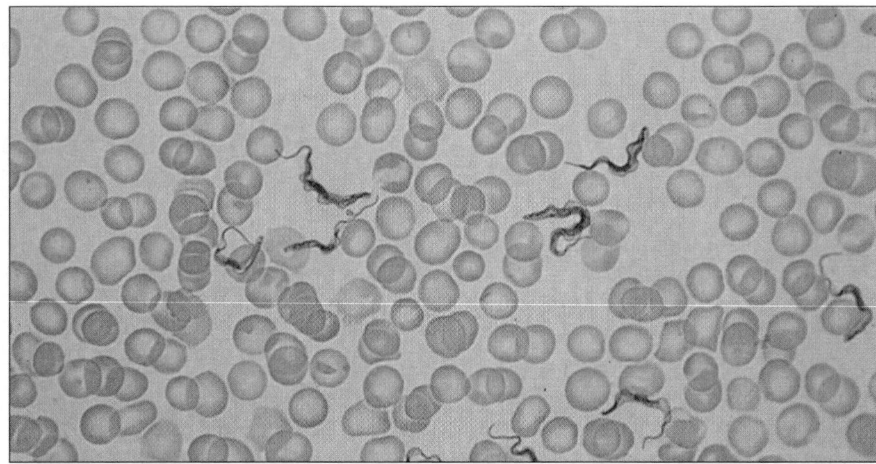

Figure 1.1.2 'Malaria' literally means 'bad air'. Until scientists showed that microbes (invisible to the naked eye) were causes of disease, common sense suggested that the air around swamps made you ill. The curtains of four-poster beds were intended to protect you from the harmful night air. When it bites people, the female Anopheles *mosquito can transmit the microscopic malarial parasite. The larvae of the mosquito live in the water of swamps and this is why malaria became associated with them.*

public health. Diseases like cholera and typhoid have been eradicated in the developed world. Polio has been significantly reduced in the UK.

Years of careful research have built up large quantities of information on the effects of smoking. Originally it was considered to be beneficial. Common sense suggested that, because it relaxed you and made you feel better, it must be good! Tobacco smoke was not recognised as a hazard.

Now the risks of smoking are well known. Scientists have established the effects of tobacco smoke in causing respiratory diseases like bronchitis, emphysema and lung cancer. It has been shown that passive smokers (including the pets of smokers) may also be harmed. The evidence is strong enough for victims of passive smoking to have a good case for suing tobacco companies for damages in court.

Scientists have provided good news, too. The respiratory system can recover to a certain extent when the smoker gives up, providing no real harm has been done. However, science can only support education. Many people still smoke – the addictive effects of tobacco are hard to suppress. Using scientific knowledge to the public good is not always easy!

Scientific research

Research is at the heart of scientific activity. Investigations are carried out to discover new information with scientists using a range of practical techniques together with their know-how to solve problems. They devise and carry out experiments to test their ideas. It is important to check that the ideas work in as many situations as possible. Experiments may lead to ideas, new or old, being rejected.

FOCUS

Scientists working in industry and services carry out research to tackle problems.

Case study

HEART DISEASE

On Tuesday July 5 1994 the *Guardian* carried an article entitled '*Heart disease toll worst but falling*'.

The article was based on information in a British Heart Foundation (BHF) report called 'Coronary Heart Disease Statistics'. It stated that deaths from heart disease were falling in Britain, but it still remained the nation's number one killer.

Professor Gerry Shaper, a member of the BHF's education committee, was quoted as saying, 'None of us can be complacent about our own lifestyles. We are a nation at risk. We live in a "coronary culture" in which high blood pressure is so widespread it is almost regarded as normal. Sixty per cent of the population are sufficiently inactive to increase their risk of heart attack and stroke, and almost three quarters of men have some experience of smoking that increases their risk.'

The report indicated that in Britain, 330 000 people a year suffered from heart attacks and 170 000 died from various forms of heart disease. About 2 million people suffer from angina. The costs to the National Health Service were estimated to be £1 billion a year, but industry is thought to lose about £3 billion in lost production.

Professor Shaper went on to say, 'While hundreds of thousands die of heart and circulatory disease each year, millions live with it. A quarter of middle aged men walking the streets of Great Britain have evidence of heart disease.'

Mike Rayner, a research officer at the Department of Public Health at Oxford University and who helped to collect the statistics said, 'Some of the statistics are encouraging: death rates are falling and some risk factor trends are in the right direction. But our fall in death rates is still far behind that achieved in other countries and the gap between social groups appears to be widening.'

Questions

1 Explain briefly what is meant by heart disease.
2 Who is Professor Shaper?
3 Why are we 'a nation at risk'?
4 What are the three causes of heart disease mentioned by Professor Shaper?
5 What is the cost to the country of heart disease?
6 Suggest some of the scientific methods that have been used to collect information on the causes and incidence of heart disease.
7 Choose one cause and explain why it is likely to lead to heart disease.
8 Using information from this case study and/or elsewhere, prepare a short health education leaflet. This should present scientific facts to support measures that people should take to reduce their risks of heart disease. You could summarise a number of issues in outline or choose one aspect to treat in more detail.
9 List some other public health campaigns that have made use of scientific data. Keep this work in your portfolio as evidence of the way science is used in supporting education and in maintaining health.

Sometimes the problems are theoretical. For example, Einstein developed his theories of relativity without using experiments.

Scientific ideas are accepted for as long as they appear to work. When they fail, new ideas replace them.

Cross breeding

Geneticists carry out important scientific research. Cross breeding different varieties of animals and plants makes it possible to combine their best qualities. Selective breeding of sheep, choosing the best animals for breeding, has allowed modern varieties to have higher yields of wool or meat. Modern wheat varieties have high yields and are disease-resistant. High yield is not the only quality that is needed in wheat varieties. Disease resistance is very important, too. Rusts are fungi which can devastate whole fields of wheat. High yielding rust-prone varieties can be crossed with low yielding rust-resistant ones (see Figure 1.1.3). The problem is that you are just as likely to get a low yielding rust-prone hybrid as the

Figure 1.1.3 Wheat should be high yielding and rust-resistant. It should also be able to withstand wind and rain and to be machine harvestable.

high-yielding, rust-resistant type that you want! New rust-resistant varieties must be bred every few years. This is because it does not take long for the rusts to mutate (change their genes) to overcome the resistance of the wheats.

Genetic engineering

Many new solutions to old problems have been made possible by the techniques of genetic engineering. Genes can be transferred from one organism to another. Will it be possible to make wheat rust-resistant using this technology?

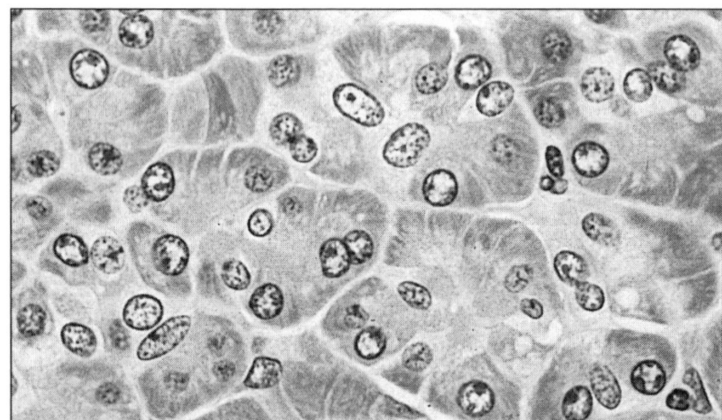

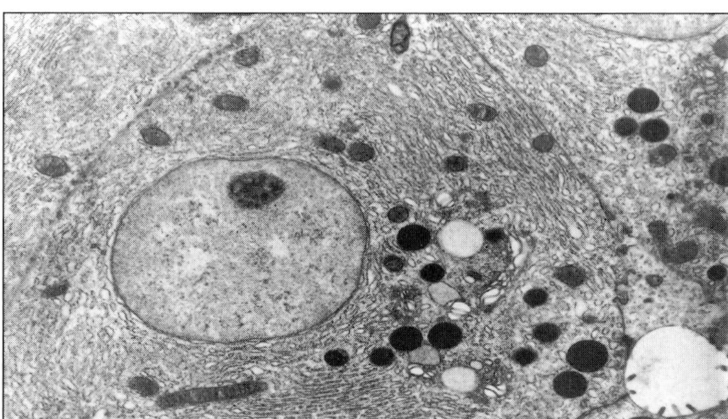

Figure 1.1.4 New ideas and new areas of research often depend on the development of new technologies. Cell biology leapt forward with the invention of the electron microscope. Details of cell structure are not visible using the light microscope **(a)**. Using electrons instead of light allows much more detail to be seen **(b)**. Note the difference in the resolution of the two images of cell structure.

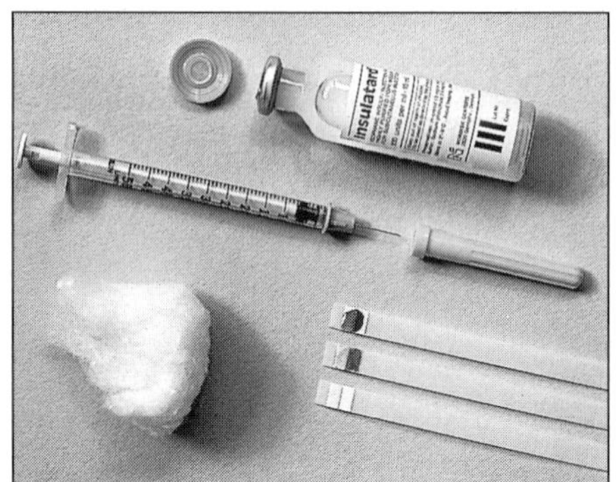

Figure 1.1.5 Bacteria can have genes added to them so that they can make medicines such as antibiotics and insulin.

Figure 1.1.6 These sheep have been given a human gene so that they produce a protein in their milk which can be used to treat emphysema in humans.

FOCUS

Analysis is an important scientific activity in industry and services.

Scientific analysis

Research often involves or leads to analysis and development.

Analysis is about taking something and breaking it down into its parts. You can identify the parts and work out how they fit together. Analysis involves characterising and, if possible, identifying:

Characterise: determine the properties of a material

Identify: recognise a material by comparing its properties with those of known materials

Scientists characterise and identify materials using practical techniques such as environmental monitoring, strength measurements and chemical tests.

In the science-based services, analytical scientists have many jobs to do. For example:

- forensic scientists collect and analyse all kinds of substances from the scene of a crime
- in hospital pathology laboratories, scientists analyse samples of such things as blood and urine to diagnose diseases and to monitor the progress of treatments.
- in industry, scientists analyse many materials. This includes the quality control of manufactured products. The analysis may need to be very careful and detailed, for example, to ensure safety in the food and drugs industries, and accuracy in the engineering of machine parts.

Investigate organisms in their environment, page 58

Investigate the properties of solid materials and relate them to their uses, page 80

Determine the composition of substances, page 99

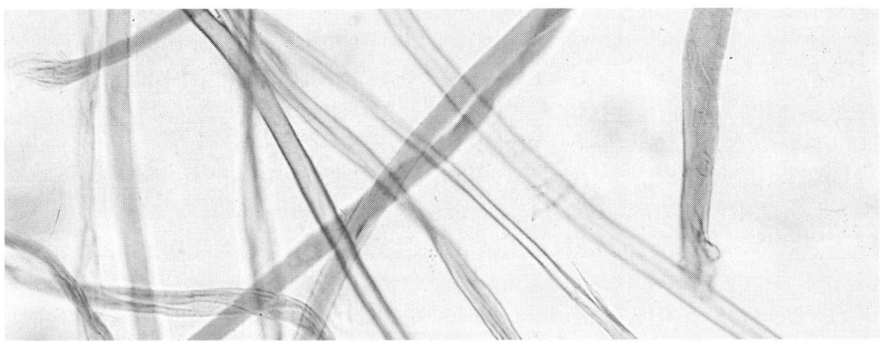

Figure 1.1.7 *Evidence can be astonishingly small! This photograph, taken using a microscope, shows fibres of red wool. Trained forensic scientists can tell from matching such samples against others where the wool was manufactured, by whom, and when. Such evidence can be very important in police investigation.*

Science and the improvement of health

Prevention is better than cure. Science is used in health education programmes to help us to make sound decisions about our lifestyles and to encourage us to maintain our health.

When things do go wrong, we rely on medical scientists to:

- diagnose the problem
- provide an appropriate treatment or therapy (course of treatment) to aid recovery
- monitor the course of the condition, to check whether:
  - the treatment is working
  - the treatment needs changing
  - the condition is getting better or worse.

FOCUS

Science is used in the health service for the diagnosis, treatment, therapy and monitoring of illnesses.

Figure 1.1.8 *Hospital pathology laboratories have an important role in diagnosis. Suspect samples of diseased tissues and body fluids can be analysed to check for problems. Treatment can be recommended and monitored. For example, the bacteria found in a urinary infection can be tested to find the best antibiotic to use. Samples of urine can be taken later to check whether the infection has cleared up.*

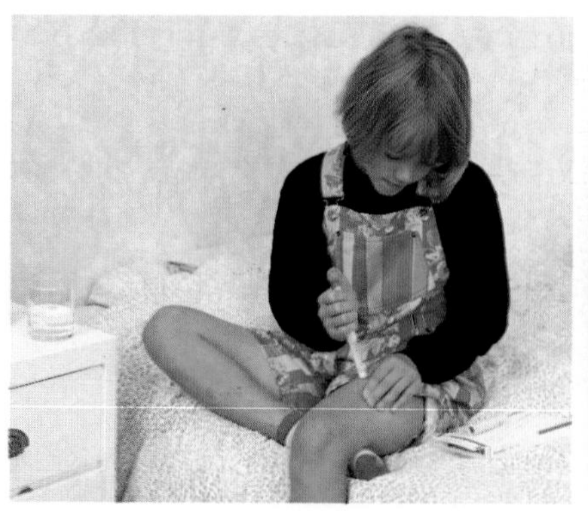

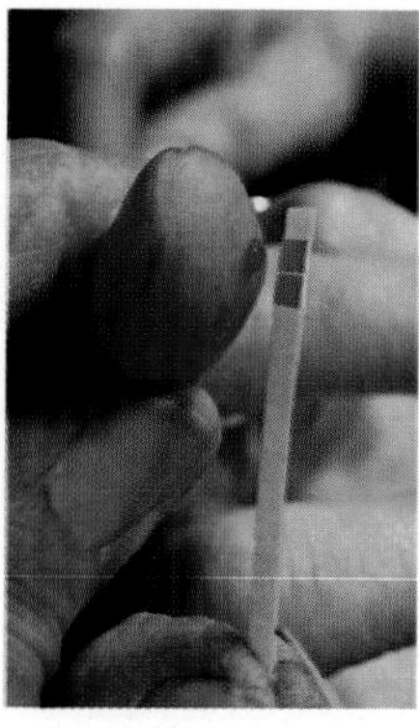

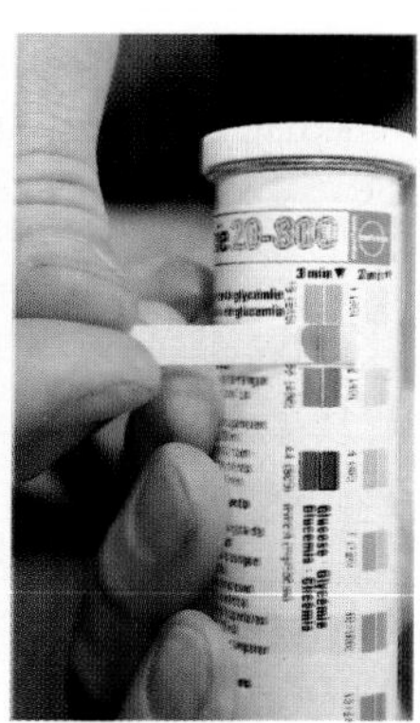

Figure 1.1.9 *Some diabetics are unable to produce sufficient insulin. Their blood sugar levels rise too high and glucose can be detected in their urine. Monitoring is important to make sure that the treatment (a carbohydrate-controlled diet and injections of insulin) is working. Scientists have produced simple-to-use test strips so that diabetics can test their own urine, to regulate their treatment themselves.*

Case study

A CAREER IN MOLECULAR CELL BIOLOGY

The following account has been adapted from an article that appeared in the University College London Science Magazine (number 8), *Molecular Cell Biology at University College London:*

'For young people looking for a career which will see them through the next forty to fifty years, science, and in particular, the science of biology and medicine, is a safe bet and a very exciting way to earn a living. In the future the use of high technology to solve the problems of society will be in great demand. In societies like ours, where the majority of people will be over fifty years of age, health care will be a central concern.

The main challenges to health care in the advanced societies of the next century will be neurodegenerative diseases (affecting the brain and nervous system) like Alzheimers, malignancy, and cardiovascular diseases, such as stroke (bursting of an artery in the brain), and arteriosclerosis (hardening of the arteries). These conditions are all caused by a breakdown in the molecular machinery of the cells of the body.

Many thousands of laboratory scientists are working in research institutes and universities throughout the world trying to understand how these breakdowns occur. Finding methods to prevent or treat the problems is mainly the job of researchers in pharmaceutical (drug) companies.

These scientists will all need a thorough knowledge of molecular cell biology.They analyse cells and tissues and the way that they work. This involves breaking them down into the molecules which make them up. Then the ways in which they work together in a living system are determined.

In the next few years, the human genome programme will provide a deluge of information about the genes in the human cell nucleus. It will be the job of molecular cell biologists to use their experimental systems to find out what the proteins that the genes code for actually do. The proteins will be analysed to test for the part that they play in causing disease. This is a job that will keep scientists busy well into the first half of the next century.

Molecular cell biology has come into its own only during the last ten years. It has been able to make use of the extraordinary advances that have been made in techniques that were developed in the late 1970s. In 1993 London University opened a large new research centre, the Laboratory for Molecular Cell Biology. This has room for up to 15 research teams. It is expected to become a major contributor to biomedical research in the UK.'

Questions

1 Why will health care be 'A central concern' through the next forty to fifty years?

2 What is meant by 'malignancy'?

3 What is the 'human genome programme' investigating?

4 Genes provide the code for making proteins. What job concerning these will 'keep scientists busy well into the first half of the next century'?

5 Suggest some other areas of health care where science will be important and many people will be employed in the future.

6 Write a short case history of someone you know who has been ill (it could be you!). Invent a name for them. Indicate:

(a) the problem/condition that they suffered from
(b) how scientific methods were used to:
  (i) diagnose the condition
  (ii) treat the condition
  (iii) monitor the course of the condition
(c) support your account with any illustrations or useful background informationthat you think is appropriate.

Scientific development

Scientific research leads to ideas, materials and products which may have the potential to benefit society. However, these discoveries must be **developed**. You may have heard of *Research and Development (R&D)* sections of industrial companies. As an example, the discovery of a new therapeutic drug is followed by years of painstaking development before it can be used to treat medical conditions.

New knowledge is of little use until it is put to use. The laser was invented before anyone could think of a use for it. It was 'a solution looking for a problem'. Lasers now have many uses, including in the telecommunications industry, where they can transmit light pulses along optical fibre cables. These lightweight cables can carry signals for long distances without needing boosters and without distortion, unlike the coaxial cables that they are replacing. Capacity is also enormously increased, with tens of thousands of signals being transmitted simultaneously. There are many other examples of 'solutions looking for a problem'.

Scientists need to carry out a great deal of additional work to develop new discoveries before they can be used in industry and services.

Figure 1.1.10 *The laser used to be a 'solution looking for a problem'. The transfer of enormous quantities of data over vast distances is the challenge for the telecommunications industry. Lasers and optical light fibres have combined to provide a solution.*

Case study

DEVELOPING A NEW CROP PROTECTION CHEMICAL

The following information on crop protection appeared in the Bayer *Research* magazine (6th edition):

Figure 1.1.11 *During the early years of crop protection efforts, enormous amounts of chemicals were sprayed onto fields. Today, only a few grams of active compound are sufficient to treat an entire hectare of farmland. The greater part of the spray liquid is water. Often less than 1 kg of active substance is distributed in 2 000 dm³ of water.*

The population of the earth is increasing by three people every second. Every single one them has a right to enough food to eat. Experts worldwide predict that starvation will be a central problem in the next 10 years.

To produce enough food, it will be necessary to maximise the yield of existing crops. This means that chemicals to protect crops from pests and diseases will be increasingly important in the years to come. This must be done without causing harm to the environment.

When a promising new chemical is discovered, scientists go through a long process of development before they can use it and market it. This is very time-consuming and very expensive.

A new crop protection chemical must be:

- able to be stored for a reasonable period of time
- harmless to the user
- easy to dissolve in water
- sprayed without difficulty
- effective against pests or diseases in the lowest possible concentrations
- harmless to the environment.

Researchers in crop protection development have to find the solutions to all of these problems.

Morestan is a product mainly used to control spider mites and mildew in fruit and vegetable crops. If a farmer wishes to use it to fight apple mildew, the recommended treatment is to use 600 g of Morestan in 2 000 dm^3 of spray for one hectare of apple trees.

Questions

1 How many people does the world population increase by every day?

2 How many people does the world population increase by every year?

3 If a new chemical is found to kill crop pests, a great deal of further development is still necessary. What are the properties that a new product must have before it can be marketed as an acceptable crop protection chemical?

4 How many m^2 are there in a hectare? (Optional: pace out a sports field taking one good long pace to be roughly one metre. Calculate its approximate area in hectares.)

5 If 25% of Morestan is the active ingredient and the rest are additives, how much of the active compound would the farmer use to treat one hectare of apple trees?

6 The leaf area of the trees is about ten times the area of the orchard. What is the area of the leaves that have to be sprayed?

7 How many grams of the active compound must be sprayed on each cm^2 of apple tree leaf?

Working safely, page 2

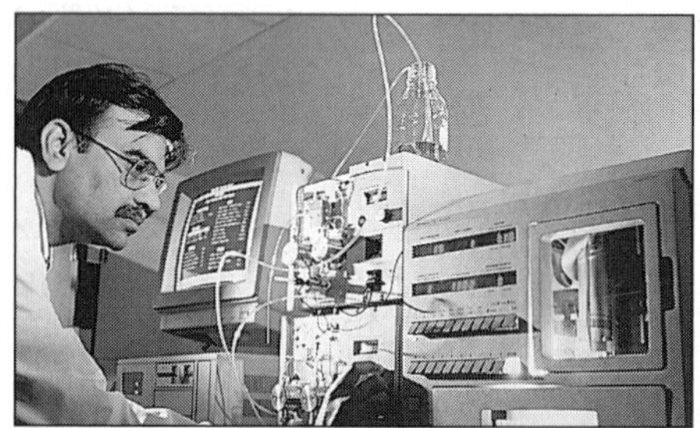

Figure 1.1.12 A research biologist using high-performance liquid chromatography (HPLC), just one of the range of analytical techniques available.

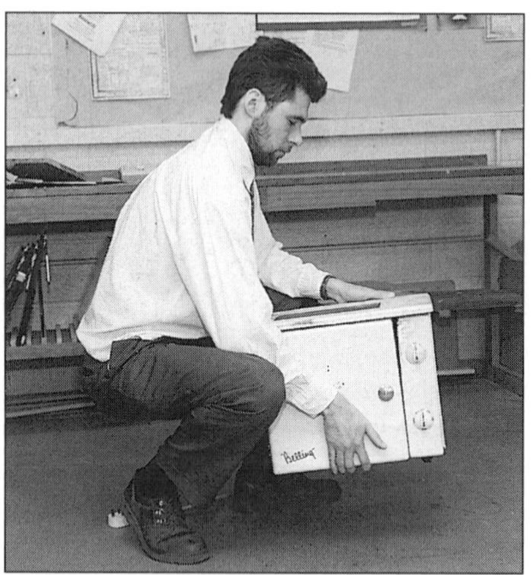

Figure 1.1.13 Straight back lifting technique is very important. Incorrect lifting is the most common cause of industrial injury, with potentially lifelong consequences.

Work practice in science-based occupations

Each area of scientific work has its own requirements and work practices. They include equipment, ways of handling material, the use of safety equipment, disposal of waste, quality control, the supervision of others and the communication of information.

Equipment

An analytical laboratory will contain a range of specialised equipment which will depend on the work the scientists have to carry out.

Handling materials

Materials may need to be handled in tiny amounts with high precision or in bulk. Some will be safe to handle without special precautions, others will need special handling techniques. Sometimes they will be handled in a laboratory, sometimes they will need transporting long distances.

Use of safety equipment

You will need to use a variety of different kinds of equipment to help you to work safely. This includes fume cupboards and personal protective equipment such as laboratory coats, goggles and gloves. Each science occupation is required by law to protect its workers with the correct type of safety equipment.

Figure 1.1.14 Some substances must be handled in very large quantities. Chemicals are often transported in bulk chemical tankers. Such tankers always carry relevant safety information about possible hazards.

Disposal of waste

In any practical work, you will need to consider how to dispose safely of waste materials. These could include microbes as well as chemicals.

Anything that goes down the sink eventually reaches sewage treatment works. These rely on living microbes to clean the water for recycling. It is essential that sewage works are not poisoned.

Solid wastes in bins are taken to open rubbish tips and eventually buried. Rain may wash materials in these tips down into underground water, so care has to be taken to prevent harmful materials reaching public water supplies. Incineration is also an option. It has the advantage of sterilising waste, so this method is frequently used by hospitals. Large amounts of incinerated waste can generate substantial amounts of heat, so this can be used for other purposes, such as heating a factory. However, smoke may need to be treated to remove poisonous or corrosive gases.

You must always dispose of wastes carefully, following any instructions that you have been given. An important but simple method to protect the environment is always to use the minimum amount of reagent or other material. Recycling is another method. For example, solvents may often be recovered. You may be asked to dispose of materials in a container for further treatment.

Figure 1.1.15 *Chemicals used to spray crops and protect them from diseases can be harmful. This employee has taken sensible precautions to minimise the risk of this hazard.*

Figure 1.1.16 *How do companies deal with their waste problems? Do they have methods to reduce waste or to treat it before disposal? Can they recycle materials?*

Quality control

Many science-based occupations make use of scientific methods because a high level of precision is essential in their products.

Sometimes testing is necessary. Starting materials, production intermediates and products must be checked for suitable purity. There are many examples of this in the food and pharmaceutical industries.

Sometimes the human factor must be checked and monitored. In health laboratories it is clearly important that patients are diagnosed correctly. Inspection of cervical smears for cells that indicate a risk of cancer is a very difficult, time-consuming and taxing job. Employees must not be allowed to work for too long and must be good at their job. In such cases work can be randomly checked: a certain proportion of slides are sent to other laboratories to see if the employees there achieve the same results.

Figure 1.1.17 *Quality control is essential on this production line. One faulty component may mean the final product will not work.*

Supervision of others

Supervision means taking responsibility for guiding the work of others and helping them to do their jobs properly. In any working situation, each employee is given certain tasks and responsibilities. The larger the organisation, the more complicated this becomes. You should have the opportunity to find out how supervision is organised in at least one science-based work area. Find out what the major responsibilities are and why it is necessary to assign them in that way.

Communication of information

Communication of ideas and new knowledge is central to the progress of science. Each scientist 'publishes' his or her work to make it available for testing by others. This is often done by writing an article for a scientific journal.

Within an organisation, communication has to be well organised to be effective. Paper systems are giving way to electronic mail. Computers linked by modems through the telephone system are giving rise to an 'information super-highway'. You should be able to find examples of different methods of communication throughout your course.

The effects of commercial factors on work practices

The success of a new product and the company that manufactures it depends on:

- the **cost** of the product
- the **price** of its production
- the **level of investment** in future developments.

Work practices described in the previous section affect these three things. Costs must be kept down, but safety and the necessary quality must not suffer. Prices must cover costs, but not be too high for the product to sell. Investment in initial outlay must pay for people as well as equipment. Profits must cover and pay off this investment and then provide for investment for expansion or the introduction of new improved methods.

FOCUS

Commercial factors that affect the success of products include costs, prices and levels of investment.

Case study

DEVELOPING A SUCCESSFUL PRODUCT

'Beano stops gas leaks'. This was the title of an article that appeared in *Biotimes*, the magazine of the Novo Nordisk company, which develops and manufactures enzymes for a wide range of purposes. Beano is a good example of how successful new products often use a combination of imagination and technical know-how. The Beano in this case is an enzyme product, not a comic! Enzymes are proteins which act as biological catalysts. They control chemical reactions inside cells and help to break down food when we digest it.

The unfortunate side effects of eating beans are well known. Flatulence is a polite term for it! Americans take the problem very seriously and spend about $800 million every year on indigestion products. Most anti-gas products treat the gas in the stomach where it actually occurs, but Beano acts on food to prevent the gas from forming in the first place.

Foods like beans, chilli and cabbage contain complex sugars that people can't digest. Instead, bacteria break them down in the stomach and form gas. Beano contains a food enzyme which breaks down complex sugars, making them digestible. This means that little or no gas is produced.

Beano is the brainchild of Alan Kligerman. He is the owner and Chief Executive Officer of AkPharma Inc. When he received a sample of a new enzyme from Novo Nordisk, with their help he was able to develop it into a successful product. Launched in 1991, Beano gained a small but profitable share of the market. It sold for $8.95 for a 16 cm^3 bottle.

Beano was originally sold as a liquid. A few drops are placed on food before eating it. Since then, tablets have been produced. This was the result of a joint project between Ferrosan and Novo Nordisk. Ferrosan is a company that specialises in vitamins and dietary supplements. They have considerable know-how in tablet formulation. Novo Nordisk are now able to supply AkPharma with a tailor-made enzyme granulate which is designed to be put straight into a tablet press.

Jan Boeg Hansen, the Project Manager for digestive aid enzymes at Novo Nordisk says, 'There is no dust formed and it is easy to handle. This is an example of how someone came to Novo Nordisk with an idea for a special project and we were able to help them to develop it.'

Questions

1 Why was Alan Kligerman able to develop the new Novo Nordisk enzyme into a successful product? Suggest both economic and scientific reasons.

2 Novo-Nordisk manufacture a large range of enzymes for a wide range ofinnovative products. Can you think of any everyday products that make use of enzymes?

3 How much would Beano cost for each cm^3 in the UK at today's exchange rate?

4 What would have had to be taken into account when deciding what the prices hould be?

Assignment

EXAMINING SCIENCE-BASED EMPLOYMENT

Setting the scene

What do scientists do? Where do they do it? The following tasks will help you to explore these questions. Scientists are found in all kinds of occupations. They work in public services such as the health service and analytical laboratories. They have vital roles in the agricultural, engineering, manufacturing, chemical and pharmaceutical industries.

In all of these areas they use science in a variety of ways, using specific working practices which are often dictated by safety considerations and regulations, and by commercial factors.

The assignment

This assignment consists of a number of tasks. Some can be completed quickly. For others you will need to maintain a record in your portfolio throughout the course.

Task 1: What do scientists do?

1 In small groups, brainstorm the question, 'What do scientists do?' Tackle this in two ways:

(a) what jobs do they do?

(b) what kinds of tasks do they perform and what kinds of equipment do they use?

Use a marker pen and a large sheet of paper to record your ideas. Continue for about ten minutes or until you run out of steam. Then skim through this book. Add to your list if you find or think of something that you missed.

2 If possible, compare your list with other groups. Add to them if you can.

3 In the introduction to this book it tells you that scientists characterise, obtain and control.

(a) Working in your group, choose ideas from your list that you think illustrate each of these things.

(b) Try to define each term by writing a brief sentence to describe what it involves.

4 Compare your lists and definitions with other groups. Write your own individual definitions and examples to include in your portfolio.

Task 2: Exploring safety issues

This task will help you to consider the safety issues that you will need to look at further in Task 3.

Part 1

1 In a small group, discuss what you think are the legal requirements for safe working in a laboratory. Make some rough notes.

2 What information on safety regulations do you think other science students (not following a GNVQ Science course) should have? Discuss this, using Unit 0 of this book and any other sources that you can.

3 Prepare a simple information sheet or leaflet of your own individual design to summarise what you consider to be the most important regulations and requirements. Illustrate it in any way that you consider effective.

Part 2

Employers and education establishments have a legal responsibility to provide you with a safe working environment. You also have a legal responsibility to work safely and to maintain that environment.

The Control of Substances Hazardous to Health (COSHH) Regulations (1988) require you to be aware of all of the hazardous substances that you use or encounter in the science laboratory and elsewhere at work. Definitions of hazard and risk and a procedure for the risk assessment of an activity can be found in Unit 0.

1 For each of the laboratories that you work in, compile a list of hazards, using these four categories (sub-divide them if you think that is useful):
   - toxic chemicals
   - high voltages
   - high temperatures
   - biological materials.

   Try to find a few examples of each to start with, but add to your lists as you find new hazards throughout your course.
2 Briefly indicate how risk may be reduced for each of your examples.
3 Keep a record of the hazard symbols that you encounter through your course.
4 Keep a record of equipment with British Standards kitemarks or with CE marks. Explain why these standards are necessary for the equipment involved.
5 Divide your GNVQ Science group into two teams. Design a safety awareness exercise. Each team should think of ten hazardous situations to simulate in a laboratory.
   SAFETY: *You must check with your supervisor before you set up this exercise,which must not put the participants at unacceptable risk.*
   When you have your supervisor's permission, teams should set up the situations in a laboratory. Each team should then to try to discover the hazards set up by the other team. You should write down your ideas and discuss them.
   Each team must explain to the other how they think the risks associated with their hazards could be reduced or eliminated.
   Make notes to include in your portfolio.

Task 3: Investigating a science based service or industry

1 What science-based employment is there in your area? Organise with other members of your GNVQ Science group to share the work for this task.
   Use libraries, the careers service, Yellow Pages and any other relevant sources to compile a list of as many different examples as you can. List them as *services* or *industries* in your portfolio.
2 What experience do you have? Have you had a full or part-time job which has involved you in or brought you into contact with scientific work? Do you have any relatives who use science in their work? Does anyone that you know, know anyone who works as a scientist?
   Find opportunities to make contacts with people working with science.

3 From your work for 1 and 2, choose an occupation to research in depth. If it is at all possible, choose one where you can talk directly with someone working in that job. Ideally, you should be able to visit them at their place of work or even work-shadow them for a period of time. Discuss this carefully with your supervisor, before you approach anyone.
Other options for gathering information include:
- arrange a visit to a scientific workplace
- arrange a visiting speaker
- explore the possibility of investigating the work of a school or college laboratory technician
- find out what videos are available
- collect careers literature, research scientific journals, etc.

4 Decide how you are going to collect and record your information so that you can cover the range and meet performance criteria for Unit 1. For your chosen service or industry, you need to find out about work practices and the effects of commercial factors and safety regulations on them. Follow this scheme:
(a) Work practices
Choose a minimum of three from those listed below to report on for your chosen area of work. Write a description in your portfolio using carefully chosen examples. Choose from:
- operation of equipment
- handling materials
- use of safety equipment
- disposal of wastes
- quality control
- supervision of others
- communicating information.

(b) Commercial factors
Identify how each of the following has an effect on some aspect of the work practices that you have described:
- cost (e.g. raw materials, labour)
- price of product
- level of investment (e.g. in people, equipment).

(c) Safety regulations
Identify how each of the following has an effect on some aspect of the work practices that you have described:
Electricity at Work Regulations
COSHH Regulations
Management of HSW Regulations
PPE Regulations

(d) Ways science is used
Keep a record of the ways in which science is used in this service or industry.In your portfolio, write descriptions of any examples of these uses of science:
- supporting education
- research
- analysis
- development
- improving health.

Design data collection sheets to help you to cover this work. You could:

- design a questionnaire for use on a visit, with a visitor or for a telephone conversation
- write a list of questions you need to answer
- construct a checklist.

Make an action plan for any visits. Give yourself guidelines of what you need to look for or ask about. Add to or modify your sheets as you progress through the task. *Word processing* gives you the flexibility to store and add to data whenever you like.

Task 4: The ways that science is used

You should consider the ways that science is used in at least two different services (including health and an analytical laboratory) and in two different industries (mentioning agriculture, mechanical and electrical engineering, manufacturing, chemical and pharmaceutical, grouping these if appropriate).

1 Write brief accounts as you find new examples during your course.
2 Make sure that you have examples to cover any gaps in your list for Task 3. Make yourself a checklist to cover the services, industries and uses of science. Tick them off as your examples cover them.

Task 5: Hazard and risk assessments

1 Keep a record of any hazard you identify, and the risk assessment resulting from the practical work that you do.
2 Keep a list of these assessments with a record of where they can be found in your portfolio.
3 *Never start work until you have had your risk assessment checked by your supervisor.*

Grading

There are a variety of tasks in this assignment. They can be developed to different levels. Discuss with your supervisor what you should do. To show good planning, you should know what are reasonable aims and objectives. Be prepared to suggest alternative or additional approaches to achieving performance criteria. You will have good opportunities to meet merit or distinction criteria. All four themes are covered: Planning, Information Seeking and Information Handling, Evaluation, Quality of Outcomes.

Opportunity to collect evidence
In completing these tasks you will have the opportunity to meet the following requirements for Intermediate GNVQ Science.

Science units
Unit 1:
Element 1.1 PCs 1,2,3,4,5,6

Core skill units

Communication:
Elements 2.1, 2.2, 2.3, 2.4

Information technology:
Elements 2.1, 2.2, 2.3, 2.5

Carry out scientific tasks using standard procedures

You will need to show that you can:

- identify the resources needed
- use a standard procedure safely
- collect, process and display data
- compare the results with data from secondary sources
- draw valid conclusions.

Assignments in other units will give you ample opportunities to meet the performance criteria and range for this element. Some of the standard procedures that you will need to use are outlined here, more specialised procedures can be found in the relevant units.

Processing and displaying data

Measurement and observation, page 12

Units for measurement, page 121

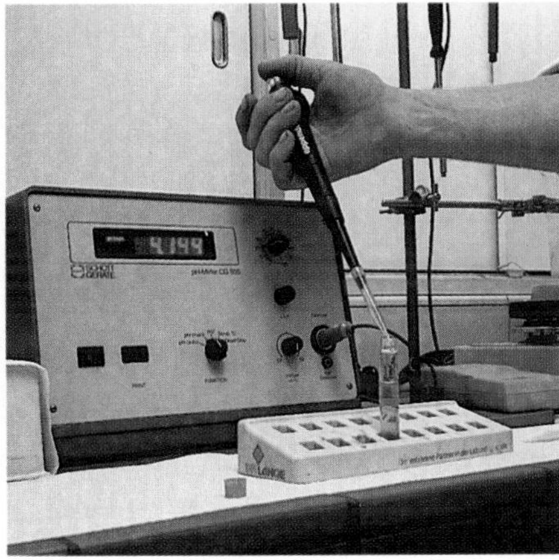

Figure 1.2.1 Scientists use a wide range of standard techniques to collect data.

Most of a practical scientist's work consists of observation. Scientists watch things to collect information or data. Data may consist of simple labels or descriptions, or they may involve measurement.

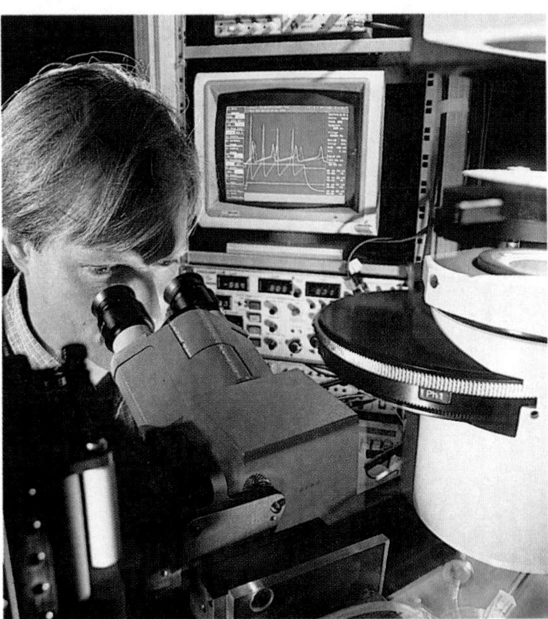

Figure 1.2.2 Relatively cheap, high performance computers have made it possible to collect, process and display data in a far more detailed and sophisticated way than was possible before.

FOCUS

Qualitative data use descriptions or references that allow grouping by similarities. Members of separate groups show recognisable differences.

Quantitative data use measurements. If necessary, calculations may be carried out to find the mean, median and mode of a set of data.

FOCUS

Qualitative data can be matched against references. They can be used to identify patterns, including similarities and differences.

Accuracy and precision in measuring length, page 15

Qualitative data use categories. Things are grouped by the selection of certain common features (qualities) such as colour or shape.
Quantitative data involve measurement so that numerical values (quantities) can be given, such as the length and mass of an object.

Comparing measurements

You cannot rely on a single measurement. Comparing measurements of the same thing allows you to check your instruments and your technique. You can also find out about variations in the things that you are measuring.

You expect your instruments to be accurate. A good way to make sure is to measure the same thing twice using two different instruments. For example a standard mass can be weighed on two different balances. If they are both accurate, they will give the same reading (within their limits of precision).

Comparing your results with those of other people, or repeating your own, is an effective way to detect and eliminate human error. You need to be careful though. An instrument like a balance can give consistent results even if it is not accurate. You can also get consistent values if you do the same thing wrong each time!

Many things that you measure will not give you consistent values because they vary. For example, the diameter of a piece of wire may vary slightly at different points along its length. The water content of soil samples will vary depending on exactly where in a field they have been taken.

When this happens, you will need to get a best estimate by taking a series of measurements and finding the arithmetic average or mean.

Mean, mode, median and range

The mean is often simply called 'the average'. It is found by taking all the measurements that have been made and adding them together. They are then divided by the number of measurements that have been made.

For example, suppose you timed an athlete over a series of 400 m races. You measured the times on six occasions, and they were 52 s, 54 s, 54 s, 53 s, 55 s, 56 s.

$$\text{Mean} = \frac{52 + 54 + 54 + 53 + 55 + 56}{6} = \frac{324}{6} = 54\ \text{s}$$

The mean, median or mode can be used as the 'average' of a set of quantitative data (measurements). Choosing which one is best depends on the way that the measurements vary and the use that is made of the 'average' value.

Often the mean alone does not tell us very much. We may need to know more about variation in the thing that we are measuring. Range, mode and median are useful when considering how something varies.

The **range** tells us how much difference there is between the largest and smallest values. It gives us a very good idea of how consistent measurements are. A small range indicates little variation in a sample, but a large range means that values can vary a great deal.

The range for the six 400 m times given above is 56 – 52 = 4 s.

Table 1.2.1 Range, mean, mode and median

Range	the difference between the maximum and the minimum value in a set of results
Mean	the arithmetic average = total of individual values divided by number of values used
Mode	the most frequently occurring value
Median	the central value found by placing all the values in order of magnitude (the average of the central values, if there is an even number of values)

The **mode** is the most commonly occurring value in a set of data. It can sometimes be a better 'average' value to use. For example, a few large values can make the mean on the large side. Consider the data:

2, 2, 3, 3, 3, 3, 3, 9, 10, 12

$$\text{Mean} = \frac{2 + 2 + 3 + 3 + 3 + 3 + 3 + 9 + 10 + 12}{10} = 5$$

Mode = 3 (the value which occurs the most number of times)

In this case, the mode would be a better 'typical value' to use.

The **median** is the central value when all of the measurements have been placed in order of size. For example:

2, 2, 2, 3, 3, 4, 4, 5, 5

Median = 3

With an even number of values you take the average of the two central values. For example:

2, 2, 2, 3, 3, 4, 4, 5, 5, 10

the median is $(3+4)/2 = 3.5$

The mean is 4. The importance, therefore, of using the median is that it offsets the effect of the single large value (in this case, the 10) to give a better estimate of a 'central value'.

Sometimes you will not expect much variation in your measurements (that is, a small range). This may be because there is little or no variation in the thing you are measuring. If you have the *whole of something* to measure, such as the length of a piece of wire or the mass of an object, for example, repeated measurements should not vary by more than the precision of your instrument. If they do, something is wrong!

If you can only measure *part of something* at a time (take samples), variation greater than the precision of the instrument indicates variation in the thing that you are measuring. For this you need to know the range.

Suppose that you have a container of ball bearings and you want to know if they are a reasonably consistent size. You use Vernier callipers to measure five and obtain the results in Table 1.2.2.

Table 1.2.2 Diameters of ball bearings

Ball bearing	1	2	3	4	5
Diameter/mm	11.3	11.0	11.6	11.0	11.1

The smallest ball bearing is 11.0 mm and the largest is 11.6 mm in diameter. The range is therefore 11.6 – 11.0 = 0.6 mm. This is well above the precision with which we can measure using Vernier callipers. This is ± 0.05 mm, a range of 0.1 mm, so we can assume that the variation is due to differences in the ball bearings, rather than to measurement errors.

$$\text{Mean} = \frac{11.3 + 11.0 + 11.6 + 11.0 + 11.1}{5} = 11.2 \text{ mm}$$

Is this a good estimate of a typical ball bearing? We only have a small number of results. What would happen to our value for the mean if the next ball bearing we measure is 11.6 mm wide?

A few exceptional values can sometimes alter the mean to make it misleading, so mode or median may be more useful. Why would manufacturers of personal protective equipment like laboratory coats and gloves be particularly interested in the mode?

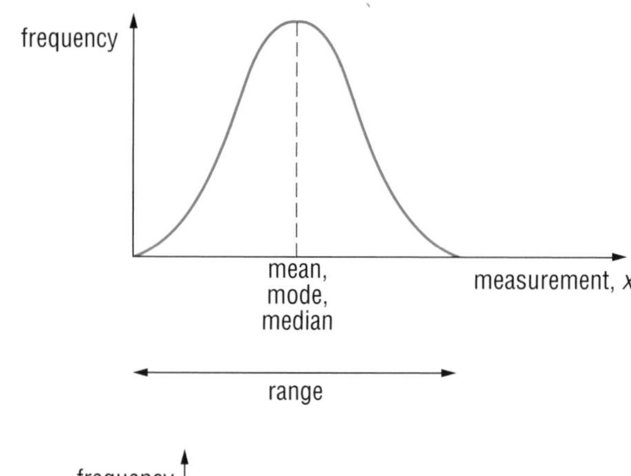

Figure 1.2.3 Gaussian or normal distribution.

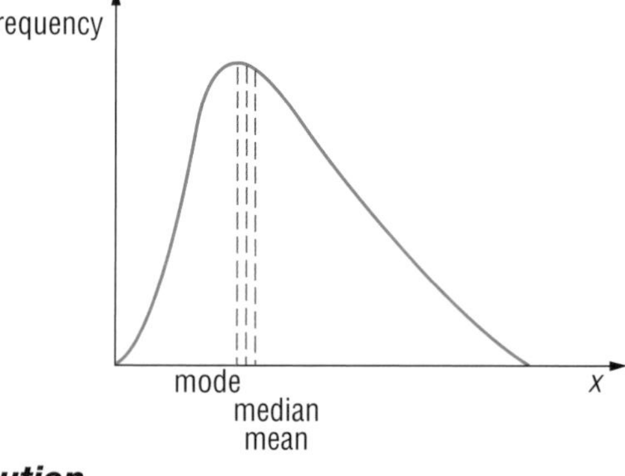

Figure 1.2.4 A skewed distribution.

The normal distribution

Many measurements show wide variation. Adult human heights and weights are examples. Such measurements often usually show a normal distribution (also called a Gaussian distribution). When you count up how many individual cases are found for each measurement you find a large number near a central value, with fewer and fewer as you get near the extremes (Figure 1.2.3).

Sometimes the mean, mode and median do not coincide (Figure 1.2.4). We say that the measurements are *skewed*. Values of mode and median may be useful, depending on what you want to use the results for.

Representing data

Tables

Data are often displayed in the form of a table. You will see many examples throughout this book. If you produce tables, make sure that each column is headed properly and, if numerical quantities are given, the correct units are shown.

Drawings

Using a microscope, page 21

Although data will often be measurements that can be presented in tables, drawings will also be necessary in reporting methods and findings, especially from microscope work.

Photographs and videotapes can also be used to record data.

Procedure

Making drawings

1. Decide if a drawing is appropriate. Is a simple description in words clear enough?
2. Decide whether to use plain paper or ruled paper. Use feint lines if you need to put a significant amount of text on the same page.
3. Use a good, sharp pencil. HB is usually hard enough to remain sharp, but gives a reasonably dark line.
4. Draw glassware, etc, in the standard way as two-dimensional line drawings of sections through equipment.
5. Make large, clear drawings with continuous pencil lines.
6. Leave room for labels/annotations (short explanatory notes). Do not label on the drawing itself.
7. Avoid shading and colour unless absolutely necessary (no 'artistic effects').
8. Arrange label lines neatly around drawing, horizontally or radiating from the centre. Do not cross them. Ensure label lines touch the structure being labelled.
9. Give a suitable title.
10. Indicate magnification, scale or actual size if this is not apparent.

Using graphs

Plotting charts and graphs can simplify the analysis of data. Trends can be seen and measured; data that is out of step with the rest can be spotted.

Bar charts and histograms

Bar charts are used for qualitative data. The lengths of bars can be used to show frequencies, that is the relative number of times that a particular effect or other occurs. A discontinuous scale is used. In other words, the categories do not have definite order and there are no intermediate values. For example, you could use colours such as red, green or blue.

Histograms are used for quantitative data. The area of the bar indicates the number of individual cases in a category. A continuous scale is used. In this the data can be arranged along a continuous scale, with intermediate values occurring at equal intervals. Length is an example.

Bar charts

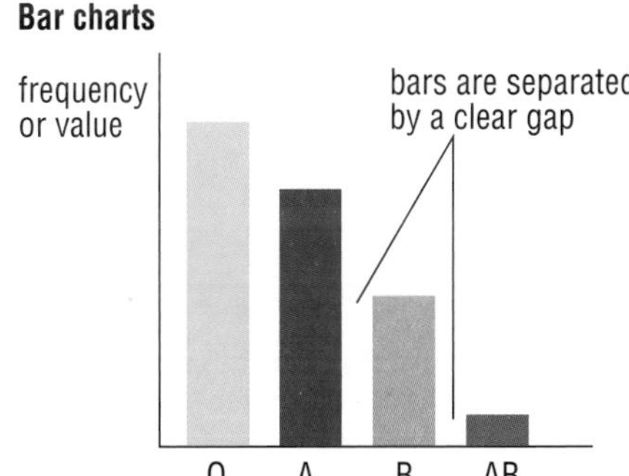

Definite categories, there may be no particular order, the scale is *discontinuous*. Use for *qualitative data*. Bar charts are used to show the pattern of variation in a set of measurements.

Histograms

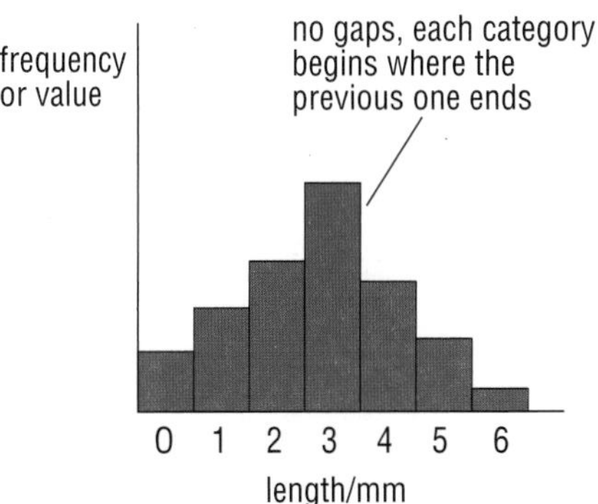

Artificial categories in a definite order on a *continuous* scale. Use for *quantitative data*.

Figure 1.2.5 *Bar charts and histograms.*

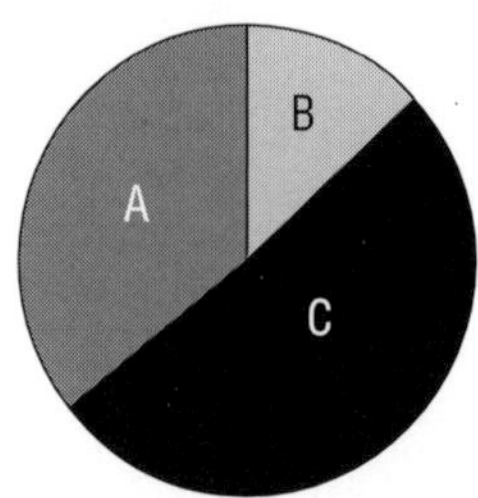

The angle of each segment is proportional to each individual value. Labels and sub-headings should indicate what each segment shows and what units are used.

The sum total of the measurements is found, here A+B+C

- For percentages this would be 100%. 360° is then proportioned for each value
- For percentages $\frac{360}{100} = 3.6°$ x each individual percentage
- For any set of results $\left(\frac{360 \times \text{individual value}}{\text{total of all values}}\right)°$

  If two charts are compared, the diameters of the circles can be made proportional to the totals of each set of values:

  Diameter of chart 2 = $\frac{\text{diameter of chart 1} \times \text{total values of chart 2}}{\text{total values of chart 1}}$

Figure 1.2.6 *Constructing a pie chart.*

Pie charts

Pie charts can also be used to compare relative frequencies or sizes. Data are converted to angles.

Straight line graphs

Straight line graphs are found in many situations.

The variable that you control (that is, deliberately change in a known way) is called the independent variable. You plot this along the horizontal or *x*-axis. The variable that you measure the changes in, caused by variations in the values of *x*, is the dependent variable. This is plotted on the vertical, *y*-axis.

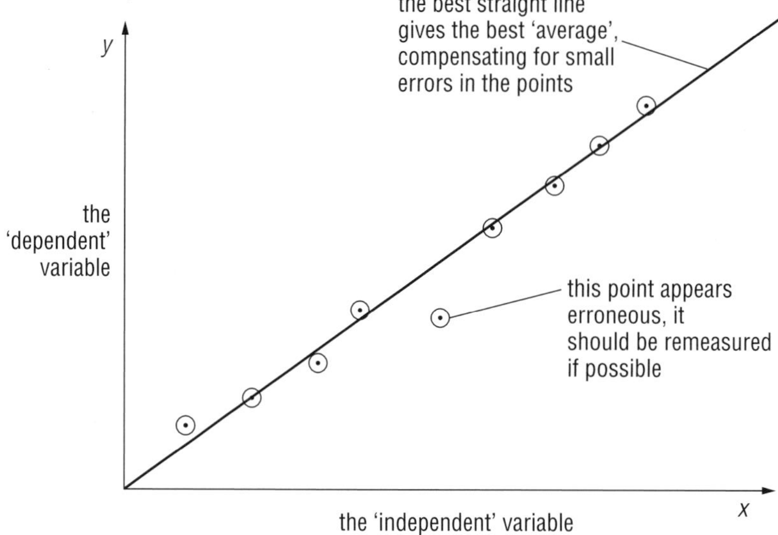

Figure 1.2.7 *Using straight line graphs.*

FOCUS

Scientists use straight line graphs to interpret sets of data. Gradients and intercepts on the axes can be found.

Two quantities may be calculated from a **straight line graph**:

- the gradient of the line – the rate of change of the dependent variable with the independent variable. For example, the **gradient** of a graph of the distance a car has travelled (y axis) against the time taken (*x* axis) gives its speed (Figure 1.2.8).
- the intercept of the line on either the *x* axis or the y axis. For example, Figure 1.2.9 shows the increase in speed of a car with time. The graph shows that timing began when the car was travelling at 30 km.p.h. (the intercept on the speed axis, when time = 0). The gradient of the straight line gives the acceleration.

the rate of change of *y* with respect to *x* can be found from the gradient of the line

$= \frac{y_2 - y_1}{x_2 - x_1} = \frac{100 - 40}{3 - 1}$

$= \frac{60}{2} = 30$ km.p.h.

distance/km; time/hours

Figure 1.2.8 *Calculating the gradient of a graph. How could you get a negative gradient.*

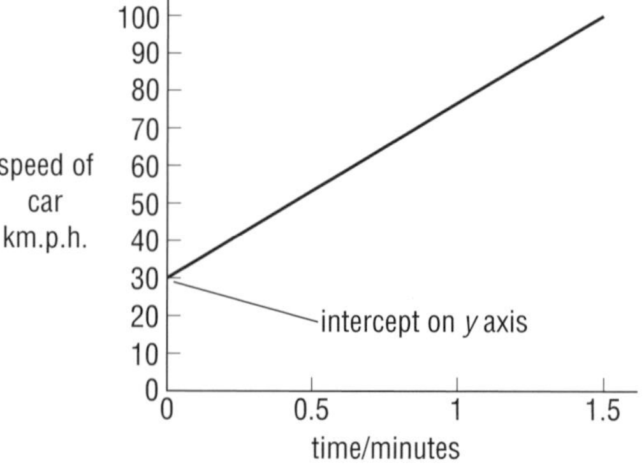

Figure 1.2.9 *Determining the intercept of a straight line graph.*

Procedure

Drawing graphs

1 Decide which variable is independent and which one is dependent. Plot the independent variable on the horizontal (*x*) axis and the dependent variable on the vertical (*y*) axis.
2 Choose scales to fit the available space, but avoid awkward multiples (e.g. use 2 s or 5 s but not 3 s).
3 If necessary, break scales to avoid crowding points in one corner of the graph paper, but make this clear.
4 Label axes and state units. An oblique line is used, e.g. length of rod / cm.
5 Use a sharp pencil to plot points clearly and accurately and to draw lines. If more than one line is plotted on the same axes, label them.
6 Only draw a best straight line (using a ruler) or smooth curves of best fit if the intermediate values are meaningful. You must be able to assume that the values in between your measured ones are an accurate estimate of real values. You need continuous scales for this. If they are not or there is any doubt, rule straight lines between the consecutive points if you wish to show a trend.
7 Give the graph a suitable title.

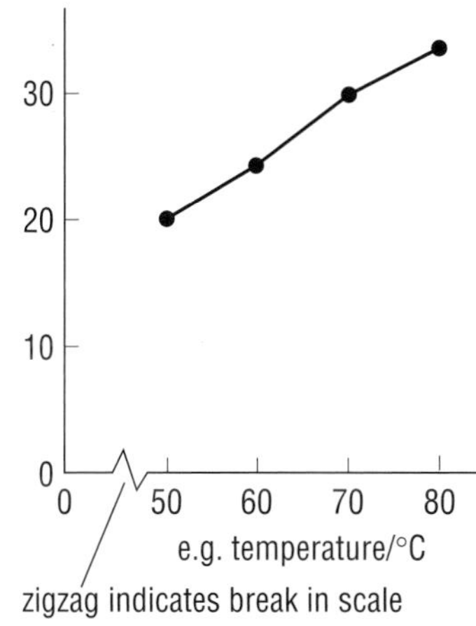

Figure 1.2.10 *How to show a broken scale on a graph.*

Graphs will often give curves rather than straight lines. You will often need to draw the smoothest curve that you can between points, so that you can read off values for points in between the ones that you have plotted. An example of this is in the use of calibration curves. By using samples of known values it is possible to calibrate an instrument such as a colorimeter.

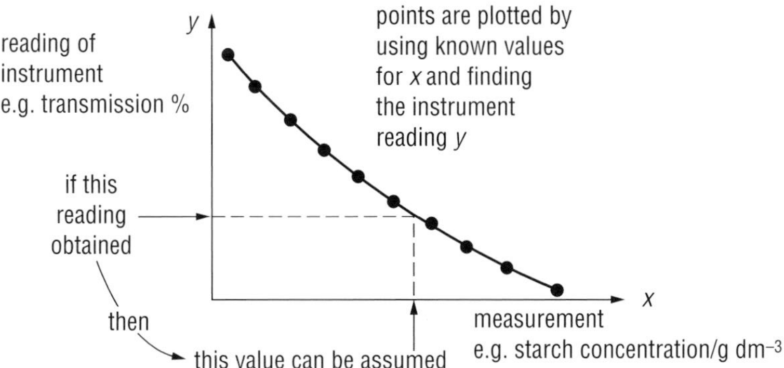

Figure 1.2.11 *A calibration curve.*

If graphs give curves rather than straight lines, rates can still be estimated by drawing a tangent to the curve. A tangent is a line at right angles to the curve at that point.

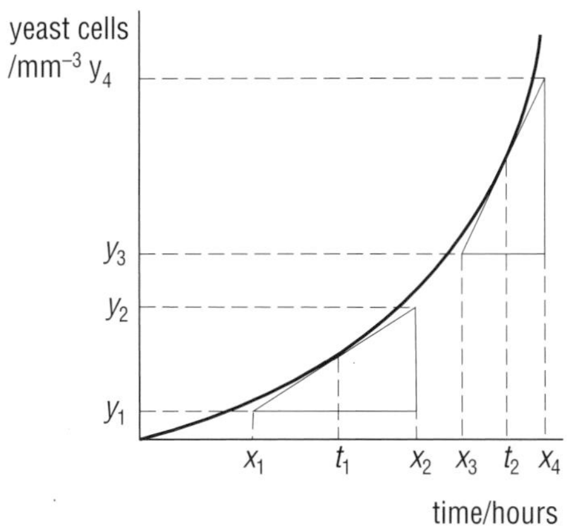

Figure 1.2.12 *Graph of the growth of yeast cells in a glucose solution.*

Mathematical formulae can be used by scientists to manipulate data.

Using formulae

The **formula** for a straight line graph, that passes through the origin (0, 0) is $y = mx$. In this formula m is the gradient. It is a constant, it always has the same value. From this we can see that the gradient $m = y/x$. Being able to rearrange formulae is very important.

The formula for a straight line graph, that intercepts the y axis at c (when x is zero) is $y = mx + c$. Again, in this formula m is the gradient and is a constant.

There is really only one rule to apply:

To rearrange a formula, do exactly the same thing to both sides.
You must remember that if you multiply or divide, you must do it to everything on both sides.

A trick that does the same thing is to cross multiply when you want to get rid of fractions:

e.g. $\frac{A}{B} = \frac{C}{D}$

Multiply the top of each side by the bottom of the other side:

$$\begin{matrix} A & & C \\ & \times & \\ B & & D \end{matrix}$$

And so, AD = BC
(This is the same as multiplying both sides by BD.)

This still works if only one side is a fraction, because you effectively treat the non-fraction as being 'over one':

Example 1

$A = \frac{B}{C}$

$\frac{A}{1} = \frac{B}{C}$

$$\begin{matrix} A & & B \\ & \times & \\ 1 & & C \end{matrix}$$

AC = B
Now find C

Example 2

$A + B = \frac{C}{D}$

$\frac{A + B}{1} = \frac{C}{D}$

$$\begin{matrix} A + B & & C \\ & \times & \\ 1 & & D \end{matrix}$$

(A + B)D = C
AD + BD = C
Now find A, B and D

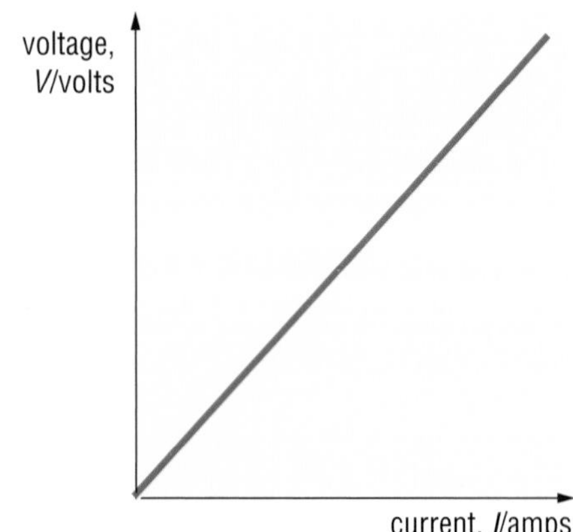

Figure 1.2.13 *A straight line graph of voltage against current. What is the formula for this graph (gradient = m)? The resistance, R, is found from the gradient. What does R equal? What does V equal in terms of I and R? What does I equal in terms of V and R?*

For electrical circuits, current (I), voltage (V) and resistance (R) can be linked by the formula for a straight line graph. You can rearrange this formula to find any one of these in terms of the other two.

Secondary sources

Often you will need to compare your results with those obtained by other scientists. This can be found in:

- databases
- textbooks
- databooks
- the scientific literature.

An experiment used to obtain data is called a primary source. Sources of information that has been collected and recorded by other scientists, and recorded in a suitable form, are called secondary sources.

Drawing valid conclusions

In any investigation a scientist sets out with an objective – to test an idea, analyse a substance and so on.

A valid conclusion is one which describes how well the original objectives of the investigation were met. It will be based on evidence (and not 'gut reaction') and will take account of any possible sources of error.

PC1 resources needed for scientific tasks are identified
equipment ☐ consumables ☐ human ☐ time ☐

PC2 task is carried out following standard procedures and observing safe practice
biology ☐ chemistry ☐ physics ☐
laboratory ☐ ☐ field ☐
working individually ☐ working as a member of a team ☐
long term sequential task (over several weeks) ☐

PC3 collected data are processed and displayed in the required form
qualitative data ☐ compare with reference ☐
search for patterns ☐
identify similarities ☐
identify differences ☐
quantitative data ☐ descriptive statistics ☐
mean ☐
median ☐
mode ☐
transformation of data:
calculate using formulae ☐
interpret straight line graph ☐
identification of units ☐
representations ☐
line graphs ☐
bar charts ☐
pie charts ☐
tables ☐

PC4 results of tasks are compared with related data from secondary sources
database ☐ textbook ☐ databook ☐ scientific literature ☐

PC5 valid conclusions are drawn
related to purpose ☐
based on evidence ☐
possible source of error taken into account ☐

Figure 1.2.14 *Element 1.2 Checklist.*

Checking the criteria for element 1.2

Assignments in other units will give you ample opportunities to meet all of the performance criteria and range for this element.

A checklist can be found in Figure 1.2.14. Make a copy of it and use it to help you. *Each box should be ticked at least once.*

Carry out scientific tasks by adapting procedures

You will need to show that you can:
- describe why a procedure needs to be adapted
- adapt the procedure and use it safely
- describe the effects of the adaptions made.

FOCUS

A procedure may be limited in its use because of its:
- **sensitivity**
- **range of application**
- **scale of operation.**

Adapting procedures

Nearly all procedures have their limitations. They often need to be adapted to do a particular task.

You may need a more **sensitive** technique, to use a procedure for a different **range of applications** or to adapt to a different **scale of operation**.

You will need to consider:
- changes in the procedure, such as the sequence of steps, or even altering a particular step
- alternative instruments (e.g. different sensitivity or range), apparatus (e.g. different size or precision), reagents (e.g. different concentration, alternative reagent).

FOCUS

Effects of adapting a procedure:
- **does it meet the need?**
- **does it give reliable results?**
- **does it lead to valid conclusions?**
- **is it easy to do?**
- **does the risk assessment change?**

The **effects** of any modifications should be noted. For example, did they meet the **need**, how **reliable** are the results, how **valid** are the conclusions that are drawn, how **easy** was it to carry out the modified procedure? Did the **risk assessment** change? (For example a large scale chemical preparation may need a fume cupboard.)

PC1 the need to adapt a procedure to carry out a task is described
sensitivity of technique ☐
range of application ☐
scale of operation ☐

PC2 procedure is adapted to meet needs

PC3 the adapted procedure is carried out observing safe practice

and

adapt to meet needs:		adapt safely
procedures	☐	☐
instruments	☐	☐
apparatus	☐	☐
reagents	☐	☐

PC4 the effects of the adaptations are described

in terms of:
meeting identified need ☐
reliability of results ☐
validity of conclusions ☐
ease of practical operation ☐

biology ☐ chemistry ☐ physics ☐
laboratory ☐ field ☐
working individually ☐ working as a member of a team ☐
short term investigation ☐ long term sequential task (over several weeks) ☐

Figure 1.3.1 *Element 1.3 Checklist.*

Checking the criteria for Element 1.3

Assignments in other units will give you ample opportunities to meet all of the performance criteria and range for this element. There will be many occasions when you need to adapt a standard procedure to meet the specific requirements of a task.

A checklist can be found in Figure 1.3.1. Make a copy of this and use it to check your progress. *Each box should be ticked at least once.*

Questions

1 Match the following lists by pairing the numbers of the examples (i) to (vi) to the letters (a) to (e) for the ways science is used. Also indicate if the examples are from industry (I) or services (S). The letters may be used more than once or not at all.
For example if you think that example (i) is development in industry, put: (i) d I
(i) Scientists working for a pharmaceutical firm are looking for new chemical compounds in a plant from a tropical rainforest.
(ii) A radiographer has used X-rays to find if a child has swallowed a button.
(iii) Plant biologists working for the Ministry of Agriculture Fisheries and Food (MAFF) have produced a new variety of potato which is resistant to attack by fungal diseases.
(iv) A chemical company is advertising a new detergent for washing clothes in cold water.
(v) A forensic scientist is given a sample of blood-stained clothing to match to the victim of a violent crime.
(vi) An engineering company is about to market a new kind of telephone.
Ways science is used:
(a) analysis
(b) research
(c) supporting education
(d) development
(e) improving health.

2 (a) Sketch a symbol which shows that a product has been made to:
(i) British standards
(ii) European standards
(b) Why are these symbols used?

3 In the Health Service, science is used to improve health. List the four methods used and give an example of each.

4 A manufacturing company employs engineers to develop new machinery to make a successful soap powder into a liquid product. Describe the commercial factors that you think will be involved in this process.

5 Work practices include:
operation of equipment
handling materials
use of safety equipment
disposal of wastes
quality control

supervision of others
communication of information

For each of the following legal requirements, give one or more examples of work practices from the categories above which are affected by them. An example would be: (b) controlling substances hazardous to health / communication of information e.g. using hazard warning labels on chemical containers in a laboratory.

(a) testing appliances regularly
(b) controlling substances hazardous to health
(c) preventing exposure to hazardous substances
(d) defining danger areas
(e) defining procedures for emergencies
(f) using personal protective equipment

6 Give an example and describe how you would reduce risk when:
(a) using a hazardous chemical
(b) working with high voltage equipment
(c) heating to a high temperature
(d) working with a hazardous biological material.

7 During the course of a week, a woman ate the following vegetables and fruit, for which the content of certain nutrients per 100 g is shown:

	vitamin A/mg	vitamin C/mg	calcium/mg
broad beans	22	30	30
Brussels sprouts	67	35	27
cauliflower	5	70	18
onions	0	10	31
parsnips	0	15	55
peas	50	25	13
potatoes	0	10	4
apples	5	5	4
oranges	8	50	41

(a) If a 'good source' of a nutrient is defined as one that contains *more* than 10 mg per 100 g (10 mg for vitamin A), construct a table to show the number of foods that she consumed that were 'good sources' of three nutrients, two nutrients, one nutrient and no nutrients.
(b) Represent this information in the form of a pie chart.

8 Find the mean, median and mode of the following measurements of the heights of a group of students:

heights / m 1.74 1.50 1.83 1.96 1.67 1.78 1.89 1.67 1.67 1.79

9 (a) If a voltage is applied across a sample of a material that conducts electricity, it will allow an electrical current to flow through it. The size of the current depends on the size of the voltage and how good a conductor the material is. It will have a certain resistance to the flow of the electrical current.
By measuring the voltage (in volts) and the current (in amperes) the electrical resistance (in ohms) can be found. This is done by dividing the voltage used by the current that flows.
This can be shown by using a formula:

$R = V/I$, where: R = resistance, V = voltage, I = current.

Rearrange the formula to find:
(i) the voltage, V
(ii) the current, I
(iii) the voltage when the resistance is 1.70 ohms and the current is 1.88 amps
(iv) the current when the voltage is 9.4 volts and the resistance is 2.5 ohms.

(b) If a rocket accelerates smoothly, the velocity (speed) at which it is travelling after a given period of time can be found from the formula:

$v = u + at$, where: v = final velocity after time = t, u = starting velocity, and a = acceleration

Use the formula to find:
(i) the velocity of the rocket in kilometres per hour after 10 seconds, if it is accelerating at 1 kilometre per second per second
(ii) the acceleration of the rocket in kilometres per second per second if it reaches 1800 kilometres per hour after 10 seconds. (Hint: be careful when using units of time in your calculations.)

10 (a) An experiment was conducted to find the resistance of a sample of material by measuring the current that passed through it when the voltage was increased by small amounts at a time. As shown in question 9, the resistance of a material can be found if the voltage applied across it is divided by the current that flows through it: $R = V/I$.
Plot a graph of the following results, with voltage plotted on the y axis and current on the x axis.

Voltage, V / volts	1.6	3.4	5.3	6.6	8.3
Current, I / amperes	2.0	4.1	6.0	7.9	10.1

(i) Comment on the results obtained in the experiment.
(ii) This graph is of the form $y = mx$. What does the m in this general formula stand for?
(iii) Rewrite the formula $y = mx$ for this graph by using R (resistance), V (voltage) and I (current).
(iv) Use your graph to find the best value that you can for the resistance of the sample.

(b) The following results were obtained when the velocity of an accelerating car was measured at 10 second intervals:

Time / secs	10	20	30	40	50
Velocity / km per hour	46	77	109	142	165

(i) Using the formula $v = u + at$, rearrange it so that it is in the form $y = mx + c$.
Plot a graph of the results above. Use it to answer the following:
(ii) Was the car accelerating smoothly? Explain your answer.
(iii) Find the initial velocity of the car, when the stop-watch was started.
(iv) Find the acceleration of the car over the period for which it was accelerating smoothly.

11 Match the data with the units by pairing the numbers and letters:
(a) time
(b) velocity
(c) temperature

(d) length
(e) electrical resistance
(f) density
(g) volume
(h) electrical current
(i) mass
(j) melting point
(k) pressure
(l) energy
(m) amount of a substance
(n) power
(o) force
(p) area
(q) concentration
(r) electrical potential difference.

- (i) moles
- (ii) metres
- (iii) joules
- (iv) kilograms
- (v) newtons
- (vi) amperes
- (vii) metres per second
- (viii) degrees centigrade
- (ix) volts
- (x) square metres
- (xi) seconds
- (xii) kelvin
- (xiii) pascals
- (xiv) moles per cubic metre
- (xv) kilograms per cubic metre
- (xvi) cubic metres
- (xvii) ohms
- (xviii) watts.

12 In August 1976, the Viking spacecraft landed on Mars. A series of tests were carried out to try to find out if life existed on the planet. One of these tests used radioactive carbon dioxide($^{14}CO_2$).

A sample of Martian soil was exposed to a sample of the Martian atmosphere to which a small amount of radioactive carbon dioxide had been added. The soil was brightly lit by a lamp for five days and then heated to 1100°C to vaporise any organic matter present. The vapours were tested for the presence of radioactive carbon.

More than six times the amount of ^{14}C was detected than would have been expected if the soil were sterile.

(a) Which of the following conclusions are valid? Explain your answers:
- (i) The scientists were testing for the Earth process of photosynthesis.
- (ii) The radioactive carbon detected in the vapour from the heated soil came from organic molecules made by photosynthesis carried out by organisms in the soil.

(b) What else do you think the scientists might have done in this investigation?

In a second test, Martian soil was warmed with a soup containing radioactive carbon dioxide ($^{14}CO_2$) in the molecules of the nutrients. The atmosphere above the soil was tested for $^{14}CO_2$ over a period of 10 hours. A second sample was heated to 160°C for three hours before the soup was added.

Samples of moon soil and antarctic soil were also tested in the same way for comparison. The results are shown in Figure 1.3.2.

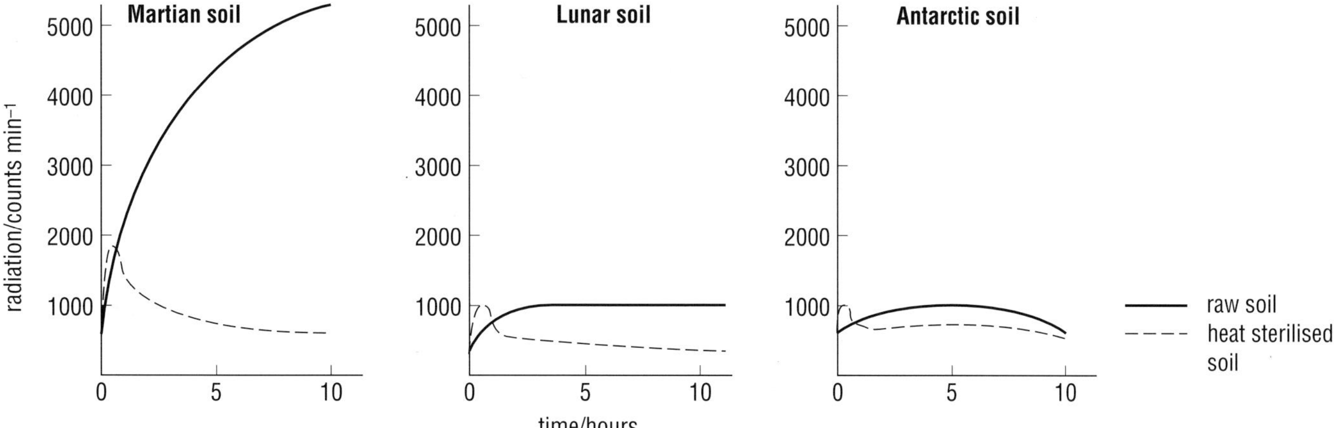

Figure 1.3.2 Soil samples.

(c) Which of the following conclusions are valid? Explain your answers.
- (i) The scientists were testing for the earth process of respiration.
- (ii) The heat treatment was to sterilise the soil so that any living organisms would be killed.
- (iii) The heat-treated soils acted as controls.
- (iv) The heated Martian soil gave off radioactive material for a while and then stopped.
- (v) The unheated Martian soil gave off radioactive material for the whole 10 hours.
- (vi) The unheated raw soils produced more radioactive material than the heated soils.
- (vii) There is life on Mars.

(d) Suggest possible sources of error in either of these investigations.

13 Choose the most appropriate piece of apparatus to carry out the measurement of the diameter of the objects by pairing the letters and numbers of each. Numbers may be used more than once or not at all.

(a) a brick	(i) tape measure
(b) a cell	(ii) micrometer
(c) a field	(iii) microscope eyepiece graticule
(d) a metal wire	(iv) Vernier callipers
(e) a table.	(v) metre rule.

14 List the pieces of apparatus that you can use to measure the volumes of liquids in order of increasing sensitivity. Give an example for each of when you might use it.

15 (a) Procedures can often be adapted to make them safer. Give some examples of this.

(b) Find out what a clinical thermometer is like. In what ways has a clinical thermometer been adapted from a standard laboratory mercury thermometer to make it more suitable for its purpose?

2 Investigating living things, materials and substances

Our environment consists of things that are living or non-living. Non-living materials may have been alive once (for example coal, fossils) or may never have lived (for example minerals). Scientists investigate the behaviour and properties of living things and materials through observation and measurement.

Living things such as plants, animals and micro-organisms are called organisms. Many people grow plants in their gardens, some grow them commercially. Other people raise animals. The improvement of, growth and well-being of animals (and 'animals' includes us), depends on scientists' knowledge and understanding. To manage and control the natural environment, scientists must know how organisms behave and what affects them.

Figure 2.0.1 Analytical kits available from garden centres can be used to determine the mineral nutrients in soil.

Much of the non-living world consists of solid materials. These include metals, ceramics (for example pottery), polymers (for example plastic, rubber) and composites (for example steel reinforced concrete). The choice and effective use of these materials depends on scientists knowing about their properties (for example strength, electrical and thermal conductivity). They need to be able to determine these. The list of objects made from solid materials and which we use daily is, of course, vast. They range from the tiny, such as microchips in computers, to the huge, such as aeroplanes and buildings.

Analysis is an essential occupation for many scientists. Chemical tests can be used to identify substances, to determine their purity or to find out how much of a substance is present in a sample. Applying their skills to analytical problems enables scientists to help fight illness and disease, monitor and control pollution and to fight crime.

Figure 2.0.2 *Scientists in this material science laboratory determine the properties of materials used in the aerospace industry.*

The Elements

Element 2.1 Investigate organisms in their environment

You will need to show that you can:

- describe the characteristic activities of plants, animals and micro-organisms
- monitor environmental variables which affect organisms
- describe how organisms respond to changes in their environment
- describe local examples of where the environment is controlled for particular purposes.

Investigate organisms in their environment, page 58

Element 2.2 Investigate the properties of solid materials and relate them to their uses

You will need to show that you can:

- measure the properties of solids safely
- relate the properties of solids to their uses and to their structures.

Investigate the properties of solid materials and relate them to their uses, page 80

Element 2.3 Determine the composition of substances

You will need to show that you can:

- prepare a sample for analysis and carry out the analysis safely
- use the results of an analysis to determine the composition of a substance.

Determine the composition of substances, page 99

Investigate organisms in their environment

You will need to show that you can:

- describe the characteristic activities of plants, animals and micro-organisms
- monitor environmental variables which affect organisms
- describe how organisms respond to changes in their environment
- describe local examples of where the environment is controlled for particular purposes.

Naming living things, page 102

Characteristic activities of living organisms

There are probably some 30 million different species of organisms alive on our planet. They vary in size and complexity from tiny one-celled organisms that are invisible to the naked eye to huge trees and massive whales. Yet all these organisms have a number of important features in common. Understanding these common features can be of great practical benefit. As we shall see, it can help:

- farmers to grow crops and keep animals
- scientists to obtain useful products, such as medicines, from plants and micro-organisms
- ecologists to look after nature reserves.

Figure 2.1.1 Plants carry out photosynthesis in which the energy from light is needed. Carbon dioxide and water combine to make glucose. Here young lettuce plants are being grown under artificial light to increase their rate of photosynthesis and so they grow more quickly.

Livings things obtain energy

All organisms need to obtain **energy**. They use this energy to grow, reproduce, react to the environment and so on.

Plants, algae and certain bacteria can obtain energy from sunlight. These organisms are known as *autotrophs*, meaning that they 'feed themselves'. Nearly all autotrophs use the energy in light (sunlight or artificial light) to carry out a series of chemical reactions called *photosynthesis* (see Figure 2.1.1). In photosynthesis, carbon dioxide and water combine in the presence of light to form glucose. Oxygen is a waste product. The overall chemical reaction for photosynthesis is:

$$\underset{\text{carbon dioxide}}{6CO_2} + \underset{\text{water}}{6H_2O} \rightarrow \underset{\text{glucose}}{C_6H_{12}O_6} + \underset{\text{oxygen}}{6O_2}$$

Animals, fungi, most bacteria and a number of other single-celled organisms get their energy from other organisms. These organisms are known as *heterotrophs*, meaning that they 'feed on others'. Humans, for example, are heterotrophs. Some heterotrophs feed on other organisms while the organisms are still alive. In this case the heterotrophs are *parasites*. Fleas and tapeworms are examples of parasites, as are disease-causing organisms such as the fungus that causes athlete's foot, and the bacterium that causes tuberculosis.

However, not all heterotrophs are parasites. Many feed off dead organisms or their excreta (their urine and faeces). Some use dead organisms for energy after they have been broken down to organic matter. For example:

- *scavengers*, such as vultures, feed off dead animals

- *decomposers*, such as earthworms and many non-parasitic fungi and bacteria, break down the organic matter from dead organisms to simpler compounds.

Living things obtain nutrients

Organisms need **nutrients** as well as energy. Nutrients are chemicals which are needed for the organism to grow and remain alive.
Photosynthetic organisms, such as green plants, obtain:

- carbon dioxide from the atmosphere
- ions such as nitrate, potassium and phosphate from the soil dissolved in water.

Heterotrophic organisms obtain their nutrients from their food:

- *carnivores*, such as wolves, polar bears and pike (a freshwater fish), feed only on meat
- *herbivores*, such as rabbits and tortoises, feed only on plants
- *omnivores*, such as pigs and humans, can eat both meat and plants (see Figure 2.1.3).

Figure 2.1.2 *Farmers have to replace nutrients lost from the soil when crops are harvested. Artificial fertilizers usually contain nitrogen (N), phosphorus (P) and potassium (K) in different proportions. By monitoring nutrient contents of soil, farmers can choose which NPK balance to use.*

Living things grow

All organisms **grow**. Growth can be defined as the increase in size of an organism as it gets older. Some organisms, including most animals, grow to a more-or-less definite adult size. Other organisms, for example trees, carry on growing throughout their lives. Some colonies of animals, such as corals, also carry on growing bigger and bigger. Recent research has shown that some of the corals in the Great Barrier Reef off Australia are more than 30 m in diameter – larger than a blue whale – and hundreds of years old (see Figure 2.1.4).

Figure 2.1.3 *Since pigs are omnivores they will eat most things. This makes them quite easy to keep even on a small holding such as this one in Malaysia. What would happen on a pig farm if there were no decomposers in the soil?*

Living things reproduce

All organisms **reproduce** – or try to. Most of the species we see around us can reproduce *sexually*. Sexual reproduction requires the production of gametes (sex cells), often by two separate individuals. Gametes fuse in pairs, one from each individual. This is fertilisation. All the animals found on British farms, such as sheep, cattle, pigs and chickens, have separate males and females. From a farmer's point of view females are often more useful than males. For instance, cows produce milk, while hens produce eggs. Bulls and cockerels are a lot less useful. For this reason, intensive research is currently under way to see if scientists can find a way to ensure that dairy cows and chickens mainly give birth to females rather than males.

Some organisms, though, can reproduce without gametes, that is *asexually*. A number of plant species can reproduce both sexually and asexually. For example, potatoes produce flowers and can use them to reproduce sexually, as pollen from the male parts of the flowers is carried to the female parts of the flowers of another individual. Fertilisation of the egg cell (female gamete) by a male gamete from the pollen then occurs. However, potatoes are normally placed in the ground as tubers when commercially grown. Each tuber grows and gives rise to a new potato plant. Towards the end of the growing season the potato plant plant uses the glucose made by photosynthesis to make many new tubers (see Figure 2.1.5). In other words, it reproduces asexually.

Figure 2.1.4 *Corals are colonies made up of millions of tiny animals. Corals carry on growing throughout their life, just as long-living plants do.*

Sexual production may give rise to considerable variation in the offspring. An advantage to the farmer of *asexual* reproduction is that all the offspring have the same genetic make up and will therefore have similar patterns of growth. However, plant breeders rely on sexual reproduction, which leads to variation among offspring, to breed new varieties.

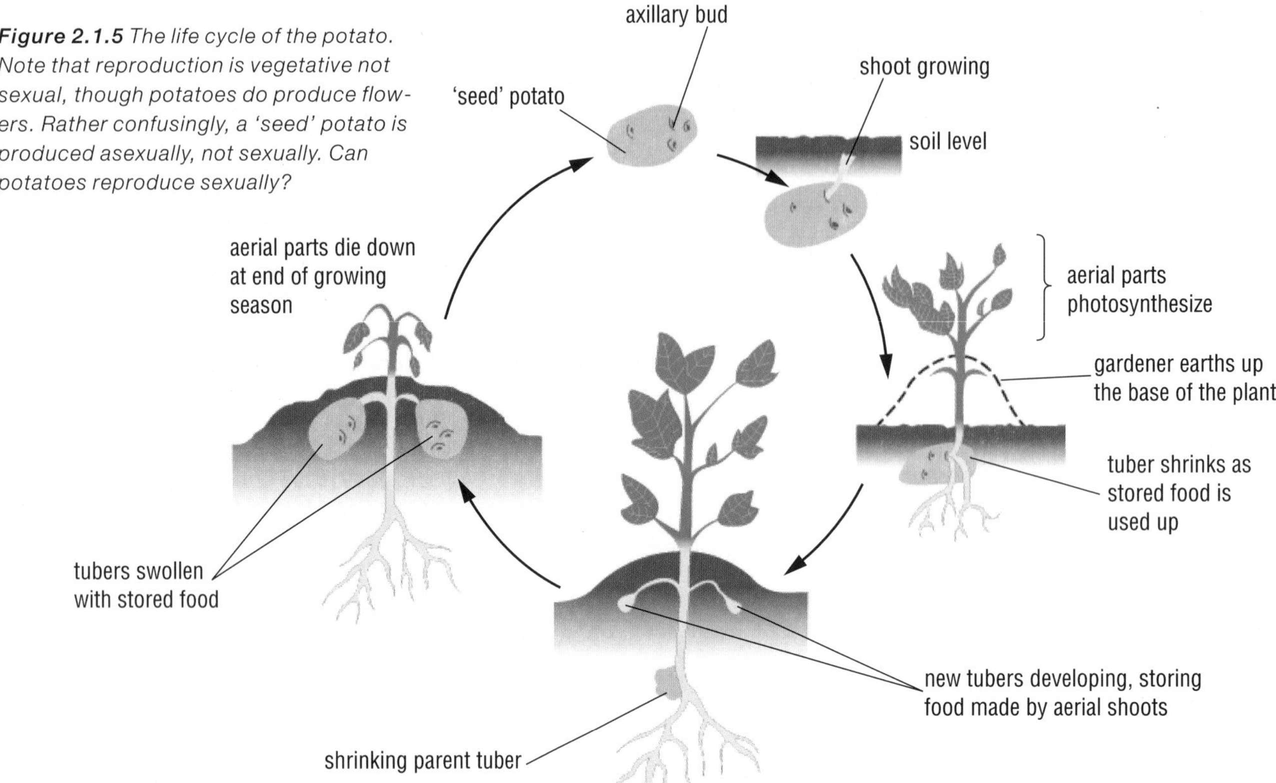

Figure 2.1.5 *The life cycle of the potato. Note that reproduction is vegetative not sexual, though potatoes do produce flowers. Rather confusingly, a 'seed' potato is produced asexually, not sexually. Can potatoes reproduce sexually?*

Figure 2.1.6 *A sheepdog at work. The natural response of a sheep to a strange dog is to run away. Each year in the UK hundreds of sheep are killed by domestic dogs. Why do dogs often chase sheep?*

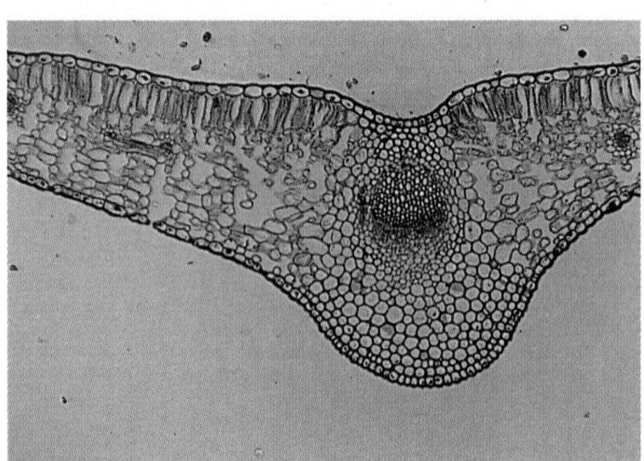

Figure 2.1.7 *A leaf as seen in cross-section under the light microscope. Carbon dioxide diffuses into the leaf through open stomata. Stomata are mainly found on the underside of the leaf.*

Living things respond to the environment

All living organisms **respond** to their **environments.** This response may be very rapid or more gradual. An example of a rapid response is the panic often shown by a sheep if it sees a strange dog (see Figure 2.1.6). Dogs have evolved from wolves and sheep are a natural prey of wolves. There is little way a sheep can defend itself from a wolf, so the best strategy is for it to run away from its perceived danger. The sheep don't do this *consciously*. In other words, they don't think about it. They just run away automatically. Sheep have evolved over countless generations to respond to wolves, especially if the wolves approach them, by running away.

Some plant responses can also be quite rapid. For example, plants can respond to changes in the intensity of sunlight within a few minutes by opening or closing the tiny holes on the undersides of their leaves, known as *stomata*. The advantages of this rapid response to the plant are as follows:

- When it is sunny, photosynthesis can take place at a rapid rate. Photosynthesis requires carbon dioxide. Carbon dioxide actually occurs in quite low concentations in the atmosphere of only about 0.035%, i.e. less than four molecules in ten thousand. The main way a plant can get its carbon dioxide is through its open stomata. Carbon dioxide diffuses in (see Figure 2.1.7).
- When it is darker (for example very cloudy or night), photosynthesis takes place more slowly, or not at all. This means that the plant closes its stomata. Consequently less carbon dioxide is needed. A major advantage of stomatal closure is that the rate of water loss from the leaves is reduced. This water loss is known as *transpiration*. Transpiration has some benefits – for example the water carries nutrients from the soil into the plant and cools the plant as it evaporates. However, plants are often short of water, so shutting the stomata can be beneficial.

Other responses by organisms to changes in their environment take much longer. For example, changes in the duration of daylight as the nights get longer in autumn cause many animals in the northern hemisphere to grow longer coats in preparation for the winter. Shorter nights also cause red deer females (hinds) to come into oestrus (i.e. become ready to mate) and male red deer (stags) to become aggressive and to start to roar. These responses mean that both sexes are ready to mate in the autumn (see Figure 2.1.8). Calves are then born in the spring eight months later. On some farms red deer are reared for meat, and it has been suggested that the fact that reproduction is triggered by night length could perhaps be used to get them to reproduce more frequently, rather than just once a year. The trick would be to change the relative lengths of day and night using artificial light. If successful, this procedure may allow more deer calves to be born each year, so potentially increasing productivity.

Figure 2.1.8 *Adult male red deer (stags) respond to longer nights in the autumn by becoming more aggressive, starting to roar and defending harems of females. Adult female red deer (hinds) respond to the longer nights by coming into oestrus and mating with a male.*

Other activities of living organisms

In addition to obtaining energy, obtaining nutrients, growth, reproduction and responding to the environment, the other activities characteristic of living organisms are:

- **excretion**
- **movement.**

Living things obtain energy, page 58

Almost all organisms produce carbon dioxide as a waste product (*excretory product*). Carbon dioxide is produced in cells as a result of *respiration*. Respiration is the process by which the energy in food or energy reserves is released. In mammals carbon dioxide is disposed of by the lungs. The other main excretory product produced by mammals is urea. Urea is a small molecule which contains nitrogen. It is made in the liver and disposed of by the kidneys, which excrete it in the urine.

> FOCUS
>
> **The characteristic activities of living organisms are:**
> - **obtaining energy**
> - **obtaining nutrients**
> - **growth**
> - **reproduction**
> - **responding to the environment**
> - **excretion**
> - **movement.**

Surprising as it may seem, the main excretory product of plants is oxygen. This is because oxygen is a waste product of photosynthesis. This means that when a plant is photosynthesising rapidly, it produces far more oxygen than it needs for respiration. Plants get rid of their oxygen by diffusion – the oxygen simply diffuses out of the leaves through the stomata.

The final activity characteristic of living things is movement. It is obvious that many animals move, but it may seem odd to think of movement as a characteristic of all organisms, even plants, for instance. Some plants can move quite quickly. Venus fly traps, for example, are carnivorous plants and can snap their modified leaves shut within a few seconds, trapping insects, or even small frogs, inside. Other plants move more slowly. Nonetheless, they may have flowers that close at night or tendrils that clasp hold of other plants and help them reach up to the light.

Living things respond to the environment, page 60

Monitoring environmental variables

As we have seen, organisms respond to their environment. The environment of an organism can be divided into two aspects:

- the biotic (biological) environment
- the abiotic (non-biological) environment.

We shall look first at how the abiotic environment can be measured. The abiotic environment is non-biological. It consists of all the **physical**

Measurement and observation, page 11

FOCUS

The abiotic environment consists of all the physical and chemical components of the environment, such as:
- **oxygen concentration**
- **light levels**
- **carbon dioxide concentration**
- **pH**
- **temperature**
- **water content**
- **nutrients.**

and chemical components of the environment, such as:
- **oxygen concentration**
- **light levels**
- **carbon dioxide concentration**
- **pH**
- **temperature**
- **water content**
- **nutrients.**

Abiotic factors such as these can often be recorded automatically by means of meters, remote sensors or electronic probes attached to some form of datalogging equipment.

Oxygen concentration

In the air, oxygen concentrations vary little, staying close to 20%. However, in water and soil they can vary a lot. Oxygen levels in water are important, as organisms vary greatly in their oxygen requirements. Fish such as trout and salmon, for example, have fast-flowing cold streams as their natural freshwater habitat. Such a habitat has oxygen levels that are close to saturation (i.e. as high as they possibly can be). In fish farms, however, oxygen levels may fall short of saturation for several reasons:
- Fish farms have high densities of fish and the fish use up much of the oxygen in the water.
- The water in a fish farm may be still, rather than fast-flowing. This means that there is less movement of oxygen across the air-water surface.
- The water in a fish farm is often quite warm. Warmer water holds less oxygen.

These factors mean that people who run trout farms may need to monitor the oxygen levels in their pools, to make sure that they don't fall too low.

There are two main ways in which the oxygen concentration of a sample of water can be obtained:
- The traditional way is to obtain a sample of the water and analyse it using the *Winkler technique*. This method is reliable, but takes a long time, and is difficult to carry out in the field away from a laboratory. It also requires the use of concentrated sulphuric acid which can be dangerous.
- The more recently developed method involves measuring oxygen levels directly using an *oxygen probe* (see Figure 2.1.9).

Figure 2.1.9 *The amount of oxygen in the water is important for fish farmers. If the amount falls too low the fish will die. Oxygen probes are easy to use but need careful calibration and can occasionally behave erratically.*

Light levels

The light that falls on photosynthetic organisms such as plants and algae has two important characteristics:
- its wavelength
- its intensity.

Wavelength (or colour) is important because chloroplasts use blue and red light more than green. There are instruments that can measure how much of the light produced by a source (e.g. a lamp or the Sun) is of a particular wavelength. Light *intensity* is an important factor affecting the rate of photosynthesis. There are various instruments used to measure light intensity. Provided a plant has enough carbon dioxide and water and isn't too cold, the greater the light intensity, the greater the rate of photosynthesis up to the pont when light intensity no longer limits photosynthesis.

Procedure

Measuring light intensity

1 Use a light meter or probe to obtain readings. It is usually not possible to calibrate light meters or probes. Ensure you know how to use the particular instrument you are using.
2 If available, use datalogging equipment.
3 At each site take three light readings with only a few seconds between each reading.

SAFETY: If working at an aquatic site (for example a river) ensure any cuts on your hands are covered with waterproof plasters before you start, and wash your hands in clean water (not river water) after taking the readings.

Requirements

- ❐ Instrument for measuring light intensity

Carbon dioxide concentration

Carbon dioxide concentrations are quite difficult to measure accurately, but are important for organisms for a number of reasons. If the weather is warm and sunny, most plant growth is *limited* by the amount of carbon dioxide. In other words, increasing the carbon dioxide level increases the rate of photosynthesis. This is exactly what happens in certain commercial greenhouses. Paraffin is burnt to produce carbon dioxide. The raised levels of carbon dioxide increase the rate of photosynthesis, allowing the plants to grow faster.

On the other hand, too much carbon dioxide can be a problem for certain organisms. For example, if micro-organisms such as bacteria are grown industrially in a large fermenter, they can produce so much carbon dioxide that the pH drops significantly. One reason for stirring a bacterial culture in a fermenter is to help remove carbon dioxide from the culture (see Figure 2.1.10).

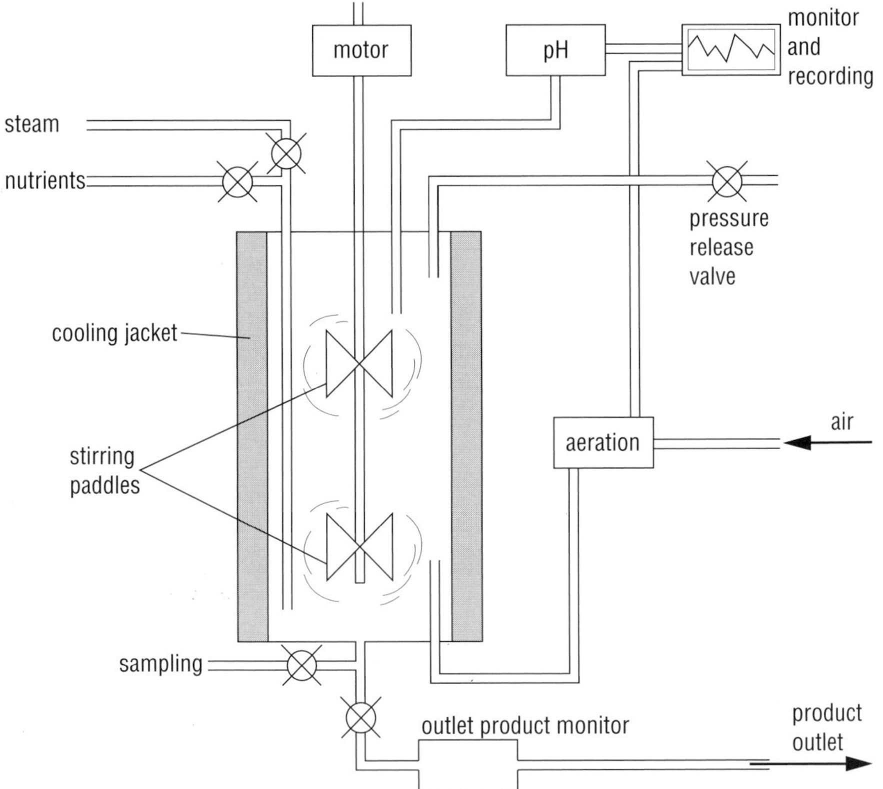

Figure 2.1.10 A diagram showing an industrial fermenter in cross-section. Nutrients, air (because of the oxygen in it) and steam (to control the temperature or sterilise the fermenter when needed) can be added. Conditions are continually monitored and the pH can be altered if need be. A motor ensures the supply of essential substances to and the removal of waste products from the centre of the vessel. Valves are indicated by ⊗. Why does a build up of carbon dioxide lead to a drop in pH? (Hint: What do you get when carbon dioxide reacts with water?)

Acids, page 99

Procedure: Measuring pH, page 210

pH

The pH of an aqueous solution is a measure of the concentration of H^+ (aq) ions in it. The more H^+ ions there are, the lower the pH. Acidic solutions have a pH of below 7. Alkaline solutions have a pH of above 7. Various types of pH meter are available. pH meters usually require careful calibration before use and the manufacturer's instructions should be followed carefully.

One reason why pH is important for many organisms is that at a pH of below about 4.5, aluminium ions, Al^{3+}, become much more soluble. The significance of this is that aluminium ions are poisonous to many organisms, especially some plants and fish. Air pollution can cause acid rain which washes aluminium out of the soil into lakes and rivers.

Figure 2.1.11 *The burning of fossil fuels that are high in sulphur and nitrogen, such as some coals, has led to the phenomenon of acid rain. Many lakes, both in this country and overseas, have lost their fish. This is because acid rain has led to a fall in the pH of the water, with consequent fish mortality.*

Temperature

Environmental temperatures are of great significance to all organisms. Many organisms, including all plants and micro-organisms, are unable to regulate their own temperatures. They have internal temperatures that are close to those of their surroundings. Somewhat misleadingly, they are often referred to as 'cold-blooded'. In fact their body temperature in general varies with the surrounding temperature. They are best called *ectothermic*, as they absorb heat from their surroundings. The *metabolism* (internal chemical activities) of such organisms rises as the temperature increases.

Birds and mammals are able to keep their body temperature fairly constant in spite of changes in the outside temperature. Such organisms are often called 'warm blooded' or, more scientifically, *endothermic*, meaning that they make heat energy within the body. The metabolism of such organisms generally rises at lower temperatures to help release energy within the body.

Measurement and observation, page 11

Temperatures can be measured by various methods including temperature probes and traditional mercury thermometers.

Water content

All organisms need water for metabolism. Soils vary in the volume of water that they hold depending on such factors as:

- composition of the soil
- time since it last rained
- presence of vegetation.

In the atmosphere, the amount of water held as water vapour is indicated by the *relative humidity*. Relative humidity equals the percentage of water vapour the air contains *relative* to that which it would hold if it was fully saturated. Relative humidity can be measured by means of a *wet and dry bulb hygrometer*.

Soils vary in the amount of water they hold. This fact is of great importance to someone growing plants, whether indoors or in a field. By considering the sizes of the inorganic particles that make up a soil, four main soil types can be identified:

- clay – in which the particles are less than 2 μm (microns – each a thousandth of a millimetre) in diameter
- silt – in which the particles are between 2 μm and 20 μm in diameter
- sand – in which the particles are between 20 μm and 2 mm in diameter
- loam – in which there is a mixture of clay, silt and sand.

Procedure

1 Determining moisture content in a soil sample

1. Weigh dish empty. Break up soil sample and spread evenly in dish. Weigh again. Find original mass of soil (w_1).
2. Place dish with soil into oven at 110 °C for at least 3 hours.
3. Remove from the oven and cool in a desiccator. (*Care: hot dish!*)
4. Weigh when cool. Find dry mass of soil (w_2).
5. Repeat 2–4 until constant weighings are obtained (constant mass).
6. Calculate % water content = $\frac{w_1 - w_2}{w_1} \times 100$

Since the moisture may vary from place to place depending on where the sample is taken from, repeat the determination with further samples.

SAFETY: *Always wash your hands after handling soil.*

Requirements

- ❒ Soil sample, 60–80 g fresh
- ❒ Heat proof dish or tray, e.g. aluminium pie dish
- ❒ Balance (measuring to at least 0.1 g)
- ❒ Thermostatically controlled oven at 110 °C
- ❒ Tongs
- ❒ Desiccator

BIOHAZARD
soil

2 Determining moisture content in the air

Use a wet and dry hygrometer in line with the manufacturer's instructions.

Requirements

- ❒ Wet and dry hygrometer

Investigation

The water-holding capacities of different soils

Requirements

- ❒ Dry clay, approx. 100 cm^3
- ❒ Dry sand, approx. 100 cm^3
- ❒ Dry loam (equal amounts of clay, silt and sand), approx. 100 cm^3
- ❒ Retort stand and clamp × 3
- ❒ 100 cm^3 graduated measuring cylinder × 3
- ❒ 250 cm^3 glass beaker × 3
- ❒ Funnel × 3
- ❒ Cotton wool

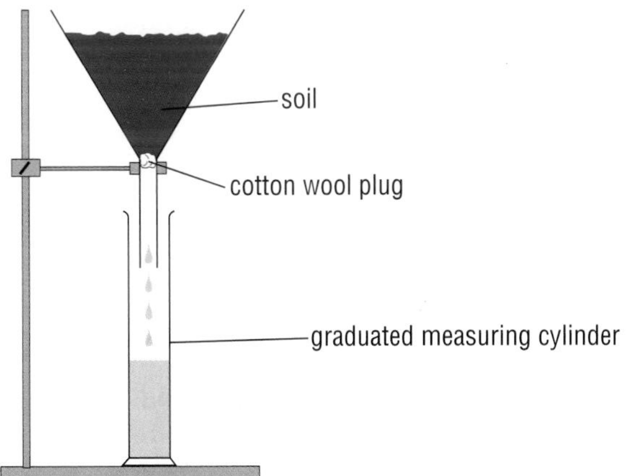

Figure 2.1.12 *A possible way to determine the water-holding capacity of a soil.*

Carry out a study to see how much water can be held by measured volumes of sand, clay and loam before any water starts to drip through. You will probably find it convenient to use apparatus similar to that shown in Figure 2.1.12. Before you start, think carefully about the following:

- How can you be sure your soils are dry before you add any water?
- How, exactly, can you work out how much water is held by a soil that is saturated with water?
- How, exactly, can you compare the water-holding capacities of three different soils?
- Do you need to repeat your measurements?

Once you have collected your results, represent them in some way. You may choose to display them in a table or on a bar chart. Try to explain your findings. Were there differences in the amount of water held by the three types of soil? If so, why do you this think this is?

SAFETY: *Always wash your hands after handling soil.*
Get your plans checked by your teacher/lecturer before you start.

BIOHAZARD
soil

Living things obtain nutrients, page 59

Nutrients

Nitrate, phosphate and potassium ions, along with a number of other minerals, are of great importance to plants and other organisms.

Requirements

- ❒ Nitrate probe or kit
- ❒ Water samples

Procedure

Determining available nutrients

Nitrate levels can be measured quite accurately using electronic probes or, less accurately, using kits that can be obtained from garden centres or aquaria suppliers (see Figure 2.1.13). Kits can also be obtained to measure the levels of some other nutrients, such as phosphate and calcium.

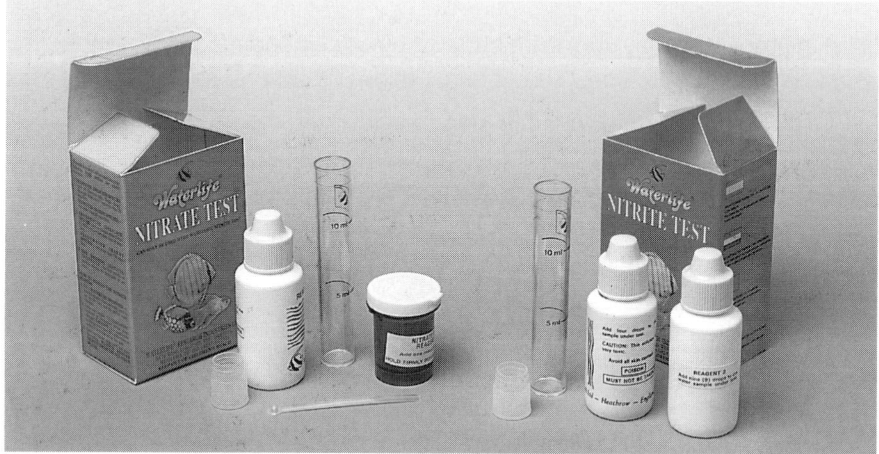

Figure 2.1.13 *Nitrate, nitrite and phosphate levels can be measured using commercial kits. Although such kits cannot always be relied on to give absolutely accurate readings, they do allow useful comparisons to made between different soils or water samples.*

An electronic probe or a kit obtained from a garden centre or aquaria supplier can be used to measure the nitrate levels of a range of waters. Carry out measurements on at least three samples from each type of water to be investigated.

SAFETY: *Pay attention to any safety warnings on the kit.*

The biotic environment

The biotic environment consists of all the other organisms that surround an individual. For example, consider a rose bush being grown commercially in a greenhouse to be cut and sold on Valentine's Day. Its biotic environment will include:

- All the other roses in the greenhouse.
- Any herbivores such as greenfly and caterpillars that feed on rose leaves.
- Any predators that feed on such herbivores. In a greenhouse such predators might be deliberately introduced as a method of *biological control* (see Figure 2.1.14).
- The people who own the business and run it on a day-to-day basis.

FOCUS

The biotic environment of an organism consists of all the ways in which other organisms affect it. These may include:
- **competition**
- **predation**
- **pollination.**

Figure 2.1.14 *Whitefly are a familiar pest in greenhouses and conservatories. Their numbers can quickly build up and cause damage to horticultural plants. Nowadays whitefly are often controlled biologically by introducing a tiny parasitic wasp,* Encarsia formosa *into their environment. The wasp does not sting humans or pets but destroys whitefly.*

Organisms are affected by the activities of other organisms in a variety of ways. For our purposes, the most significant of these activities are:

- **competition**
- **predation**
- **pollination.**

Competition

Within a species individuals may *compete* with one another for something that is in short supply. For example, wheat plants compete with other wheat plants for light, nutrients, water and space. Similarly, in a culture of micro-organisms, the individual cells may compete with one another for food and space.

Competition can also occur between members of different species. For example, plants such as wild oats or bindweed, which grow as weeds in crops such as wheat or barley, compete with the crops for nutrients, water, space and light. Some weeds germinate only at some times of the year; others can germinate throughout the year (see Figure 2.1.15).

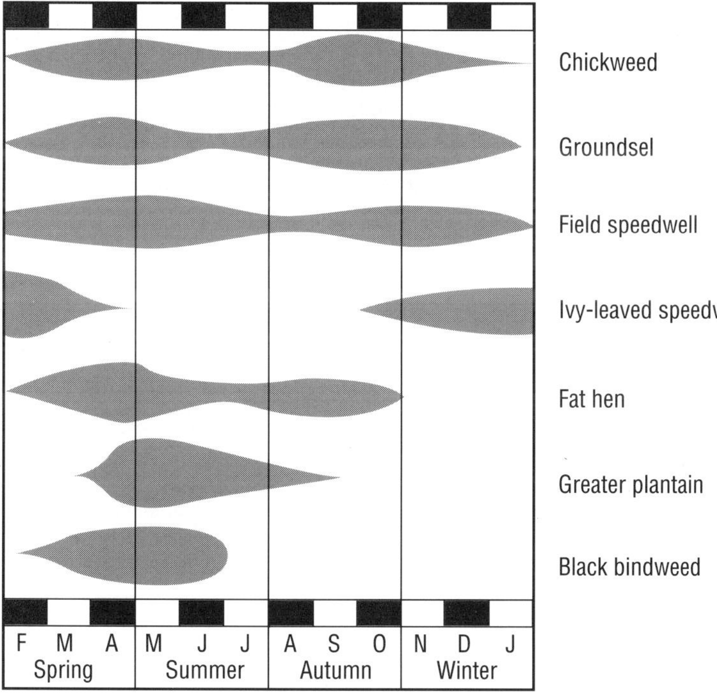

Figure 2.1.15 *The times of the year when the seeds of some common British weeds typically germinate. Other things being equal, would you expect a bare field to have more or less water in its soil than a field with vegetation on it? Why?*

Predation

Predation occurs when one organism, the *predator*, feeds on another organism, the *prey*. We are used to thinking of predators as large animals, such as foxes, that catch and eat smaller animals, such as mice and rabbits, killing them in the process. However, from the point of view of the organisms concerned, the following can perhaps also be considered as example of predation:

- One organism (a parasite) feeds on part of another organism (the host) which continues to live. For example, mildew grows on wheat or a tick gorges itself on blood from a sheep (see Figure 2.1.16).
- One animal (a grazer) feeds on parts of or all of large numbers of plants. For example, a cow eats grass.
- One or more animals (parasites) eats part of a single plant (the host). For example, a large white caterpillar eats part of a cabbage.

Figure 2.1.16 *A tick parasitising a sheep. How does this (i) resemble and (ii) differ from 'normal' predation? Why, when the air temperature is low, will the tick's metabolic rate fall, but the sheep's metabolic rate rise?*

Investigation

How much damage can caterpillars cause?

Requirements

- ❒ Access to caterpillar-infested cabbages

It is quite difficult to determine the effects of herbivores on the plants they eat. One possibility is for you to find a gardener who is growing cabbages which become attacked by caterpillars. Try to persuade the gardener not to use a chemical spray. Then devise a method to quantify how much damage the caterpillars are causing. You might, for example, use graph paper to find out what area of cabbage leaves the caterpillars eat each day.

SAFETY: Some caterpillars have hairs which are irritants; some people are allergic to them. If you handle caterpillars, wear gloves.

BIOHAZARD
caterpillars

Pollination

Competition and predation are both ways in which organisms interfere with the growth and reproduction of other organisms. However, organisms may interact more positively, to the mutual benefit of each organism. A classic case is insect pollination. In *insect pollination*, the plant benefits because pollen grains are carried from it to another plant, and to it from another plant (see Figure 2.1.17). This enables the plant to reproduce. The insect benefits because it is, in a sense, 'rewarded' by the plant for its efforts. It may be given nectar (rich in sugars) or eat some of the pollen (rich in proteins).

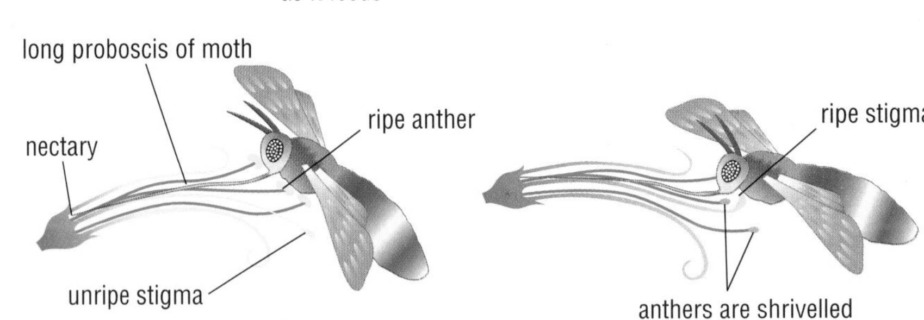

Figure 2.1.17 *Honeysuckle flowers are pollinated by hawk moths. The anthers ripen before the stigmas, so that a young flower deposits pollen onto the underside of a hovering moth. If the moth visits an older flower on another honeysuckle, there is a good chance that the second honeysuckle will be pollinated by pollen from the first one. From the honeysuckle's point of view, what might happen if it tried to 'cheat' by producing less nectar than usual? From the moth's point of view, what might happen if it tried to 'cheat' by eating all the pollen instead of carrying most of it from one honeysuckle to another?*

How do organisms respond to changes in their environment?

FOCUS

Organisms may respond to changes in their environment by showing growth, reproduction, movement or death.

Organisms respond to changes in their environment in a number of ways:

- their **growth** is affected
- their **reproduction** is affected
- individuals **move**
- individuals **die**.

Growth is affected

Changes in the environment may accelerate (speed up) the growth of an organism or retard it (slow it down). For example, piglets grow faster if kept in warm conditions indoors (see Figure 2.1.18). This is because when outside they need to spend more of the energy they obtain from their food on thermoregulation (keeping warm).

Figure 2.1.18 *Farmers want their young animals to survive and grow quickly. Keeping young animals indoors helps to keep any deaths to a minimum and maximise growth.*

Plants, too, grow better under certain conditions. Part of the skill in growing plants, whether in horticulture or agriculture, is in getting the best growing conditions for the plants. Plants generally need plenty of light, carbon dioxide, moisture and nutrients. These allow them to photosynthesise and so grow.

Living things obtain energy, page 58
What factors affect the successful cultivation of plants?, page 122

People often talk about the *growth* of micro-organisms, such as bacteria and yeast. What is meant, though, is an increase in the *number* of individuals, rather than an increase in the size of each individual. For this reason, we shall consider 'growth' of micro-organisms under reproduction.

Reproduction is affected, page 69

Reproduction is affected

Changes in the environment may allow an organism to reproduce. As we have seen, many organisms – plants and animals – use changes in day length as triggers to prepare them for the next season.

Most micro-organisms are sensitive to changes in the environment. In micro-organisms that can be grown in culture in a Petri dish, reproduction leads to the **growth** of a colony (see Figure 2.1.19).

FOCUS

Plants and animals respond to some changes in the environment by growing faster; to others by growing more slowly. Plant growth is usually increased by increases in light intensity, temperature, moisture level, nutrient level and carbon dioxide concentration.

Living things respond to the environment, page 60

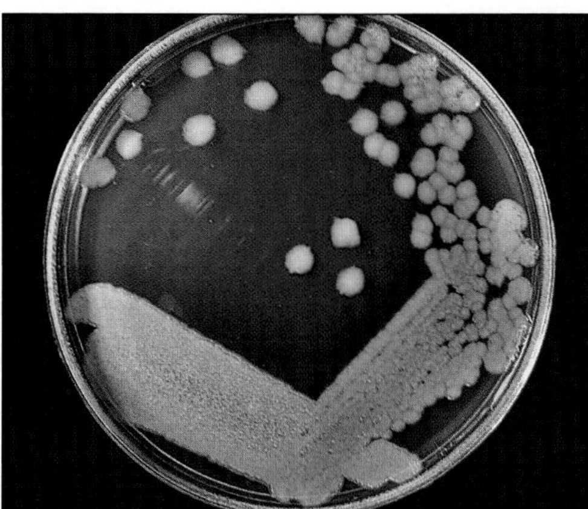

Figure 2.1.19 *This Petri dish shows many colonies of the bacterium* Pseudomonas aeruginosa, *which is found in pus. Each colony consists of many thousands of individual bacteria.*

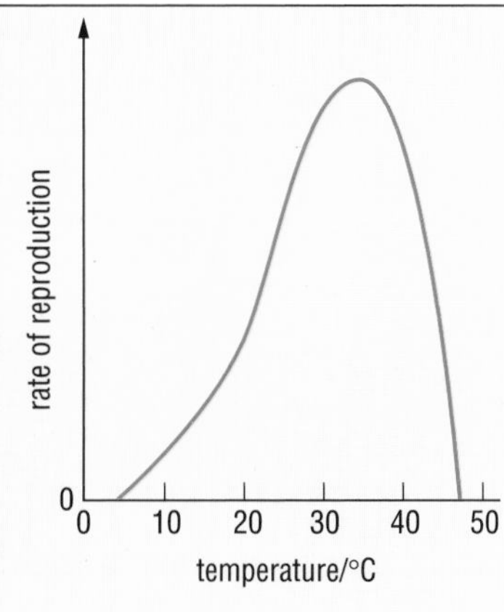

Figure 2.1.20 *For most micro-organisms, the optimal temperature for reproduction is around 35 °C. At temperatures below about 5 °C most micro-organisms cannot reproduce. Above about 45 °C most micro-organisms are killed by the heat but some do really well. Why do micro-organisms that reproduce best at 60 – 70 °C sometimes survive common food sterilisation procedures?*

Many micro-organisms have very specific nutrient requirements. In the absence of these nutrients they will fail to grow. Others are less precise in their requirements and can grow on a variety of media. Most micro-organisms have an optimum temperature for reproduction. Usually this is at about 35 °C (see Figure 2.1.20). However, some micro-organisms

Requirements

- ❒ Petri dishes
- ❒ Non-pathogenic bacteria suitable for media used, from approved list and reputable source
- ❒ Light microscope
- ❒ Microscope slides
- ❒ Cover slips
- ❒ Colorimeter (if available)
- ❒ Haemocytometer (if available)

Note: For further information on micro-organisms and safety see either *Microbiology: an HMI Guide for Schools and FE*, DFE, (1985) or *Topics in Safety*, 2nd Edition, ASE, (1988).

Procedure: Using a colorimeter, page 210

Procedure

Determining the growth of micro-organisms

A measure of the growth in the population size of a micro-organism such as a colony of bacteria can be made in a number of ways:

- If the micro-organism is growing on the surface of a solid substrate (surface), such as the agar in a Petri dish, the area of the substrate covered by the micro-organism can be measured. This measure has the units of 'mm^2 of colony'.
- If the micro-organism is growing in a liquid medium, such as a culture medium in a fermenter, one method is to take small samples, place them on a microscope slide under a cover slip and count the number of individual cells visible under a light microscope. This measure has the units of 'number of cells per mm^2 of microscope slide'.
- If the micro-organism is growing in a liquid medium, a second method is to use a *colorimeter* to measure the opacity of the solution, namely the resistance of the solution to the transmission of light. The more cells there are, the less light passes through. This measure has the units of 'percentage of light absorbed'.
- If the micro-organism is growing in a liquid medium, a third method is to take a small sample of known volume and count all the cells in it under the microscope. This measure has the units of 'number of cells per mm^3 of culture'. A haemocytometer can be used for counting cells in known volumes.

BIOHAZARD
micro-organisms

SAFETY: Consult your supervisor before beginning any practical work with micro-organisms. Always carry out a risk assessment before starting. Use only non-pathogenic (non-disease-causing micro-organisms). Use sterile procedures, which must be demonstrated by members of staff who have had the appropriate training. Dispose of all cultures safely.

FOCUS

Some changes in the environment cause organisms to reproduce; other changes prevent reproduction. Colonies of micro-organisms usually grow faster when it is warm, and when nutrients and space are available.

grow best at about 10 °C. Such micro-organisms can be a real nuisance in refrigerators. A few micro-organisms grow best at 60–70 °C. These micro-organisms may survive common food sterilisation procedures.

Most organisms, whether micro-organisms, plants or animals, respond to improvements in their **environment** by increasing in numbers. For example, during summer the number of aphids in a garden may increase greatly as it becomes warmer and as they feed on sugars which they obtain from plants (see Figure 2.1.21).

Figure 2.1.21 *Aphids feed by sticking their mouthparts into plants. This allows them to obtain the sugars and amino acids carried in the phloem of the plant. In good weather aphid numbers can shoot up as they tap into this abundant source of nutrients.*

The typical shape of the curve relating the number of individuals of a particular species in an area (e.g. aphids in a garden) to time is illustrated in Figure 2.1.22.

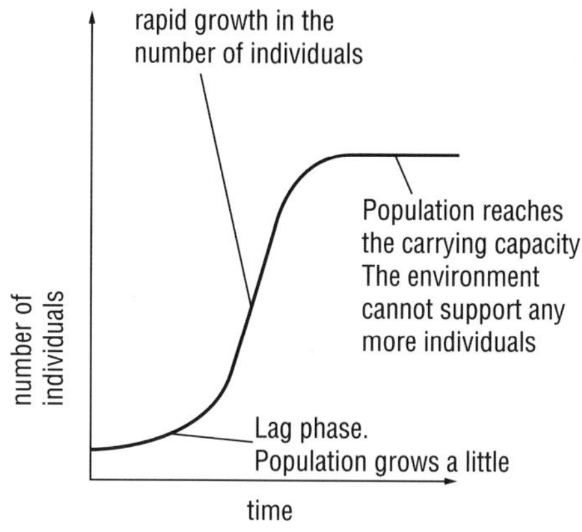

Figure 2.1.22 A generalised graph showing how the number of individuals of a species can build up in an area given favourable environmental circumstances. Ladybird larvae feed on aphids. Draw a graph to suggest how ladybird numbers might change in relation to changes in the numbers of aphids.

Individuals move

Most animals can respond to **changes in the environment** by moving to another place – though there are animals such as barnacles where the adults are unable to move. Animals may move in response to temperature, to areas where there is a greater availability of food, and to avoid predation. Animals move in different ways at different stages of their life cycle:

- Juveniles (young individuals) often disperse considerable distances. For instance, in an attempt to find a suitable place to live, juvenile birds and mammals may move a long way from their parents once they have fledged (left the nest) or weaned (stopped receiving milk).
- Adults generally only move if the local habitat gets worse. In some species this happens every year with the result that the animals may *migrate* each year to another country. For example, swallows breed in the United Kingdom in summer, but then fly to Africa during our winter (see Figure 2.1.23).

FOCUS

Many animals can respond to changes in the environment by moving away from unfavourable conditions and towards favourable ones. Animals may move in response to temperature, to areas where there is a greater availability of food, and to avoid predation.

Figure 2.1.23 Swallows fly south in winter. This allows them to avoid the cold and find richer sources of food. Can you suggest a disadvantage to a swallow of migrating to Africa each year?

Individuals die

Finally, too great a change in the environment may mean that organisms are unable to respond, and instead die. Some species are particularly susceptible to *pollution* or *disturbance*. Such species are known as *indicator species*. Their presence indicates that the local environment is relatively undisturbed and unpolluted. For example, the presence of otters in a river indicates that the river is clean and suitable for the growth and reproduction of a wide range of animals, plants and other organisms (see Figure 2.1.24).

FOCUS

Some changes in the environment are so great that they lead to the death of organisms.

Case Study: An astonishing year, page 74

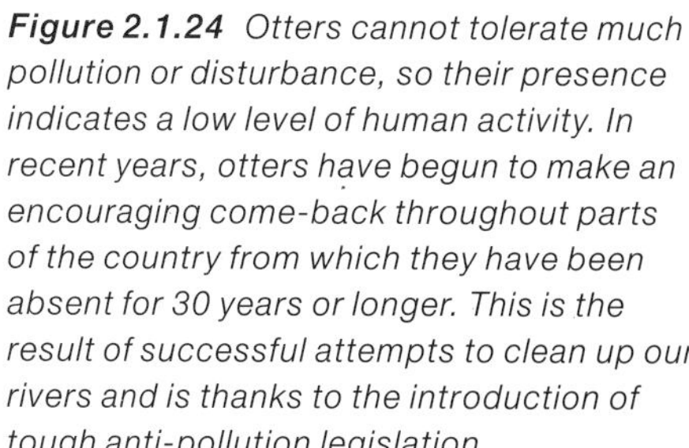

Figure 2.1.24 Otters cannot tolerate much pollution or disturbance, so their presence indicates a low level of human activity. In recent years, otters have begun to make an encouraging come-back throughout parts of the country from which they have been absent for 30 years or longer. This is the result of successful attempts to clean up our rivers and is thanks to the introduction of tough anti-pollution legislation.

How can the environment of organisms usefully be controlled?

There are many circumstances under which it is to our benefit to be able to **control the environment** of organisms, These include controlling the environment of organisms for:

- domestic reasons, e.g. gardening, cooking
- commercial reasons, e.g. agriculture and horticulture
- pollution monitoring
- nature conservation.

We shall look at these in turn.

FOCUS

Reasons for controlling the environment of organisms include

- **gardening**
- **cooking**
- **agriculture**
- **horticulture**
- **pollution monitoring and nature conservation.**

Domestic benefits of controlling the environment of organisms

Many of the activities a gardener carries out are to provide the best environment for particular organisms. For example, a gardener keen to grow vegetables may:

- sow the seed at an appropriate depth
- fertilise the soil
- water the plants as they grow
- remove competing plants by weeding
- apply insecticides and fungicides to kill insects (such as aphids) and fungi (such as mildew).

Oxygen concentration, page 62
Temperature, page 64
Water content, page 64

In the kitchen, many of the ways in which we treat our foods serve to preserve them. For example:

- We cook many foods. This kills any micro-organisms in the food, effectively sterilising it.
- We store many foods in refrigerators or tins. Most refrigerators provide a temperature of about 4 °C. At this temperature micro-organisms that could spoil the food grow slowly, if at all. Food in tins is first heat sterilised to kill the micro-organisms. The tins are sealed so as to keep micro-organisms and oxygen (needed for the growth of most micro-organisms) out.
- We store other foods dry (e.g. rice). This makes it almost impossible for micro-organisms to grow, as all organisms need water.
- We turn fruit into jams and marmalades (see Figure 2.1.25). The high sugar content of jams makes it very difficult for most micro-organisms to colonise, as the water in them is lost by osmosis.

Figure 2.1.25 Jam making is a traditional activity, usually carried out in late autumn as a way of making use of excess fruit. It is a very effective way of ensuring that micro-organisms are unable to colonise a highly nutritious food. In most cases jam making involves adding sugar, boiling at about 105 °C for 15 minutes or more, and covering while still hot. Micro-organisms are destroyed by the boiling. Their subsequent entry is prevented by covering the jam while it is still hot. Any micro-organisms that do survive or get in find growth difficult as the effect of the sugar is to keep the water content of the jam very low. Another way to kill micro-organisms is to cook food. Why is it very important to allow a frozen chicken to defrost completely before cooking it?

Commercial benefits of controlling the environment of organisms

The commercial benefits that may result from controlling the environment of organisms are huge. For example, whether or not you approve of factory farming, there is no doubt that rearing animals under intensive conditions often makes commercial sense for a farmer. In modern battery farms, just one or two people can look after over a million hens. The temperature and food supply can be regulated to maximise the economic return from the farmer's investment. By keeping the animals in cages, the farmer ensures that they expend little energy on exercise, devoting it instead to growth (meat production) and reproduction (egg laying). You might like to list arguments for and against intensive farming. You will need to consider both economic and ethical arguments.

We shall look at the commercial benefits to be obtained from controlling the environment of organisms in more detail in Element 3.1, when we consider how food can be obtained from plants.

Pollution monitoring

A quite different example of the way in which we can take advantage of the fact that organisms respond to changes in their environment comes from pollution monitoring. A *pollutant* is a substance which is released into the environment as a result of human activity and subsequently damages the environment. Examples of pollutants include:

- Oxides of sulphur and nitrogen released from the burning of coal and oil. When these oxides dissolve in rainwater, they produce sulphuric and nitric acid. As a result, the pH of the rain water drops, giving rise to acid rain. Acid rain kills many organisms, including certain plants, invertebrates and fish (see Figure 2.1.26).
- Nitrate and phosphate ions released into rivers as a result of fertiliser run-off from farms. When nitrates and phosphates get into water, they can cause a population explosion of algae and blue-green bacteria (see Figure 2.1.27). Eventually these organisms die. When they do so they are decomposed (broken down) by organisms that use up much of the oxygen in the water. As a result organisms such as fish, that require high oxygen levels, may die.

One way of monitoring pollution is to use monitoring equipment directly to measure altered environmental variables. For instance:

- a pH meter can tell you whether the water is acid
- a nitrate meter can tell you if nitrate levels are high
- an oxygen meter can tell you if oxygen levels have fallen.

This approach is sometimes called *chemical monitoring*. Another way to monitor pollution is to look to see whether certain *organisms* are absent from the place you are interested in. This approach is known as *biological monitoring*. For example, many lichens are killed by high levels of sulphur dioxide. This means that areas of Britain with high levels of sulphur dioxide pollution have few species of lichens (see Figure 2.1.28).

Obtain products from cultivated plants, page 120

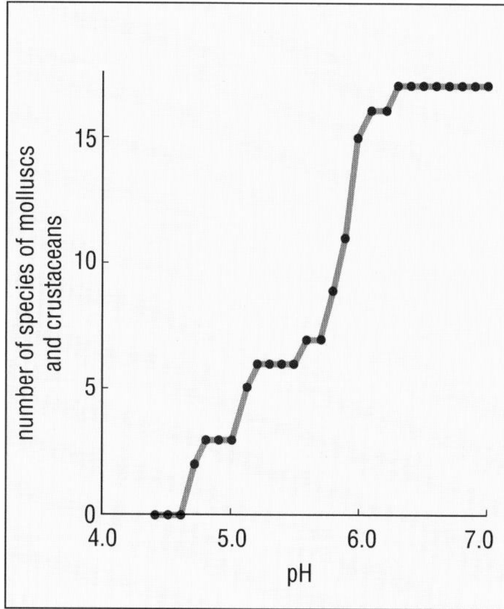

Figure 2.1.26 *The number of different species of molluscs (snails) and crustaceans (water fleas, etc.) found in Norwegian lakes as a function of the pH. The more acid the water, the fewer the number of species.*

Figure 2.1.27 *Excessive levels of nitrates and phosphates can cause an algal bloom. This is a population explosion of unicellular photosynthetic organisms.*

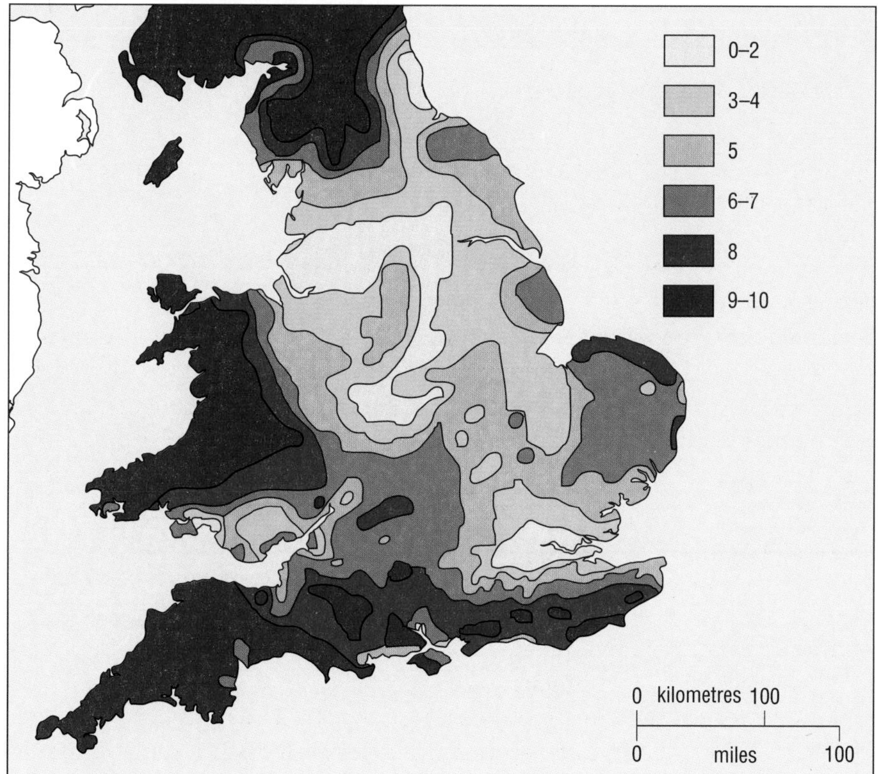

Figure 2.1.28 *The distribution of lichen zones in England and Wales. Zones 0,– 2 have the fewest species of lichens, zone 10 the most. In which zones are large cities mainly found? Why is this?*

Because lichens are killed by sulphur dioxide, counting the number of lichen species present in an area gives you an indication of how bad pollution by sulphur dioxide is. As lichens grow slowly, counting the number of lichen species gives you an indication not so much of today's pollution – which could be measured by chemical monitoring – but of what pollution was like *in the recent past*. Biological monitoring and chemical monitoring can therefore complement one another. Each tells you something different about the overall picture.

Figure 2.1.29 *Chalk grassland in Oxfordshire. Such grassland is only preserved through grazing by sheep or rabbits, or by deliberate mowing. Grazing and mowing help prevent the invasion of taller plants, such as hawthorn bushes.*

Nature conservation

At first sight, the idea that the environment of organisms can usefully be controlled for the purposes of nature conservation may sound odd. Isn't nature conservation all about not interfering, letting nature take her course? Well, yes and no. The truth is that many nature reserves benefit from some sort of management. One example is chalk grassland (see Figure 2.1.29). Chalk grassland may have as many as 50 plant species in each square metre. However, this is only the case if the grassland is grazed or mown regularly. In the absence of grazing and mowing, many of the delicate, beautiful small plants soon become crowded out.

Another example of controlling the environment of organisms for the benefit of nature conservation comes from the burning of heaths and moors. While burning too often can damage moors, preventing any burning from taking place leads, eventually, to the loss of heathland and moorland. The reason is as follows. After a fire, seeds of heathers and other plants characteristic of such areas germinate. Within a couple of years the moor will have regenerated and the young plants provide valuable grazing for many animals. However, in the absence of any burning, trees such as birch begin to invade. The continued prevention of burning eventually leads to the existence, not of a heath or moor, but of a wood.

Case study

An astonishing year

In 1993 the naturalist Robin Page founded the charity 'The Countryside Restoration Trust'. Robin Page is a farmer with a passion for wildlife. He wanted to see if farms could be run both to produce food and to benefit wildlife. Here is an extract from an article he wrote in the Summer of 1994 to describe how the first year of the Trust went. Read it and then answer the questions that follow.

It has been an astonishing year. Twelve months ago we were unsure of the future and we were worried that we might not be able to buy our first forty acres of land. Consultants I spoke with were not encouraging; they told us that neither the time nor our approach were right and that we could only hope to raise £2,000. So, against the odds, we went public – the rest is history. Twelve months later we have just reached £100,000. We do not consult consultants anymore.

Just as remarkable is what the money has achieved. I would not have believed that restoration could be well on the way so quickly. On a cold, wet winter's day, twenty Friends planted nearly 500 yards of hedgerow. It was hard, heavy work, with the clay sticking to boots and hands – one local Friend, Jill Geering, at over seventy, put in a marvellous stint on hands and knees. However, our Friends literally 'stuck it out' and at the end of the day there was a real feeling of achievement. Despite the summer drought most of the 1,800 saplings

Illustration 1 *Members of the Countryside Restoration Trust planting a hedge in the Cambridgeshire countryside. Cambridgeshire is the least wooded of all the counties in the UK. The UK is the least wooded country in Europe.*

in the hedge have survived extremely well, some have even withstood the attention of hares intent on pruning. Hawthorn, blackthorn, field maple, wild privet, dogwood, wild rose, wild crab apple, oak, ash, spindle, wild pear, hazel and a sweet chestnut are all flourishing. Next winter we plan to add holly and a few purging buckthorn, the food-plant of the brimstone caterpillar.

The new hedge has divided the field into two. On one side Tim Scott, our Management Committee farmer, is growing barley with unsprayed headlands full of 'weeds' and insects. On the other side we have planted Miriam Rothschild's hay meadow mixture. It was planted in the wet and cold; it has survived the hot and dry and is doing extremely well. Arable weeds are still much in evidence in this area – but as the hay meadow mixture becomes established, its plants will gradually dominate.

Then came the National Rivers Authority which has co-operated with us in a really exciting way. It has dug out an old meander that was filled in by the now defunct Great Ouse River Board in 1971. By doing so, an island has been created on which we will soon build an artificial otter holt. To raise the water level, the NRA has also tipped nearly 200 tonnes of flint into two 'riffles' (dams to you and me), around which we have planted marsh marigold, yellow iris, monkey flower, ragged robin, water avens, purple loosestrife, hemp agrimony, water mint, water forget-me-not and water lilies.

The wildlife has also been exciting. A hobby has been hunting regularly over the field; a pair of Mandarin duck nested in old willows; Robert Goodden, the butterfly expert, found several beautiful brown argus butterflies feeding on the flowers of bird's foot trefoil in the new hay meadow; and yes, the otters are still active. There have been several sightings, but we are making every effort to minimise disturbance – I personally have not seen them, and have not tried to. I am just happy to know that they are there from their tracks and 'spraints' (droppings).

Questions

1 From the figures in the first paragraph, work out approximately how much an acre of good quality arable land cost at 1993 prices. How many acres are there in a hectare (100 m × 100 m)?

2 Give two reasons why the Trust planted a hedge.

3 State two problems the young hedgerow trees (saplings) faced in their first year.

4 Find out how many of the species planted in the hedgerow are native to Britain.

5 How might you expect the yield on the half of the field planted with barley to compare with that on a conventional, high intensity farm? Explain your answer.

6 Explain how the environment has been managed to encourage otters.

7 Why do you think Robin Page has not tried to see the otters?

8 Describe one way in which your local environment has recently changed. Has this change been for the better or the worse?

Assignment

RECORDING CHANGES IN THE PHYSICAL ENVIRONMENT OVER TIME

Setting the scene

Aspects of the abiotic environment, such as temperature, pH and nutrient status, can be recorded at regular intervals using instruments such as thermometers, pH meters and nitrate meters or test kits. The physical environment is of great importance for living organisms, as different species of organism are adapted for different physical environments.

SAFETY: *Always work in pairs, never alone. Tell your teacher/lecturer when and where you are going. Make sure a responsible family member knows where you are. Cover any cuts or grazes with waterproof plasters. Take care not to fall into any water. If you do fall in, report to your GP within 12 hours – every year a number of people in the UK die as a result of diseases caused by falling into freshwater. For example, Weil's disease, carried by rats, gives 'flu-like symptoms.*

The assignment

You will be provided with access to a safe aquatic habitat, such as a pond or stream, and with appropriate instruments.

Before you set off, make absolutely sure you know how to obtain readings from each of the instruments you take with you. Practise in the laboratory beforehand. Some instruments, e.g. oxygen meters, may need careful calibration. Follow the maker's instructions. If possible, use some sort of datalogging equipment.

Either take readings every two hours from dawn to dusk *or* take readings at the same time of day for a week or two.
In addition to recording the physical environment of the water, make records of the weather, e.g. air temperature and cloud cover, and on any other points of interest, such as whether the water is clear or cloudy, and whether you can see any organisms.

Presenting your assignment

1 Once you have collected your results, plot them out. For instance, plot temperature on the vertical axis against time on the horizontal axis.
2 Try to identify and explain any patterns you observe. For example, does pH vary during the day? If so, how and can you suggest why?
3 Try also to suggest what significance your results might have for the organisms in the water.
4 You may need to do some background reading to help you interpret your findings. For example, are your readings typical of clean or polluted freshwater?
5 Finally, write up your work. Think about what sort of scientists would carry out this kind of work, and why.

Additional information

The following Procedures and Investigations are available:
(a) Measuring light intensity, page 63
(b) Determining moisture content in a soil sample, page 65
(c) Determining moisture content in the air, page 65
(d) The water-holding capacities of different soils, page 65
(e) Determining available nutrients, page 66

Grading

This assignment gives you an opportunity to meet merit or distinction criteria. All four themes are covered: Planning, Information Seeking and Information Handling, Evaluation, Quality of Outcomes.

Opportunity to collect evidence
In completing this assignment you will have the opportunity to meet the following requirements for Intermediate GNVQ Science:

Science units
Unit 1:
Element 1.2, PCs 1, 2, 3, 4, 5
Unit 2:
Element 2.1, PCs 2, 3

Core skill units

Application of Number:
Elements 2.1, 2.2, 2.3

Communication:
Elements 2.1, 2.2, 2.3

Information Technology:
Elements 2.1, 2.2, 2.3, 2.4, 2.5

Assignment

WHAT EFFECT DOES CHANGING THE ENVIRONMENT OF AN ANIMAL HAVE?

Setting the scene

Humans keep animals in captivity for all sorts of reasons. Most of us eat meat as part of our diet. Many of us have pets. Then there are animals kept in zoos for conservation and entertainment, and the animals kept in research establishments used to check that new medicines and veterinary products are safe.

You may or may not approve of the various reasons why we keep animals. However, given that we do keep animals, we have a duty to care for them. Indeed, from a farmer's point of view, an unhealthy animal is a liability. It won't grow or reproduce as it should, and it may infect other animals.

The assignment

Your objectives are to:

- keep an animal in a controlled environment
- devise a way of recording its behaviour
- alter its environment and determine what effect this has on its behaviour.

Task 1: Keeping an animal in a controlled environment

You will need to choose an animal to work on. You may have access to a farm or poultry unit. If so, this will enable you to work on an animal from which we obtain food or other useful products (e.g. wool from sheep). It may be that your school or college has facilities for keeping small mammals (e.g. gerbils or rats). If so this will allow you to work on the sort of animal used in the testing of drugs and other products, as these products are often tested on small mammals as the final stage in their (the drugs') development. Finally, you may decide to keep a suitable organism at home. Fish are ideal. However, you should only keep an animal at home if you have at least two year's experience of looking after that species.

SAFETY: Whatever organism you choose to work on, keep in mind your safety and its well-being (see 'Additional information' below). Only use animals from approved sources. Strictly speaking you should wear protective gloves before handling any animal. Always wash your hands after any investigation. Never eat or drink anything while working. If a bite causes you to bleed, immediately contact a nurse or your GP. Should you suspect that your animal is unwell, ensure you know to whom to turn – for example, to an experienced technician or to a vet.

BIOHAZARD
farm and
laboratory
animals

Task 2: Recording an animal's behaviour

Having chosen your experimental animal, you need to devise some systematic way of recording its behaviour. Here are some suggestions, but that's all they are – mostly it's up to you:

- Divide the animal's home into about a dozen different areas. For example, you might rule lines onto the front of an aquarium, or the insides of a small mammal cage.
- Work in pairs, one of you holding a watch with a second hand. Every 60 seconds write down what the animal is doing. You will have to do some preliminary work to identify the range of behaviours shown by your animal. Try to identify about 6 to 10 different behaviours, e.g., for a small mammal: feeding; drinking; grooming; sniffing; moving; sleeping; sitting inactive; standing inactive.
- Use a camcorder to record aspects of an animal's behaviour. This can be especially valuable for allowing analysis of rapid behaviours, such as feeding or grooming.

Task 3: Altering an animal's environment to determine what effect this has or its behaviour

Change the animal's environment in some way and see what effect this has on its behaviour. For instance:

- introduce more fish into an aquarium
- move a small mammal into a new cage
- change the animal's food.

You must, of course, only carry out such a change if you are certain that the animal will not be harmed as a result. Consult your supervisor first.

Use the same recording methods as before to quantify any changes in the animal's behaviour.

Presenting your assignment

When you have finished your study write it up clearly so that someone unfamiliar with what you have done can understand it. A good report will demonstrate that you can independently draw up plans of action and change them when needed. You will need to show that you can collect appropriate background information and suggest how your work could be extended and improved. You should also relate your findings to the real world. If possible, visit a farm or zoo and, after obtaining permission, make some recordings of the animals' behaviour and compare them with your animal's behaviour. Think carefully about how to present your results in your final report – by means of writing, drawings, graphs, tables, photographs and video footage, for example.

Additional information

Many pet shops and garden centres have useful booklets about how to keep and look after small mammals, birds, fish and other pets. Relevant publications are also produced by:

- RSPCA Education Department, Causeway, Horsham, West Sussex RH12 1HG – Tel: 01403 64181 (e.g. *Animals in Schools* and *Small Mammals in Schools*)
- Institute of Biology, 20–22 Queensberry Place, London SW7 2DZ - Tel: 0171 581 8333 (e.g. *Living Biology in Schools*)
- CLEAPPS School Science Service, Brunel University, Uxbridge UB8 3PH – Tel: 01895 251496 (e.g. *Small Mammals* and *Giant African Land Snails*)
- Bookshops (e.g. Sainsbury, D. (1992). *Poultry Health and Management: Chickens, Turkeys, Ducks, Geese, Quail, 3rd edn*, Blackwell Scientific Publications).

Grading

This assignment gives you an opportunity to meet merit or distinction criteria. All four themes are covered: Planning, Information Seeking and Information Handling, Evaluation, Quality of Outcomes.

Opportunity to collect evidence
In completing this assignment you will have the opportunity to meet the following requirements for Intermediate GNVQ Science:

Science units
Unit 1:
Element 1.1, PCs 1, 2, 3
Element 1.3, PCs 1, 2, 3, 4
Unit 2:
Element 2.1, PCs 1, 2, 3, 4

Core skill units

Application of Number:
Elements 2.1, 2.3

Communication:
Elements 2.1, 2.2, 2.3

Information Technology:
Elements 2.1, 2.2, 2.3, 2.4, 2.5

Questions

1 List the various activities that are characteristic of living organisms.

2 Describe how (a) plants, (b) animals and (c) micro-organisms obtain their energy.

3 Describe how (a) plants, (b) herbivores and (c) carnivores obtain their nutrients.

4 What is meant by 'growth'?

5 Distinguish between sexual and asexual reproduction.

6 Summarise the four main ways in which organisms may respond to changes in their environment.

7 Describe how each of the following may affect the growth of plants: (a) light intensity and (b) moisture level.

8 Give three reasons why animals might move in response to changes in their environment.

9 Describe how each of the following may affect the growth of colonies of micro-organisms: (a) temperature and (b) availability of nutrients.

Figure 2.2.1 Each item in this kitchen has been made for a purpose. The materials used to make those items must have the right properties. What properties do different kitchen utensils need to have?

Measuring properties, page 82

FOCUS

The important properties of materials are strength, stiffness, hardness, toughness, transparency, electrical resistance, thermal conduction and density.

Figure 2.2.2 Different materials are used to make different parts of this bridge. Each material has been chosen because it has the properties needed for that part of the bridge.

Investigate the properties of solid materials and relate them to their uses

You will need to show that you can:

- measure the properties of solids safely
- relate the properties of solids to their uses and to their structures.

Investigating materials

You use a wide variety of solid materials all the time. The bed you sleep in at night. The mug you use for coffee. The house you live in. The clothes you wear. All of these items are made of materials which have been specially selected for a purpose. They can only accomplish that purpose if they have the right mixture of properties.

Properties and uses

Any object that we build has a purpose. It has to do something. For example, the purpose of a chair is to support your weight when you sit on it. The chair will only do this if its materials have the right **properties**. The materials have to be strong, hard, stiff and have a low density.

Construction

A chair is an example of a structure. This is something which we build to support other things. It has to hold up its own weight as well as the weight of other things we put into or onto it.

Materials which are used to build structures have to be **strong.** They must be able to withstand large forces before they break. Steel is stronger than wood.

Quite often, structural materials also need to be **stiff.** They must not change their shape when forces are applied to them. For example, concrete is stiffer than polythene.

It is often important that structural materials are **hard** or resistant to bumps and scratches. For example, pottery is much harder than wood. Think about work surfaces in a kitchen. A bare wooden surface is easily dented or scratched. It can be protected by covering it with ceramic tiles, or by treating it with a polyurethane varnish which dries to a hard, scratch-resistant finish.

Any structure which is unable to support itself will be useless. Most structures are therefore built from materials which have a low **density**, so that their own weight is kept low. Because wood has a low density it is often used to make roofs.

Larger structures have to let light into them, so some of their materials must be **transparent**. Glass is transparent, brick is not. Other materials are also transparent (for example, perspex and some other polymers). Therefore, other considerations come into play when making a final choice. Think about suitable materials for a greenhouse.

Buildings need to be heated when the weather is cold. They ought to be made from materials which will not let that expensive heat energy leak out quickly. The materials on their outside have to be **thermal insulators.**

Finally, some structures need to be resistant to sudden shocks. Their materials must be **tough**, not brittle. Metals are tough, ceramics are not. A hammer with a ceramic head rather than a metal one would be of little use.

Equipment

Many of the smaller objects that we build are *implements*. Tools, crockery, televisions and bags fall into this class. They often contain a variety of materials, each chosen for a specific purpose.

For example, consider a small screwdriver (see Figure 2.2.3). It has been designed for use by an electrician. Two materials are used. The handle must be an *electrical insulator*, so it has been made from a polymer. The shaft needs to be stiff and strong, so it has been made out of metal.

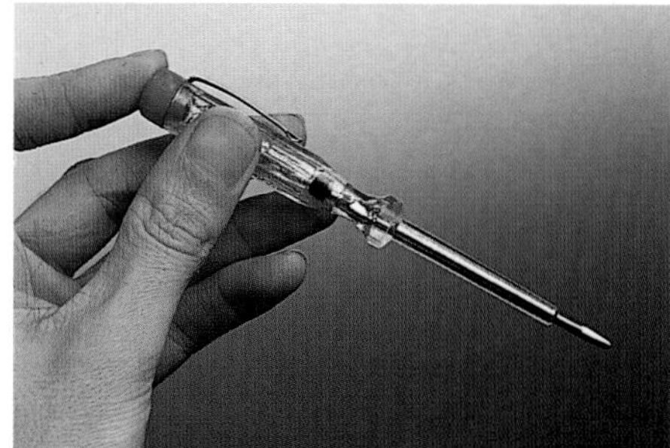

Figure 2.2.3 *An electrician's screwdriver. Why does it have a steel shaft and a polymer handle?*

A cooking pot is shown in Figure 2.2.4. Its material has to be a *good thermal conductor* so that heat energy can pass easily from the stove to the food inside the pot. It also ought to have a low density so that it is easy to lift and move around. The material must also be stiff and hard, but above all it must have a high *melting point*. Otherwise, it will melt when it is put on the stove.

Figure 2.2.4 *Cooking pots must always have a high melting point. What other properties should they have?*

Think about the properties needed by materials which make the following objects: cooking spoons, hammers, electrical switches, pens and fences. Can you list them?

Types of material

There are four different types of **material** which are used to make structures and equipment.

FOCUS

The four types of material are metals, ceramics, polymers and composites.

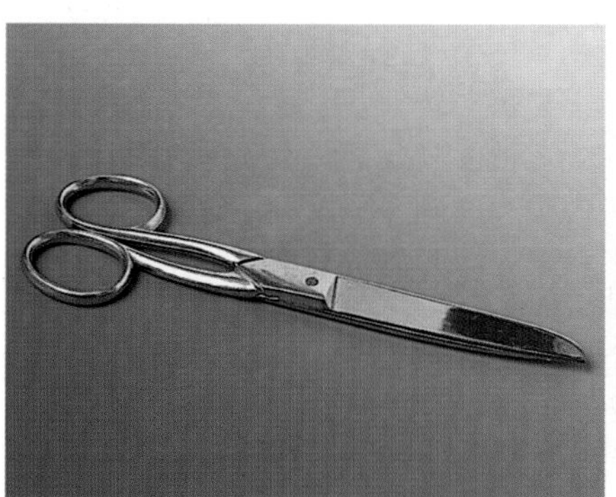

Figure 2.2.5 *Examples of the four different types of material.*

▶ Properties and structure, page 88

Metals

Commonly used metals are iron, copper and aluminium. They are all excellent electrical and thermal conductors, as well as being strong and tough. Most metals have high densities (see Figure 2.2.5a).

Ceramics

Glass, pottery and cement are ceramic materials. They are strong and hard but also lack toughness. Ceramics other than glass have high melting points. They are good electrical and thermal insulators, with a low density (see Figure 2.2.5b).

Polymers

Nylon and polythene are polymers. They are not very good structural materials. This is because they have only moderate strength and are not very stiff or hard. However, they are tough. They can be transparent, are good electrical insulators and have low densities (see Figure 2.2.5c).

Composites

A composite material is a mixture of two other materials. One has to be strong and hard, the other has to be tough and stiff. The result is a material which is strong, hard, tough and stiff. No single material has this useful set of properties.

Wood, steel reinforced concrete and glass reinforced plastic are widely used examples of composites (see Figure 2.2.5d).

Table 2.2.1 A summary of typical properties of the four main types of material. However, there are many exceptions

Property	Metals	Ceramics	Polymers	Composites
Strength	high	high	low	high
Hardness	medium	high	low	high
Stiffness	high	high	low	high
Toughness	high	low	high	high
Transparency	low	high	high	low
Electrical resistance	low	high	high	high
Thermal conduction	high	low	low	low
Melting point	medium	high	low	medium
Density	high	medium	low	medium

Figure 2.2.6 Testing materials as part of the quality control in a factory.

FOCUS

Measurements made on samples of materials from a structure allow scientists to assess its safety.

Measuring properties

Scientists routinely **measure** the properties of materials. For example, they are part of the quality control at factories where materials are made or used (see Figure 2.2.6).

Tensile strength

The easiest way of measuring the *tensile strength* of a sample is to add weights to one end until it snaps.

Comparing samples

The tensile strength of a sample depends on its size. If you need to compare the strength of two samples, it must be a fair test. Make sure that both samples have the same shape and size.

Figure 2.2.7 Testing the materials in a large structure to assess its safety.

Procedure

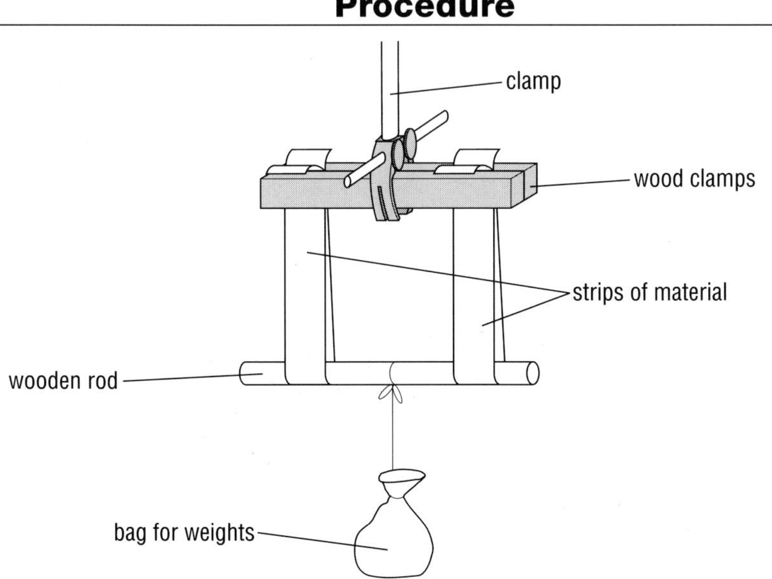

Figure 2.2.8 Measuring the tensile strength of a material.

Requirements

- ❒ Two identical strips or wires of material to be tested
- ❒ Clamp
- ❒ Wood clamps
- ❒ Stand
- ❒ Wooden rod
- ❒ strong bag(if available)
- ❒ Wire or strong thread
- ❒ Selection of weights

SAFETY: *Wear eye protection; the sample may snap suddenly. Make sure that heavy weights have somewhere safe to fall.*

Eye protection must be worn

1. Obtain two identical samples of the material in the form of uniform thin strips or wires.
2. Suspend them securely with a clamp and stand so that they hang as two loops (see Figure 2.2.8).
3. Place a wooden rod through the loops and suspend a strong bag from its centre (see Figure 2.2.8).
4. Place a box with some cushioning (such as waste paper) under the bag.
5. Add weights to the bag until the sample snaps.
6. Calculate the tensile strength as follows. Find the mass of the weights in the bag in kilograms. Multiply this by 9.8 to find the snapping force in newtons.

Relative hardness

Relative hardness is a comparison of the hardness of two or more materials. You can decide which of two materials is the harder by ramming them into each other. The softer material is the one which gets dented.

Table 2.2.2 gives Mohs's scale of hardness for minerals. The hardness of any material on this scale can be found by attempting to scratch it with each of the materials in the table.

Comparing samples

The procedure described below allows you to compare the hardness of several different materials with some degree of accuracy.

The 'denting height' of the cylinder is a measure of the hardness of the sample. Provided that you stick to the same ball-bearing and cylinder, you can use this procedure to compare the hardness of different materials.

Table 2.2.2 Mohs's scale of mineral hardness

Mineral	Hardness
Talc	1
Rock salt	2
Calcspar	3
Fluorspar	4
Apatite	5
Felspar	6
Quartz	7
Topaz	8
Corundum	9
Diamond	10

Procedure

Measuring relative hardness

WARNING

SAFETY: The procedure involves dropping heavy weights onto samples of material. Make sure that the weights cannot tumble onto your feet or hands.

Requirements

- Sample slabs
- Clear plastic tube
- Metal cylinder to fit into tube
- Stand and clamp
- String
- Ball bearing

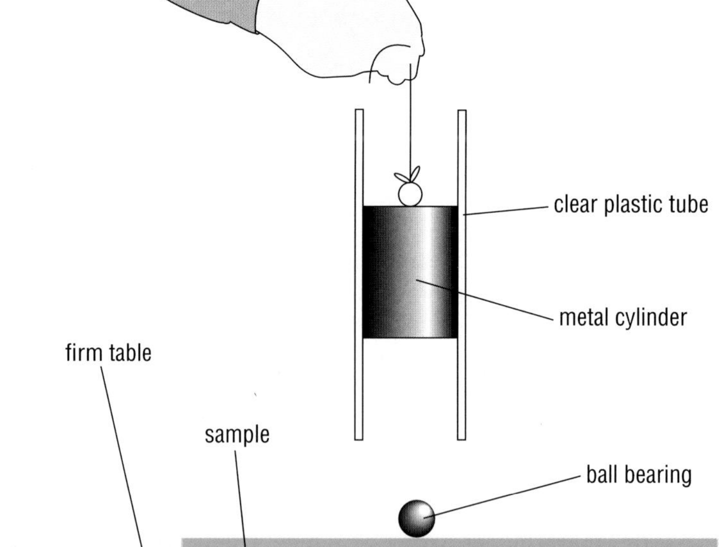

Figure 2.2.9 *Measuring the relative hardness of a material.*

1 Obtain a flat smooth slab of the material and place it on a firm table.
2 Suspend a long clear plastic tube above the sample (see Figure 2.2.9).
3 Select a cylinder of metal which fits the tube loosely. Fasten a length of string to one end of it (see Figure 2.2.9).
4 Place a small steel ball bearing on the sample directly under the tube.
5 Holding the string, lower the cylinder down the tube until it is a known height (say 10 cm) above the sample (see Figure 2.2.9). Let go of the string.

6 Look at the surface of the sample. Note whether or not it has been dented by the ball-bearing.
7 Repeat steps 4 to 6 until you have found the minimum initial height for the cylinder which leaves a visible dent in the sample.

Stiffness

The *stiffness* of a material is measured by measuring the force needed to stretch or bend it by a given amount.

Comparing samples

The stiffness of a sample depends on its size. If you need to compare the stiffness of two samples, it must be a fair test. Make sure that both samples have the same shape and size.

Procedure

Measuring stiffness

SAFETY : *Wear eye protection; the sample may snap suddenly. Make sure that heavy weights have somewhere safe to fall.*

Eye protection must be worn

Requirements

- ❒ Two identical strips or wires of material to be tested
- ❒ Clamp
- ❒ Wood clamps
- ❒ Stand
- ❒ Wooden rod
- ❒ Strong bag
- ❒ Wire or strong thread
- ❒ Selection of weights
- ❒ Pin
- ❒ Tape or rubber band to fasten pin
- ❒ Ruler

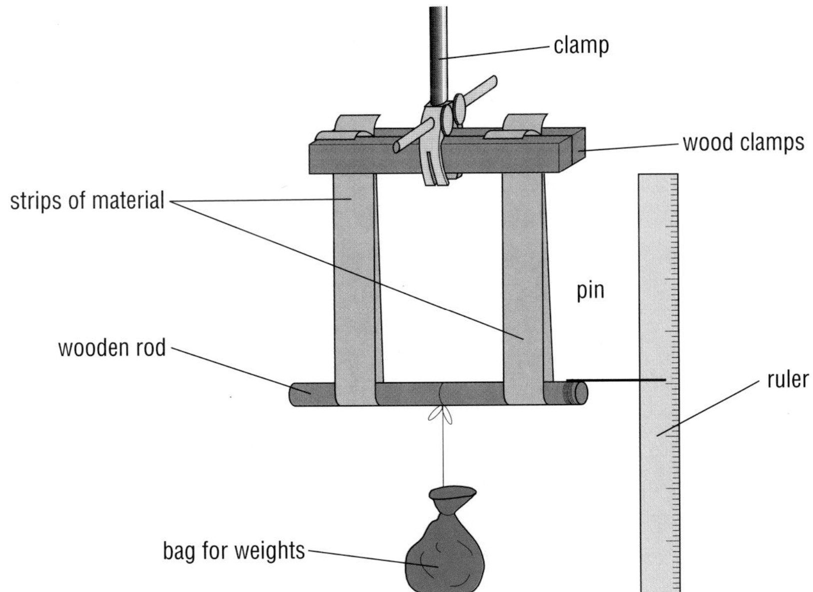

Figure 2.2.10 *Measuring the stiffness of a material.*

You will need to do some trial runs to find a suitable size for the sample. If it is too thick or short, you won't be able to extend it by 5 mm.

1 Obtain two identical samples of the material in the form of uniform thin strips or wires.
2 Suspend them securely with a clamp and stand so that they hang in two loops (see Figure 2.2.10).
3 Place a wooden rod through the loops and suspend a strong bag from its centre.
4 Place a box with some cushioning under the bag.
5 Place a ruler at the end of the rod. Fasten a pin to the end of the rod so that it acts as a pointer on the rule (see Figure 2.2.10).
6 Add weights to the bag until the sample has extended by exactly 5 mm.
7 Calculate the stretching force as follows. Find the mass of the weights in the bag in kilograms. Multiply this by 9.8 to find the stiffness in newtons.

Electrical resistance

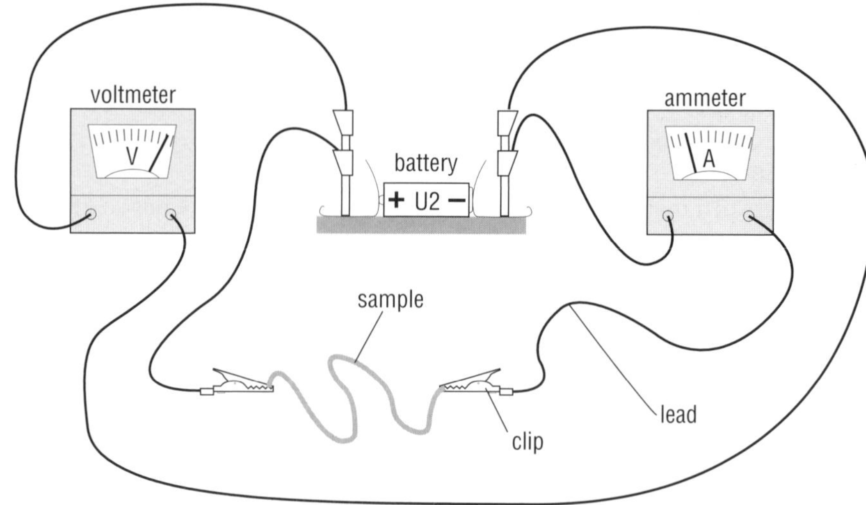

Figure 2.2.11 Measuring the resistance of a material.

Figure 2.2.11 shows how the electrical resistance of a sample can be measured. The sample is connected to a battery via an ammeter. The meter measures how much current is forced through the sample by the battery.

The resistance can be calculated if you know the voltage across the battery terminals. The voltmeter connected to the battery tells you this.

$$\text{resistance (ohms)} = \frac{\text{voltage (volts)}}{\text{current (amps)}}$$

Suppose that the current is 0.45 A and the voltage is 1.5 V. The resistance of the sample is then $\frac{1.5}{0.45} = 3.3\ \Omega$.

Comparing samples

The resistance of a sample depends on its size and shape. Short fat samples have lower resistances than long thin ones. If you need to compare the resistance of two samples, it must be a fair test. Make sure that both samples have the same shape and size.

Procedure

Measuring electrical resistance

Electrical hazard

Requirements

- ❒ 1.5 V battery in holder
- ❒ Voltmeter (0–2V)
- ❒ Ammeter (0–5A)
- ❒ Connecting wires
- ❒ Crocodile clips
- ❒ Samples

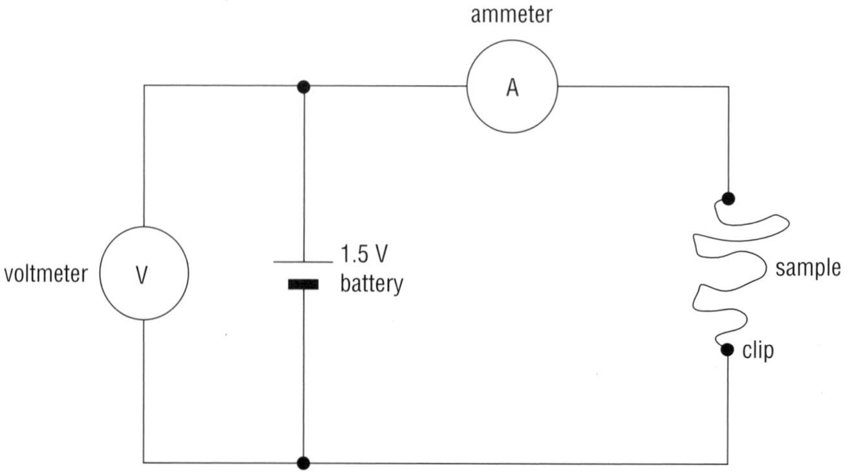

Figure 2.2.12 Circuit diagram for measuring resistance.

1 Obtain a sample of the material in the form of a strip or wire.
2 Clip it into the circuit shown in Figure 2.2.12. Use an ammeter rated at 5 A full scale.
3 Note the ammeter and voltmeter readings. You may need to use a more sensitive ammeter if its reading is very small.
4 Calculate the resistance (in ohms) by dividing the voltage (in volts) by the current (in amps).

Thermal conduction

The *thermal conduction* of a sample tells you how easily heat energy flows through it. It is quite difficult to measure accurately.

Thermal conduction can be measured by making a box out of six squares of the material under investigation. It can be heated from the inside using an electrical resistor. The temperature rise of the air in the box is a measure of how difficult it is for the heat energy coming out of the resistor to flow through the walls of the box. The final temperature of the box depends on its size and the power of the resistor.

Comparing samples

If you need to compare the thermal conduction of two samples, it must be a fair test. Make sure that both boxes are the same size, and that the resistors have the same voltage and current.

Procedure

Measuring thermal conduction

SAFETY: The sample may get hot enough to burn you. Touch it with care. Take the usual precautions when handling apparatus which is connected to the mains electricity supply.

Requirements

- ❒ Six square slabs of material to be tested
- ❒ 15 ohm resistor rated at 11 watts
- ❒ Connecting leads
- ❒ Temperature probe/electronic thermometer
- ❒ 12 V d. c. supply
- ❒ 1 A full-scale ammeter

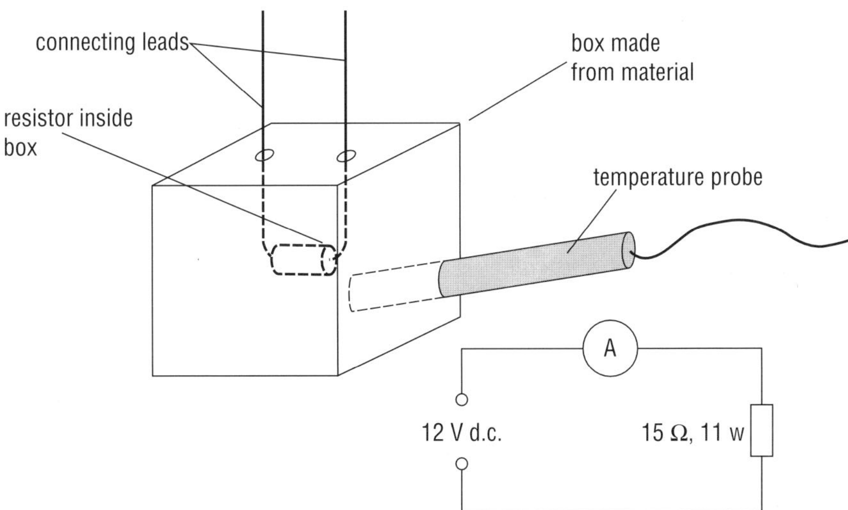

Figure 2.2.13 Measuring the thermal conduction of a material.

1 Make a small cubical box out of six identical square slabs of the material. It must be large enough to fit a 15 ohm resistor rated at 11 watts. It must also have a small hole for the probe of an electronic thermometer (see Figure 2.2.13).
2 Suspend the box in mid-air by the leads which deliver current to the resistor (see Figure 2.2.13).

3 Connect the leads to a 12 V d.c. supply via an ammeter (1 A full scale) (see Figure 2.2.13).
4 Note the initial temperature of the air in the box.
5 Switch on the d.c. supply. The ammeter should read about 0.8 A.
6 Wait until the temperature inside the box reaches a steady value. This may take some time. Record the temperature.

Density

The **density** of a material is the mass of a cubic metre of it. Once you know the mass and volume of a sample, you can use these rules to calculate the density.

$$\text{density (g cm}^{-3}\text{)} = \frac{\text{mass (g)}}{\text{volume (cm}^3\text{)}}$$

$$\text{density (kg m}^{-3}\text{)} = \text{density (g cm}^{-3}\text{)} \times 1\,000$$

For example, a cube of wood has sides of length 5 cm. Its mass is 20 g. The density is therefore $\frac{20}{(5 \times 5 \times 5)} = 0.16\ \text{g cm}^{-3}$ or $160\ \text{kg m}^{-3}$.

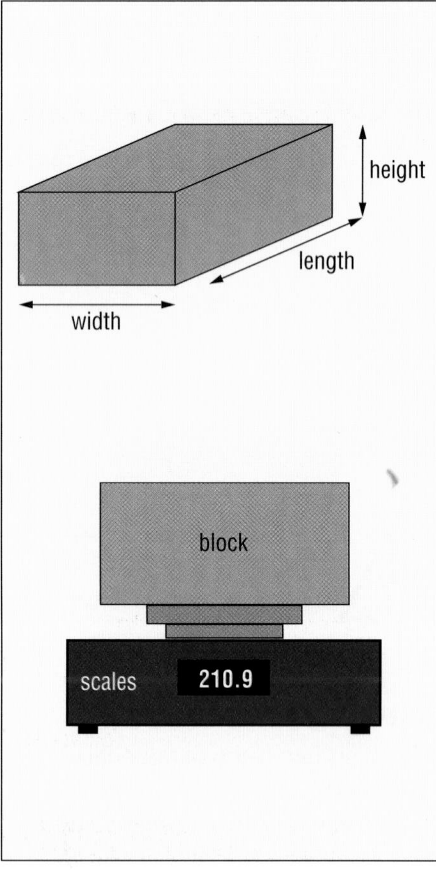

Figure 2.2.14 *Measuring the density of a material.*

Procedure

Measuring density

1 Obtain a block of the material which is rectangular (see Figure 2.2.14a). If the material comes as sheets, you will need to stack them together like a book.
2 Measure the width, length and height of the block with a ruler. Record the results in cm.
3 Calculate the volume of the block in cm^3 by multiplying the width by the length by the height.
4 Use a set of scales to find the mass of the block in grams. Check that the scales have been zeroed before you place the block on the scale pan.
5 Calculate the density of the block using the formula:

$$\text{density (g cm}^{-3}\text{)} = \frac{\text{mass (g)}}{\text{volume (cm}^3\text{)}}$$

FOCUS

Solids have macroscopic structures. They may be
- **amorphous: particles arranged in a random fashion**
- **crystalline: particles arranged in a regular, repeating way**
- **polymeric: particles consist of extremely long strings of atoms.**

Properties and structure

Metals, ceramics, polymers and composites each have a different set of properties (see Table 2.2.1). This is because of the different way in which their atoms are arranged. Each has a different **structure**. The structure of each class of material gives it its unique mixture of properties.

Scientists have developed their ideas about how atoms interact with each other. These ideas can be used to explain the properties of materials. They can also be used by scientists to work out how materials can be modified to make them more useful.

Some basic ideas

All materials are made out of **atoms**. They can bond with each other to form *chemical compounds*. These compounds can have molecular or giant structures.

In *molecular structures*, the smallest particles present are **molecules**.

Bonding between atoms in a molecule is strong (covalent bonding) but between one molecule and another is weak.

In *giant structures*, the smallest particles may be atoms or **ions**. There are three types of giant structure:

- metals, ions held together by lose electrons by metallic bonds
- ionic compounds, oppositely charged ions held together by ionic bonds in crystalline lattices
- giant covalent compounds, atoms held together by covalent bonds in lattices (some are crystalline, others are amorphous).

Atoms and elements, page 8

Structure of elements and compounds, page 10

FOCUS

The properties of a material arise from the strength and nature of the bonds between its atoms. Strong bonds make the material stiff and hard, with a high melting point. Bonds which allow atoms to move past each other make the material tough and plastic.

FOCUS

The particles present in a material may be atoms, molecules or ions.

Strength

A strong material will have strong bonds holding all of its particles in place. This means that a large force has to be applied to persuade the particles to move apart from each other.

Some materials will have weak bonds between their particles. When these materials are stretched, the weak bonds give way relatively easily, allowing the sample to break.

Toughness

In a tough material the particles can change their position when enough force is applied. The material is plastic. In brittle materials the particles cannot change their position without allowing the sample to break into pieces.

Heat energy

All of the particles in a solid are in continual motion. They are locked in place by the bonds between neighbouring particles, so this motion makes them vibrate back and forth. The energy of this motion is called thermal energy or heat.

Raising the temperature of a solid increases the amount of vibration of its particles. When the temperature reaches the melting point of the material, its particles have enough energy to break free from each other. The solid becomes a liquid.

Thermal conduction

When a solid is given extra heat energy, its particles vibrate more. If each particle is firmly bound to its neighbours, it cannot vibrate without moving its neighbours. So heat energy injected at one end of a solid must inevitably get shared amongst more and more particles as time goes on. Heat energy is conducted along all solids; it flows from the hot end to the cold end.

Electrical conduction

An electric current in a solid is a flow of electrons. When a solid is connected to a battery (see Figure 2.2.15), the electrons at the negative terminal have more electrical energy than those at the positive terminal. If they are free to move in the solid, electrons will drift down the sample, converting electrical energy into heat energy.

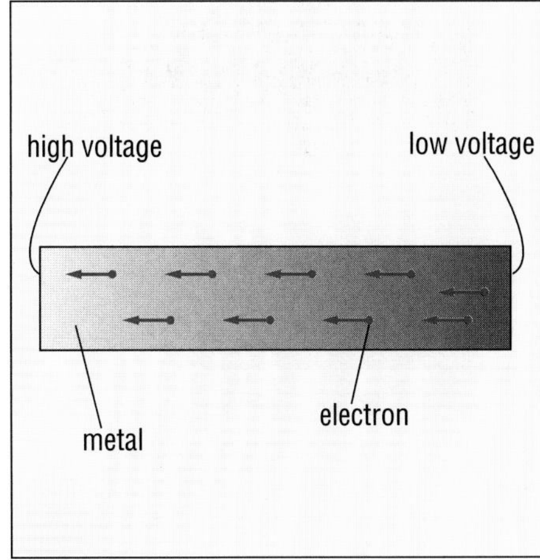

Figure 2.2.15 An electric current is a flow of electrons.

Metals

Metals have giant structures.

When metal atoms are placed close to each other, they each lose one or more **electrons**. Each atom becomes a positive ion. The electrons floating around in the space between the atoms provide the strong force which tugs the atoms together. This metallic bonding is strong.

> **FOCUS**
> **Metals consist of ions bonded to each other by loose electrons. The bonds are strong, so metals are stiff. The ions can slip past each other, so metals are also tough. The loose electrons allow metals to conduct heat and electricity easily.**

High density and strength

Metals are dense because the bonds between their ions are strong. The electrons floating between them pull them into regular structures known as lattices (see Figure 2.2.17). Materials which have their particles arranged in regular arrays are crystalline.

Each ion is pulled strongly towards its neighbours, locking it firmly into place in the lattice. The ions are packed closely together, giving a high density.

This sort of structure is strong. You need to apply a large force to wrench the ions apart.

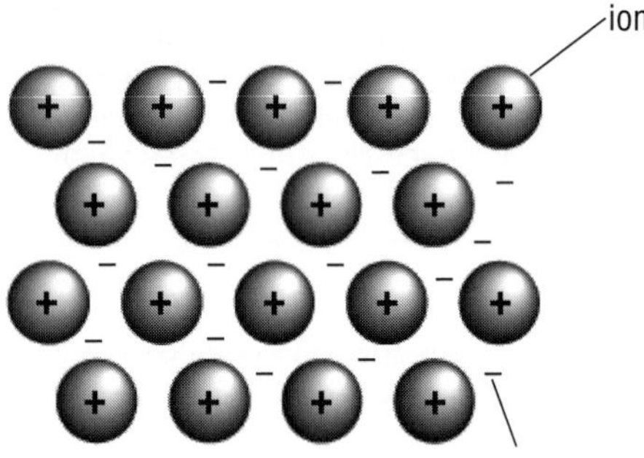

Figure 2.2.16 *The electrons in the spaces between the ions bind them together into regular crystalline structures.*

Figure 2.2.17 *Ions in a metal are packed close each other, giving a material which is dense and strong.*

Toughness

Metals are tough. When large forces are applied to them, they change shape before they break. This is because the electrons which hold the ions in place can move. Planes of ions in the lattice can slip past each other, taking the electrons with them (see Figure 2.2.18). So as a metal changes shape, the forces which bind its ions together stay the same.

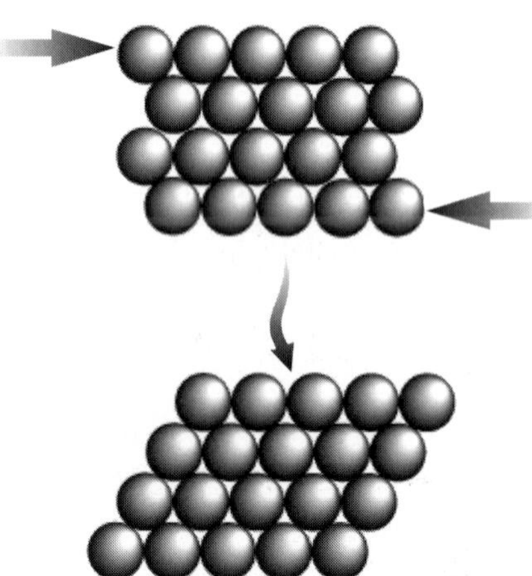

Figure 2.2.18 *Planes of atoms can slip past each other in metals without breaking apart.*

Electrical conduction

The electrons in a metal are free to move through the gaps between the ions. So when a metal is made part of an electric circuit its electrons move easily from one end to the other.

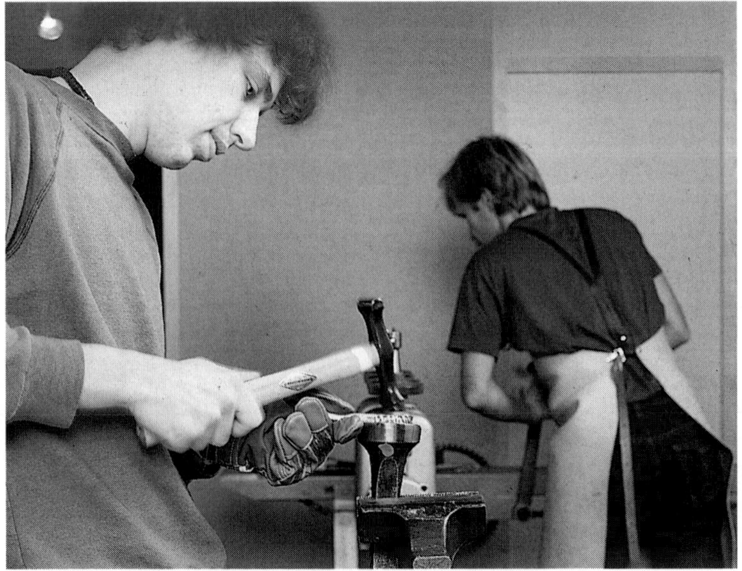

Figure 2.2.19 *Metals can be hammered into new shapes because of their structure.*

Thermal conduction

Heat energy put in at one end of a solid gets shared amongst more and more of its particles as time goes on. This is because the bonds between the particles transfer the heat energy from one particle to the next.

Metals are different. Heat energy injected at one end still flows to the cold end, but it does so relatively quickly. It is carried by the electrons which bind the atoms together. So metals are good conductors of heat.

Melting point

A solid melts when its atoms have enough heat energy to escape from the lattice and move freely past each other. The amount of energy needed depends on the strength of the bonds which hold the atoms in place in the lattice.

Since the bonds of metals are strong, they need a lot of heat energy before they break. So most metals have high melting points. Their atoms need a lot of heat energy before they can break free from their neighbours.

Ceramics

Ceramics have giant structures. Unlike metals, ceramics contain more than one type of atom. Two sorts of bonds occur, depending on the type of atoms involved.

Ionic bonding happens when one type of atom completely loses electrons to the other type of atom. This leaves some atoms positively charged, others negatively charged. The strong electrical forces between these ions jam them into lattices, regular arrangements in space (see Figure 2.2.20). Materials with ionic bonding are crystalline.

Covalent bonding occurs when electrons from one atom are shared by another atom. This gives a strong bond which forces the atoms to sit in fixed positions relative to each other. This can give rise to a crystalline structure (see Figure 2.2.21 (left)) but is more likely to lead to an amorphous structure (see Figure 2.2.21(right)), with atoms bonded strongly to each other with no overall regularity in their arrangement.

FOCUS

The particles in ceramics are held together by strong ionic or covalent bonds. Ceramics are therefore hard, strong and stiff. The particles cannot slip past each other, so ceramics are brittle.

Structures of elements and compounds page 10

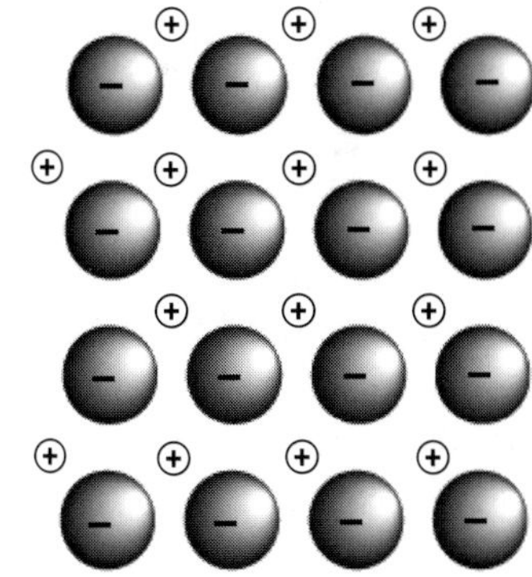

Figure 2.2.20 *Ionic bonding between atoms.*

Figure 2.2.21 *Strong bonds between atoms can give crystalline (left) or amorphous (right) structures.*

Strength, stiffness and hardness

The strong bonding between particles in ceramics makes them strong, stiff and hard. You need a large force to pull one particle away from its neighbours.

Brittleness and melting point

Ionic and covalent bonds force atoms to sit in particular places relative to each other, with gaps between them. Metallic bonding forces the atoms together until they touch. So ceramics have lower densities than metals.

Ceramics are brittle because their atoms cannot slip past each other without totally disrupting the lattice. As you force one plane of atoms apart from another, the arrangement becomes unstable and the solid suddenly falls apart.

The melting point of all ceramics is very high. A great deal of heat energy is required to break the strong bonds between their atoms.

Electrical and thermal conduction

There are no loose electrons in a ceramic, so it can't conduct electricity.

Any heat energy injected at one end of a ceramic will be conducted slowly to the other end. As each atom increases its vibration, this will get passed onto its neighbours via the bonds which connect them. Many ceramics contain small gaps in their structure (pores) which contain air. This makes them into very good thermal insulators.

Polymers

FOCUS

Polymers contain very long molecules which are weakly bonded to each other. This makes polymers tough, but not very stiff or strong.

Polymers consist of molecules which contain a large number of atoms. These are arranged in very long strings. The atoms are held together by strong covalent bonds.

Many polymers are based on carbon. In these, each polymer string has a central thread of carbon atoms, surrounded by other atoms (in many cases hydrogen) (see Figure 2.2.22). There are weak forces between the molecules, but each atom is firmly bonded to its neighbours within a molecule.

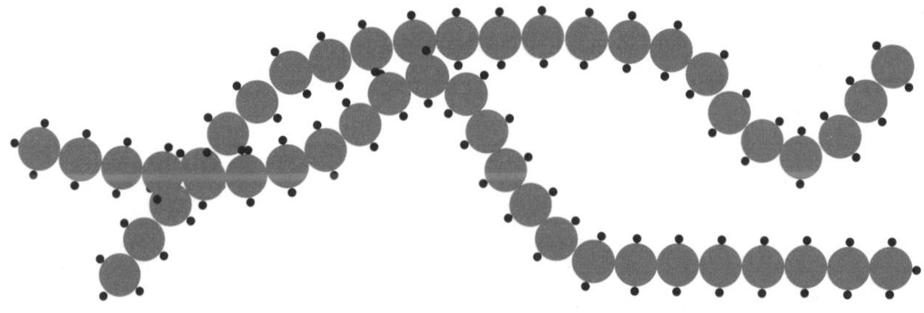

Figure 2.2.22 *Polymeric structure of long molecules.*

Melting point

Each molecule does not require very much heat energy to liberate it from the weak clutches of its neighbours. So polymers tend to have low melting points.

Stiffness, strength and toughness

Polymers are not stiff. When forces act on them, their molecules slide past each other without much difficulty. So when a polymer is stretched, it gets longer. If the forces are large enough, the polymer will not return to its original shape when the forces are removed. This means that polymers, like metals, are plastic. Plastic materials are tough; they change shape rather than snap when subjected to sudden shocks.

Polymers are not very strong. Although it is difficult to break the covalent bonds within each molecule, it is not difficult to separate the molecules from each other.

Thermal and electrical conduction

There are no loose electrons in a polymer, so they can't conduct electricity.

Any heat energy injected at one end of a polymer will be conducted very slowly to the other end. As each molecule increases its vibration, this will get passed onto its neighbours via the weak bonds which connect them.

Composites

Ceramic materials have one major defect. They are brittle. Were it not for this, ceramics would be ideal for many purposes because they are so stiff, hard and strong. However, a material which consists of a ceramic mixed with another material which is tough (such as a metal or a polymer) has the best properties of both materials. It can be stiff, hard, strong and tough.

FOCUS

Composites are mixtures of ceramics with either plastics or metals. They combine the best properties of these materials to achieve materials which are both tough and strong.

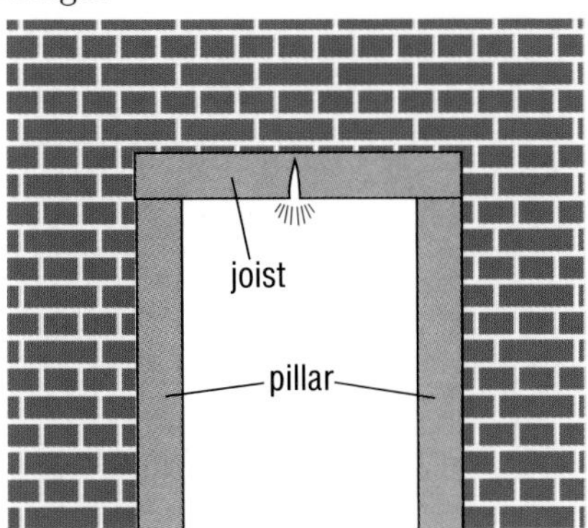

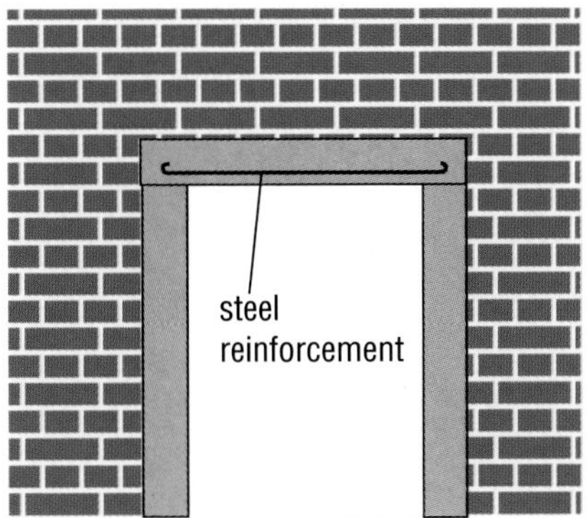

Figure 2.2.23 *Steel reinforced concrete is strong under both tension and compression.*

Reinforced concrete

Pure concrete is very strong when it is compressed. But, like all ceramics, it is very weak when you stretch it. It suddenly cracks open.

So beams and joists in structures cannot be made with pure concrete (see Figure 2.2.23a). If they didn't crack under their own weight, they certainly would when the rest of the structure was placed on top of them.

Steel reinforcements are added to concrete before it sets to get around this problem. The steel is in the form of mesh or wire. The result is a composite material (steel reinforced concrete) which combines the hardness of a ceramic with the toughness of a metal (see Figure 2.2.23b).

Reinforced concrete is widely used in large structures such as buildings, roads and bridges. Like all ceramics, it is too hard to be shaped easily, so it has to be cast in moulds. Its combination of strength, hardness and cheapness is unrivalled.

Figure 2.2.24 *Making car body shells from GRP at Lotus Cars, Norwich. Mats of glass fibres are soaked in a polymeric resin. When the resin sets, the result is a sheet of material which is stiff and tough. The fibres can be seen at the edge of the resin bath.*

Glass reinforced plastic

Figure 2.2.24 shows an object being made out of glass reinforced plastic (GRP). This material has the toughness of a polymer with the hardness and stiffness of a ceramic. It is particularly good for making stiff sheets. GRP is therefore widely used for making small boats and car panels.

Case study

Power transmission lines

Electricity supply is a serious business. We all need it in our homes and workplaces and get very annoyed if the supply is cut off. Many people are involved in maintaining the systems which transfer electrical energy from where it is generated (Illustration 1a) to where it is used (Illustration 1b). In particular, scientists make decisions about the best materials to use for each part of the system.

a

b

Illustration 1 Electricity is generated far away from where it is needed.

Overhead cables

The cheapest way of insulating high voltage wires is to hold them well away from other conductors. This is the method used with long distance overhead transmission lines (Illustration 2). Each cable has to be suspended from the pylons by supports.

Illustration 2 High voltage overhead cables.

The supports

Each support must obviously be a very good electrical insulator. So it can't be a metal. It must also be strong, because the cables are heavy. Finally, it must be tough so that it doesn't snap in high winds.

The solution is to make the supports from a jointed ceramic. Each glass segment hooks into the one above, so that the support is strong but flexible. The shape of each segment keeps most of it dry when it rains. This is very important as water is a conductor.

The cables

Each cable is made from a composite material. It has to be light, to have low resistance and be strong. No one material has all of these properties.

Most of a cable is strands of aluminium. This metal combines a high electrical conductivity with a low density, giving a cable which has a low resistance and is light.

The rest of the cable is strands of steel. This provides strength for the cable. Without it, the aluminium strands would be unable to hold up their own weight. They would stretch and break.

Underground cables

Electricity is delivered to most homes and factories by underground cable. Naked overhead cables are not only unsightly, they are also dangerous. Putting cables under the ground keeps them well away from people.

Underground cables are surrounded by cladding. This has several purposes. It must insulate the cable from

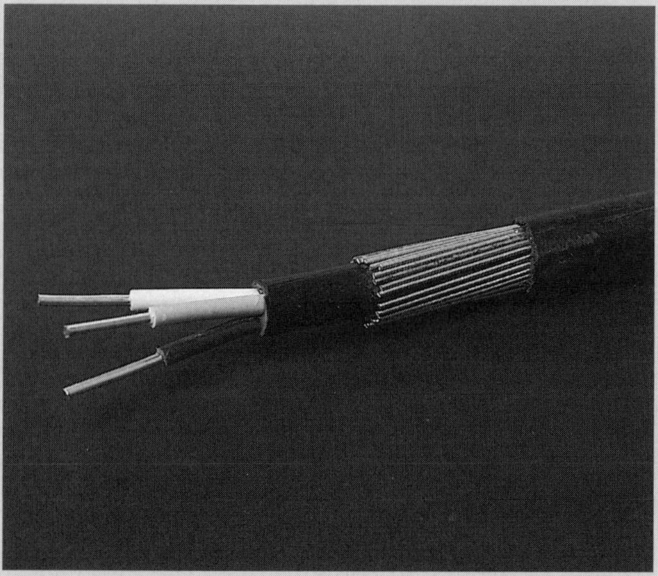

Illustration 3 Underground cables.

other cables in the duct. It must protect the cable from water. It must also keep people and their sharp tools away from the cable!

So the cladding must be an electrical insulator, tough, waterproof and flexible. Polymers are the only materials which have all of these properties. Steel reinforcing wires are embedded in the cladding to provide extra safety for people who attempt to cut into the cables!

Questions

1 Describe the structure of a metal. Explain why metals are good conductors of electricity.

2 Describe the structure of a ceramic. Explain why ceramics are strong electrical insulators.

3 Describe the structure of a polymer. Explain why polymers are tough electrical insulators.

4 List the various materials which are used to make a light bulb. Describe the properties which each material must have for the light bulb to work. Explain those properties by describing the structure of each material.

5 GRP is widely used to make the cupboards which hold electricity fuses, switches and meters in houses. Describe the properties that GRP must have for this purpose. Explain those properties by describing the structure of GRP.

6 The pylons which hold up overhead cables can be made out of steel or reinforced concrete. List the properties which the pylon material must have. Relate this to the properties of steel and reinforced concrete. Which material should be used?

Assignment

FOOD CONTAINERS

Setting the scene

A food company would like to operate in large cities in the UK. They sell high quality (and expensive) take-away food to the business community at lunchtime. Clients phone in their order by reading from a menu. The food is then delivered to the client an hour later.

The company has a problem. Some clients have been complaining that their food has been arriving cold. Others have found that the food containers have arrived dented and split. Therefore, the company has commissioned a study to determine what material they should use for their food containers.

The company has narrowed the choice down to three reusable containers. They are made from aluminium, polythene and glass. The ideal container is hard, light and a good thermal insulator.

The assignment

1 You are given samples of aluminium, polythene and glass (all of these are, of course, waterproof). They will be in the form of flat sheets. In each case, determine the hardness, density and thermal conduction of the material.

2 Decide which material will be best for the food box.

3 Explain the properties of the materials investigated in terms of their structure.

Presenting your results

You should write a laboratory report of your investigation. You will be asked to discuss this with your supervisor. Make sure you:

- record your initial ideas and plans in an appendix to the report (the appendix should show how these were modified during the course of the investigation)
- look back in the conclusion to the report at what you did – state what changes or improvements you would make if the work was carried out again
- list all sources of information at the end of the report. This should be cross-referenced in the report itself.

Opportunity to collect evidence
In completing this task you will have the opportunity to meet the following requirements for GNVQ Intermediate Science:

Science units
Unit 1:
Element 1.2 PCs 1, 2, 3, 4, 5
Unit 2:
Element 2.2 PCs 1, 2, 3

Core skill units

Application of number:
Elements 2.2, 2.3

Communication:
Element 2.1, 2.2, 2.3, 2.4

Grading

This assignment gives you the opportunity to meet merit or distinction criteria. All four themes are covered: Planning; Information Seeking and Information Handling; Evaluation; Quality of Outcomes.

Additional Information

The following procedures are available:
(a) Measuring relative hardness, page 84
(b) Measuring thermal conduction, page 87
(c) Measuring density, page 88

Procedure

Measuring the thermal conduction of waterproof materials

SAFETY: Wear eye protection. The procedure employs hot water. Use a kettle to heat the water. Hot water can scald your skin.

Eye protection must be worn

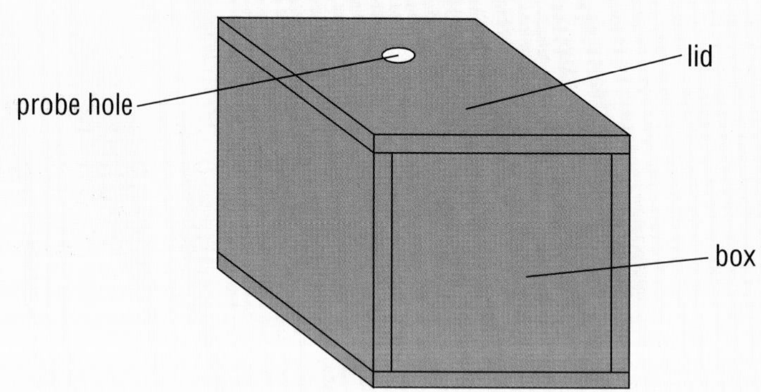

Figure 2.2.25 *Measuring the thermal conduction of a food box.*

Make up a box from flat plates of the material to be investigated. Glue the sides together. The glue may not be waterproof and may go soft at high temperatures, so place each box in a large tray to catch spillages.

Care: Glass can crack when exposed to boiling water.

1. Obtain three boxes, each made of a different material. The boxes must be the same shape and size, with a lid (see Figure 2.2.25).

2 Fill each box with hot water. Put the lid on.
3 Insert thermometers or temperature probes and record how the temperature changes with time.
4 The box which stays at the highest temperature is made of the material which is the best thermal insulator.

Questions

1 List the properties of
  (a) metals
  (b) ceramics
  (c) polymers and
  (d) composites
  which make them useful materials for particular applications.

2 For each of the structures listed below, state three important properties for their materials.
  (a) Window
  (b) Table
  (c) Shopping bag
  (d) Car jack
  (e) Ice cream container
  (f) Light switch
  (g) Fire hose.

3 For each of the properties listed below, give the names of the types of materials which have that property.
  (a) Transparency
  (b) High strength
  (c) High melting point
  (d) Low electrical resistance
  (e) High density.

4 Name the type of material which is most likely to have this set of properties:
  (a) Tough, high density, good electrical and thermal conduction.
  (b) Poor thermal conduction, stiff, low density and hard.
  (c) Tough, low density, low melting point and transparent.
  (d) Tough, hard, stiff and strong.

5 What is the difference between an amorphous structure and a crystalline structure?

6 Consider the following materials: metals, ceramics, polymers and composites. Which have strong bonding between the atoms present and which have weak bonding between molecules?

7 Fill the gaps in these sentences.
  (a) Materials are made out of ......
  (b) All atoms have a .... at their centre, surrounded by shells of ....
  (c) Atoms bond to each other to form ....

(d) Materials with weak bonds between their particles have a low .... point.
(e) An electric current is a flow of ....
(f) Atoms which share electrons with each other have .... bonds.
(h) Atoms which give or receive electrons from each have .... bonds.
(i) Metallic bonds are formed when each atom loses an ....
(j) Materials whose particles form regular arrays have a .... structure.
(k) A material with long string-like molecules is a ....
(l) A material which is a mixture of a ceramic and a metal has a .... structure.

Determine the composition of substances

You will need to show that you can:
- prepare a sample for analysis and carry out the analysis safely
- use the results of an analysis to determine the composition of a substance.

Reasons for analysing substances

Chemists are employed as analysts in different laboratories. For example, they work in industrial laboratories (undertaking research or quality control), forensic science laboratories and hospital pharmacies. Many analysts collect samples for analysis from the outdoors, for example, rivers, soil and the air. They are said to be working *in the field*.

There are two types of chemical analyses which you will carry out. **Qualitative analysis** involves identifying a substance. To do this you will need to know how to use chemical tests to identify various ions and gases, and flame tests to identify certain metal ions. **Quantitative analysis** involves determining how much of a substance is present. One example is an acid-base titration. You will need to know how to carry out such a titration.

There are two types of substance which you may be required to analyse:
- compounds: acids, alkalis (bases which are soluble in water), salts
- mixtures: impure compounds, aqueous solutions.

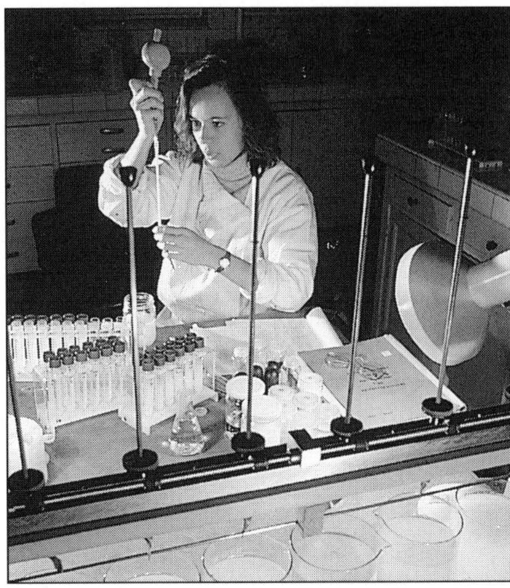

Figure 2.3.1 This chemist is preparing a sample of a colloid for analysis.

FOCUS
- **Qualitative analysis – finding out what a substance is**
- **Quantitative analysis – finding out how much of a substance is present**

Substances to be analysed

Acids

Most people have heard of acids. There are two types: *mineral acids* and *organic acids*. Most mineral acids are manufactured on a large scale from rocks and minerals in the Earth's crust. One exception is nitric acid. The starting material for its manufacture is air. Mineral acids are used in a wide range of industrial processes, for example, in the manufacture of fertilisers and some plastics.

An important type of organic acid is the group called the *carboxylic* acids. Many of these occur naturally in plants and animals. For example, citric acid is found in many fruits and methanoic acid is found in ants. These acids can also be manufactured, often using crude oil as the starting material. They are used, amongst other things, to make *esters*, compounds which have many uses, ranging from solvents to fragrances.

All acids have the following properties:
- distinct sharp taste (but don't try it!)
- soluble in water, giving a solution with a pH of less than 7
- change the colour of indicators
- react with the more reactive metals to give a salt and hydrogen
  acid + metal → salt + hydrogen
- react with carbonates to give a salt, carbon dioxide and water
  acid + carbonate → salt + carbon dioxide + water
- react with bases to give a salt and water only
  acid + base → salt + water.

Figure 2.3.2 Oxalic acid is an organic acid. It is found in rhubarb. Oxalic acid is a typical acid and, because of this, it is unwise to cook rhubarb in aluminum saucepans. Do you know why? Look at the properties of acids.

Table 2.3.1 Some important acids (in each case hydrogen atoms which can be replaced by metal ions to form salts are shown in bold italics)

Name	Formula	Name of salt
Mineral acids		
hydrochloric acid	$\boldsymbol{H}Cl$	chloride
nitric acid	$\boldsymbol{H}NO_3$	nitrate
sulphuric acid	$\boldsymbol{H}_2SO_4$	sulphate
phosphoric acid	$\boldsymbol{H}_3PO_4$	phosphate
Carboxylic acids		
methanoic acid	$HCOO\boldsymbol{H}$	methanoate
ethanoic acid	$CH_3COO\boldsymbol{H}$	ethanoate
lactic acid (2-hydroxypropanoic acid)	$CH_3CH(OH)COO\boldsymbol{H}$	lactate
oxalic acid (ethanedioic acid)	$COO\boldsymbol{H}$ | $COO\boldsymbol{H}$	oxalate
citric acid	$CH_2COO\boldsymbol{H}$ | $C(OH)COO\boldsymbol{H}$ | $CH_2COO\boldsymbol{H}$	citrate

Figure 2.3.3 Kettle descalers are usually solutions of methanoic acid. They are effective because the fur (or limescale) in kettles, and similar appliances, is calcium carbonate. Why does the fur fizz when the descaler is added? Why is it better to use a hot solution of the descaler?

Acids dissolve in water to give a solution of *hydrogen ions*, $H^+(aq)$. The other ions present depend on the acid (see Table 2.3.2). For example, hydrochloric acid contains hydrogen ions, $H^+(aq)$, and chloride ions, $Cl^-(aq)$:

$$HCl(g) + aq \rightarrow H^+(aq) + Cl^-(aq)$$

In equations like this, 'aq' is used to represent an excess of water.

Strong acids split freely into ions. Solutions of *weak acids* will contain many acid molecules which have not split into ions.

Table 2.3.2 Ions present when acids dissolve in water

Acid	Ions in solution	
hydrochloric acid, $HCl(aq)$	$H^+(aq)$	$Cl^-(aq)$
sulphuric acid, $H_2SO_4(aq)$	$2H^+(aq)$	$SO_4^{2-}(aq)$
nitric acid, $HNO_3(aq)$	$H^+(aq)$	$NO^-_3(aq)$
methanoic acid, $HCOOH(aq)$	$H^+(aq)$	$HCOO^-(aq)$
ethanoic acid, $CH_3COOH(aq)$	$H^+(aq)$	$CH_3COO^-(aq)$
oxalic acid, $(COOH)_2(aq)$	$2H^+(aq)$	$(COO)_2^{2-}(aq)$

Analysing acids

An acid solution can be identified by its effect on *acid-base indicators*. The concentration of an acid can be determined by an *acid-base titration*. The end-point in the titration (when the acid has just been **neutralised** by the base) can be detected with an acid-base indicator.

Acid-base reactions, page140

Procedure: Carrying out an acid-base titration, page 107

An acid is neutralised by a base when sufficient has been added to form a salt and water only.

FOCUS

Acids dissolve in water to give solutions of hydrogen ions, $H^+(aq)$. Alkalis dissolve to give solutions of hydroxide ions, $OH^-(aq)$. Acid-alkali indicators can be used to determine whether a solution is acidic or alkaline.

Table 2.3.3 Acid-base indicators

Type of acid-base reaction	Suitable indicator	Colour in acid	Colour in alkali
Strong acid – strong base	methyl red bromothymol blue phenol red	red yellow yellow	yellow blue red
Weak acid – strong base	methyl orange	red	yellow
Strong acid – weak base	phenolphthalein	colourless	red

Figure 2.3.4 Methyl red is a typical acid-base indicator. It is red in acids and yellow in alkalis. What colour would you see if methyl red were added to potassium hydroxide solution?

Bases

A *base* is a compound which neutralises an acid to give a salt and water only. Bases which dissolve in water are called *alkalis*. Metal oxides and hydroxides are bases. A base may be *strong* or *weak*, depending on how freely it splits into ions in water.

Table 2.3.4 Ions present when alkalis dissolve in water

Alkali	Ions in solution	
sodium hydroxide, NaOH(aq)	$Na^+(aq)$	$OH^-(aq)$
potassium hydroxide, KOH(aq)	$K^+(aq)$	$OH^-(aq)$
ammonia, $NH_3(aq)$	$NH_4^+(aq)$	$OH^-(aq)$
calcium hydroxide, $Ca(OH)_2(aq)$	$Ca^{2+}(aq)$	$2OH^-(aq)$

Alkalis dissolve in water to give *hydroxide ions*, $OH^-(aq)$. The other ions depend on the alkali. For example, sodium hydroxide dissolves in water to give sodium ions, $Na^+(aq)$, and hydroxide ions, $OH^-(aq)$:

$$NaOH(s) + aq \rightarrow Na^+(aq) + OH^-(aq)$$

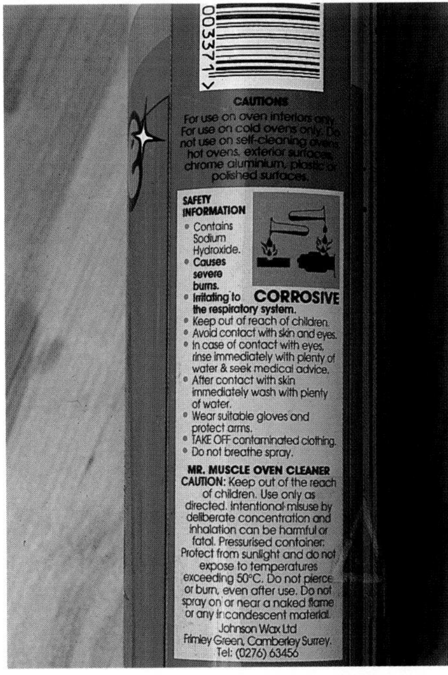

Figure 2.3.5 Sodium hydroxide (often known as caustic soda) can be bought in shops such as Boots. It dissolves grease and is useful for clearing blocked drains. Many brand name oven cleaners contain strong alkalis such as sodium hydroxide. How could you determine the purity of a sample of sodium hydroxide bought from a shop?

Carrying out an acid-base titration, page 107

FOCUS

The concentrations of acids and alkalis can be found using acid-base titrations.

Acid-base reactions, page 140

Precipitation, page 140

Figure 2.3.6 *These 'iron tablets' contain the salt iron(II) sulphate. They are used in the treatment of anaemia. Salts are the active ingredient in a number of medicines.*

Analysing alkalis

An alkaline solution can be identified by its effect on acid-base indicators. The concentration of an alkali can be determined by an **acid-base titration**. The end-point in the titration (when the alkali has just been neutralised by the acid) can be detected with an acid-base indicator.

Salts

Salts are an important type of chemical substance. You are no doubt familiar with the most common example, sodium chloride. However, there are many other examples which you may come across perhaps without realising it. Salts have numerous uses. They are found in foodstuffs (e.g. acidity regulators, preservatives), medicines (e.g. astringents, laxatives, purgatives, antacids, treatment of anaemia), agrochemicals (e.g. fertilisers, fungicides), explosives and photography. In addition, there is a vast range of specialist applications.

Table 2.3.5 Some salts and their uses

Name	Formula	Uses
ammonium nitrate	NH_4NO_3	fertiliser, explosives
ammonium sulphate	$(NH_4)_2SO_4$	fertiliser
ammonium chloride	NH_4Cl	batteries, medicines
copper(II) sulphate	$CuSO_4$	fungicides, wood preservatives
iron(II) sulphate	$FeSO_4$	medicines
magnesium sulphate	$MgSO_4$	medicines
zinc sulphate	$ZnSO_4$	medicines
zinc chloride	$ZnCl_2$	batteries
sodium chlorate(I)	$NaOCl$	liquid bleach
calcium chlorate(I)	$Ca(OCl)_2$	bleaching powder
sodium hydrogencarbonate	$NaHCO_3$	antacid, baking powder
sodium carbonate	Na_2CO_3	water softeners
calcium carbonate	$CaCO_3$	antacids
magnesium carbonate	$MgCO_3$	antacids
sodium chloride	$NaCl$	'common salt' – flavour enhancer, de-icer
potassium chloride	KCl	LO-SALT, fertiliser
silver chloride	$AgCl$	photography
silver bromide	$AgBr$	photography
silver iodide	AgI	photography
sodium citrate	$C_6H_5O_7Na_3$	foodstuffs
sodium benzoate	C_6H_5COONa	foodstuffs
calcium sulphate	$CaSO_4$	Plaster of Paris

Salts are formed when an acid is **neutralised** by a base. Salts are soluble in water to a greater or lesser extent. They are ionic compounds, made up of *cations* (positively charged ions) and *anions* (negatively charged ions). They dissolve to give a solution of their ions. For example, potassium nitrate dissolves to give a solution of potassium ions, $K^+(aq)$, and nitrate ions, $NO_3^-(aq)$.

Preparing salts, page 149

FOCUS

An acid is neutralised by a base to give a salt and water only.

Ions present in solution can be identified by qualitative chemical tests. The metal ions present can often be identified by carrying out a flame test on the solid salt.

Qualitative chemical tests, page 104

Mixtures

Mixtures consist of more than one pure chemical substance (either *elements* or *compounds*). An impure substance is an example of a mixture. It consists largely of the substance but has small quantities of other substances present as impurities. Qualitative analysis enables the impurities to be identified. Quantitative analysis enables the amount of purity to be determined (this is sometimes called assaying).

Solutions are mixtures. The dissolved substance (called the *solute*) is mixed with the *solvent* (often water). Qualitative analysis enables the solute to be identified. Quantitative analysis enables the concentration of the solute to be determined, for example the concentration of an acid.

FOCUS

Mixtures contain more than one pure chemical substance (elements or compounds). They can usually be separated easily using techniques such as filtration, distillation and crystallisation.

Preparing a sample for analysis

How you take samples of a substance for analysis depends on where it comes from and what you want to know about it. An important question is 'Does the composition of a substance depend on where in the source it is taken from?' To check you should take samples from different places.

If the sample is a pure substance, only a single sample needs to be taken for an analysis. This is not to say that it is sufficient to carry out one analysis. The sample will need to be divided into separate portions to repeat the analysis. This is how you can check the accuracy of the analysis.

The composition of a mixture may vary from one sample to another. Therefore, you need to take a number of **representative samples** and analyse each of these before you can come to any conclusions.

The preparation of a sample for analysis depends on the analytical techniques to be used. A number of things need to be considered:

- from whereabouts should the sample be taken? (e.g. the composition of soil depends on where it is taken from)
- how much is needed for analysis?
- does the sample need to be ground into a powder before analysis? (e.g. to help it dissolve more readily)
- does the sample need to be dissolved and, if so, at what concentration?
- if the sample is already a solution, does it need to be diluted before analysis and, if so, to what concentration?

FOCUS

For a pure substance a single sample is taken for analysis.

For a mixture one or more representative samples are taken for analysis.

Figure 2.3.7 *Sodium chloride dissolves in water. The solution which forms consists of a solute (the dissolved sodium chloride) and a solvent (the water). It is a mixture. Which ions will be present in solution?*

Qualitative chemical tests

Chemical substances often have at least one characteristic reaction which may be used to identify them. These qualitative chemical tests can be used to identify ions in aqueous solution and gases. Some metal ions can be identified in a solid by using a flame test. Details of the methods are given in the procedure below.

Requirements

- ❒ Test tubes and rack to hold them
- ❒ Bunsen burner and mat to protect bench from heat
- ❒ Delivery tube
- ❒ Dropping pipette
- ❒ Wooden splints
- ❒ Nichrome wire
- ❒ Watch glasses

Eye protection must be worn

CORROSIVE dilute nitric acid

CORROSIVE AND OXIDISING concentrated nitric acid

IRRITANT dilute hydrochloric acid

IRRITANT silver nitrate solution

Procedure

SAFETY: Wear eye protection.

Qualitative chemical tests

1 Chemical tests for ions

Substances for analysis must be in solution (the test for carbonates is an exception). If the substance is solid, try dissolving it in distilled water. If it does not dissolve, try:

- dilute nitric acid (warming if necessary).
- concentrated nitric acid (warming if necessary)

Once a suitable method has been found, take a small quantity of solid (equivalent to 2–3 grains of rice) and prepare about 10 cm^3 of stock solution. Store in a boiling tube. Keep a sample of the original substance (things may go wrong!). The following tests for ions should be carried out on 1–2 cm^3 samples of the stock solution.

Carbonate, CO_3^{2-} Add dilute hydrochloric acid to the sample (which may be either a solid or an aqueous solution). Pass any gas given off through calcium hydroxide solution ('limewater'). Formation of a white precipitate (calcium carbonate) confirms that the gas is carbon dioxide and, therefore, indicates the presence of carbonate ions in the sample (see Figure 2.3.8)

Chloride, Cl^- Add an equal volume of dilute nitric acid (unless nitric acid was used to dissolve the substance) followed by a few drops of silver nitrate solution. Formation of a white precipitate (silver chloride) indicates chloride ions in solution.

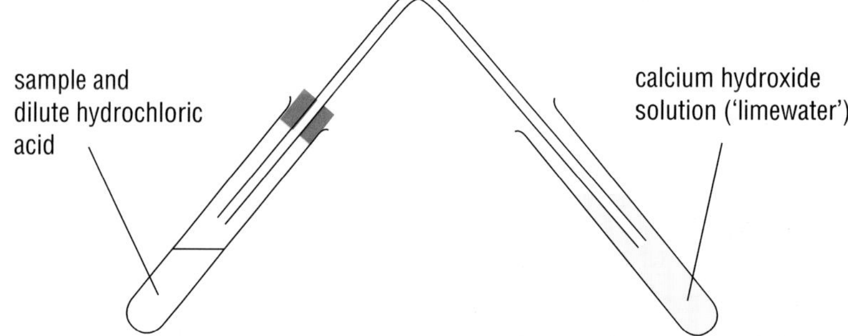

Figure 2.3.8 *Apparatus for testing that a gas evolved in a chemical reaction is carbon dioxide.*

Sulphate, SO_4^{2-} Add an equal volume of dilute hydrochloric acid followed by a few drops of barium chloride solution. A white precipitate of barium sulphate indicates sulphate ions in solution (see Figure 2.3.9).

Copper(II), Cu^{2+} Solutions of copper(II) ions are usually green or blue. Add dilute aqueous ammonia drop by drop. Formation of a blue precipitate which dissolves to give a deep blue solution when further ammonia is added indicates copper(II) ions in solution (see Figure 2.3.10).

Iron(III), Fe^{3+} Solutions of iron(III) ions are usually yellow. Add dilute sodium hydroxide until the solution is alkaline. Formation of a rusty brown precipitate suggests the presence of iron(III) ions. To confirm, add hydrochloric acid until the precipitate just dissolves, followed by 2 drops ammonium thiocyanate solution. Formation of an intense red solution indicates iron(III) ions are present in solution.

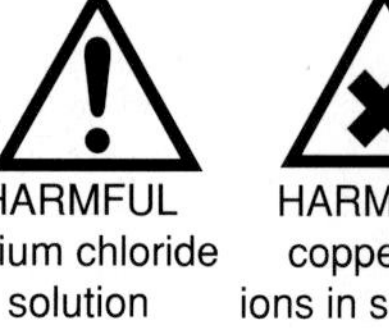

HARMFUL barium chloride solution

HARMFUL copper(II) ions in solution

CORROSIVE dilute sodium hydroxide

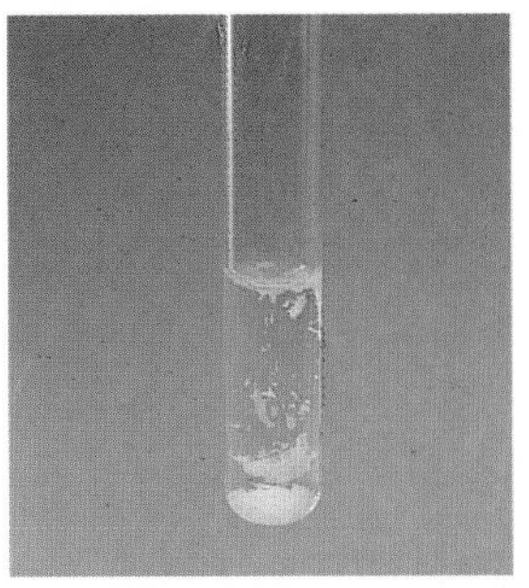

Figure 2.3.9 The formation of barium sulphate.

Figure 2.3.10 Identifying copper(II) ions in solution by adding dilute aqueous ammonia.

Figure 2.3.11 The intense red colour formed when iron(III) ions react with ammonium thiocyanate.

2 Chemical tests for gases

If a gas is given off at any stage, it can be identified as oxygen, carbon dioxide or hydrogen using the following tests:

Oxygen Place a glowing splint into the gas. If the splint begins to burn, the gas is oxygen (see Figure 2.3.12).

OXIDISING
oxygen

Carbon dioxide Pass the gas through calcium hydroxide solution ('limewater'). Formation of a white precipitate (calcium carbonate) confirms that the gas is carbon dioxide (see Figure 2.3.8).

Hydrogen Hold a burning splint in the mouth of the test tube containing the gas. If there is a small explosion (a 'popping' sound), the gas is hydrogen.

EXTREMELY FLAMMABLE
hydrogen

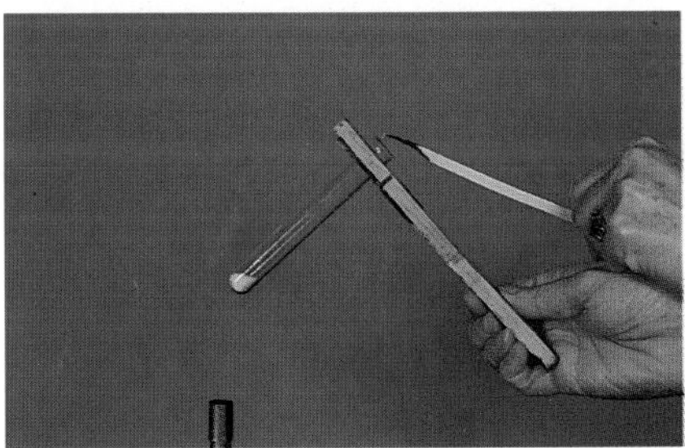

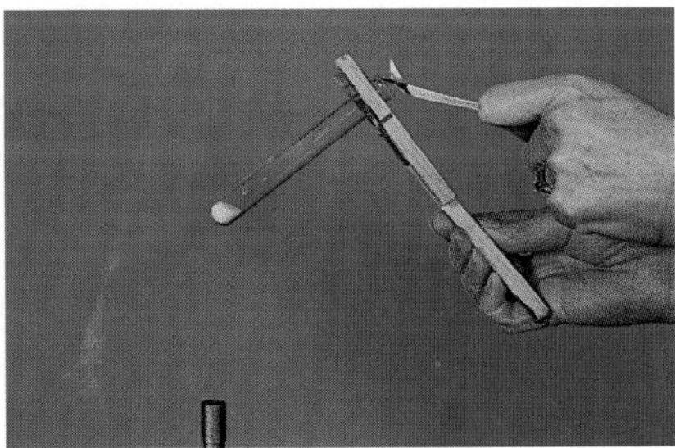

Figure 2.3.12 Testing for oxygen.

3 Flame tests

Place a small sample of the solid on a watch glass. Add a few drops of concentrated hydrochloric acid. Moisten a piece of Nichrome wire with the mixture and hold it in a Bunsen flame (see Figure 2.3.13). Colour of flame:

- bright yellow: indicates **sodium ions**
- lilac (still visible through blue glass): indicates **potassium ions**
- green: indicates **copper ions**
- brick red: indicates **calcium ions.**

CORROSIVE
hydrochloric acid

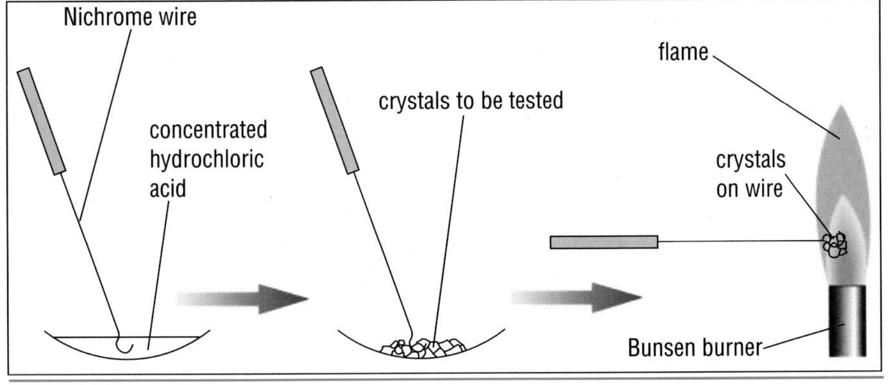

Figure 2.3.13a The steps in carrying out a flame test

Figure 2.3.13b A positive flame test for calcium ions.

Quantitative chemical tests

Quantitative chemical tests involve chemical reactions. They are used to determine how much of a substance is present in a mixture. An important example is the use of acid-base reactions for quantitative analysis.

Standard solutions are often used in acid-base titrations. A standard solution is one whose concentration is known accurately. It can be used to determine the concentration of other solutions.

Balanced chemical equations for acid-base titrations

The type of acid is characterised by the number of moles of hydrogen ions which can form when one mole of acid dissolves in water. For example, one mole of hydrochloric acid, $HCl(aq)$, forms one mole of hydrogen ions, $H^+(aq)$. It is said to be *monobasic*. Other examples of monobasic acids are nitric acid, methanoic acid and ethanoic acid. On the other hand, one mole of sulphuric acid, $H_2SO_4(aq)$, forms two moles of hydrogen ions, $2H^+(aq)$. It is said to be *dibasic*. See Table 2.3.2 on page 100.

Similarly an alkali is characterised by the number of moles of hydroxide ions which can form when one mole of an alkali dissolves in water. For example, one mole of sodium hydroxide, $NaOH(aq)$, forms one mole of hydroxide ions, $OH^-(aq)$. However, calcium hydroxide, $Ca(OH)_2(aq)$, forms two moles of hydroxide ions, $2OH^-(aq)$. See Table 2.3.4 on page 101.

The simple rule in a neutralisation reaction is that one mole of hydrogen ions react with one mole of hydroxide ions to form water:

$$H^+(aq) + OH^-(aq) \rightarrow H_2O(l)$$

> **FOCUS**
> **1 mole of a monobasic acid gives 1 mole of hydrogen ions.**
> **1 mole of a dibasic acid gives 2 moles of hydrogen ions.**
> **1 mole of a tribasic acid gives 3 moles of hydrogen ions.**

So, if one **mole** of an acid gives one mole of hydrogen ions (e.g. nitric acid), it requires one mole of an alkali that gives one mole of hydroxide ions (e.g. sodium hydroxide). Similarly, if one mole of an acid gives two moles of hydrogen ions (e.g. sulphuric acid), it requires two moles of an alkali that gives one mole of hydroxide ions (e.g. potassium hydroxide).

In the following summary,
M = cation with a single positive charge, e.g. Na^+, K^+
A = anion with a single negative charge, e.g. Cl^-, NO_3^-, $HCOO^-$, CH_3COO^-
B = anion with a double negative charge, e.g. SO_4^{2-}, $(COO)_2^{2-}$

- $HA(aq) + MOH(aq) \rightarrow MA(aq) + H_2O(l)$

  e.g. $HCl(aq) + NaOH(aq) \rightarrow NaCl(aq) + H_2O(l)$
  $HNO_3(aq) + NaOH(aq) \rightarrow NaNO_3(aq) + H_2O(l)$

- $HA(aq) + NH_3(aq) \rightarrow NH_4A(aq)$

  e.g. $HCl(aq) + NH_3(aq) \rightarrow NH_4Cl(aq)$
  $CH_3COOH(aq) + NH_3(aq) \rightarrow CH_3COONH_4(aq)$

- $2HA(aq) + Ca(OH)_2(aq) \rightarrow CaA_2(aq) + 2H_2O(l)$

  e.g. $2HNO_3(aq) + Ca(OH)_2(aq) \rightarrow Ca(NO_3)_2(aq) + 2H_2O(l)$

- $H_2B(aq) + 2MOH(aq) \rightarrow M_2B(aq) + 2H_2O(l)$

  e.g. $H_2SO_4(aq) + 2NaOH(aq) \rightarrow Na_2SO_4(aq) + 2H_2O(l)$

- $H_2B(aq) + Ca(OH)_2(aq) \rightarrow CaB(aq) + 2H_2O(l)$

  e.g. $H_2SO_4(aq) + Ca(OH)_2(aq) \rightarrow CaSO_4(aq) + 2H_2O(l)$

Table 2.3.6 Hazards of some common acids and alkalis

Hydrochloric acid	greater than 2 mol dm^{-3}: irritant greater than 6 mol dm^{-3}: corrosive
Sulphuric acid	greater than 0.5 mol dm^{-3}: irritant greater than 1.5 mol dm^{-3}: corrosive
Nitric acid	greater than 0.1 mol dm^{-3}: irritant greater than 0.5 mol dm^{-3}: corrosive greater than 3 mol dm^{-3}: corrosive and oxidising
Ethanoic acid	greater than 1.5 mol dm^{-3}: irritant greater than 4 mol dm^{-3}: corrosive
Sodium hydroxide	greater than 0.05 mol dm^{-3}: irritant greater than 0.5 mol dm^{-3}: corrosive
Potassium hydroxide	greater than 0.05 mol dm^{-3}: irritant greater than 0.5 mol dm^{-3}: corrosive
Aqueous ammonia	greater than 3 mol dm^{-3}: irritant greater than 6 mol dm^{-3}: corrosive

Procedure

SAFETY: Wear eye protection. Remember many substances are hazardous – avoid breathing dust, or getting solids or liquids on your skin.

Eye protection must be worn

WARNING

Requirements

- ❒ Volumetric flask
- ❒ Balance
- ❒ Burette and stand
- ❒ Pipette
- ❒ White tile
- ❒ Conical flasks

Carrying out an acid-base titration

1 Sample preparation

(a) Transfer a measured quantity of substance to a volumetric flask.

(i) For a **solid**: weigh the required quantity of sample in a weighing bottle. Use a glass funnel to transfer the powdered solid into a volumetric flask. Ensure all the solid has been transferred by using a squeezy bottle containing distilled water to wash out the weighing bottle and funnel. Make sure the solid has dissolved before making the solution up to the volume of the volumetric flask with distilled water.

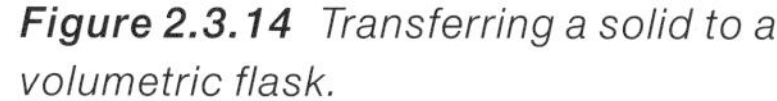

Figure 2.3.14 Transferring a solid to a volumetric flask.

(ii) For a **liquid**: use a pipette to measure a precise volume of the liquid which needs to be diluted (remember to use a pipette safety filler). The pipette should be held vertically and the bottom of the meniscus should be level with the graduations used.

(b) Make the solution up to the required volume with distilled water. The bottom of the meniscus must be level with the graduation mark on the flask. The final few drops must be added carefully. A dropping pipette is a convenient way of doing this.

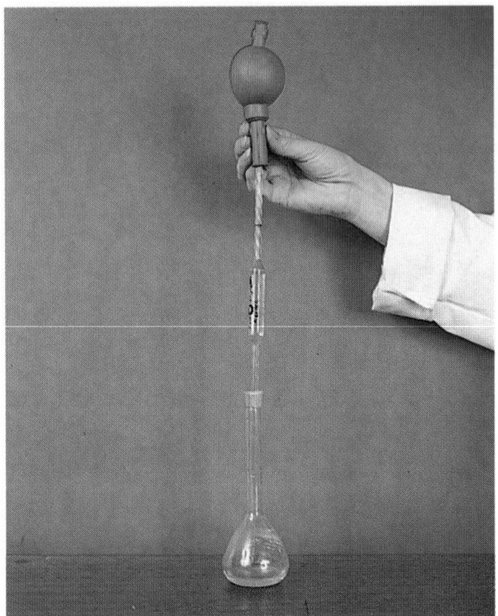

Figure 2.3.15 *Transferring a liquid to a volumetric flask.*

2 Carrying out a titration

Use a pipette to transfer a known volume of the prepared solution to a conical flask. Remember to use a pipette safety filler. The bottom of the meniscus must be level with the graduation mark on the pipette. Allow the solution to run out freely and then touch the solution in the flask with the pipette tip. Do not blow out the pipette unless the instructions tell you to do so. Add 2–3 drops of a suitable acid-alkali indicator. Titrate with a standard acid (if the sample is an alkali) or a standard alkali (if the sample is an acid) from a burette.

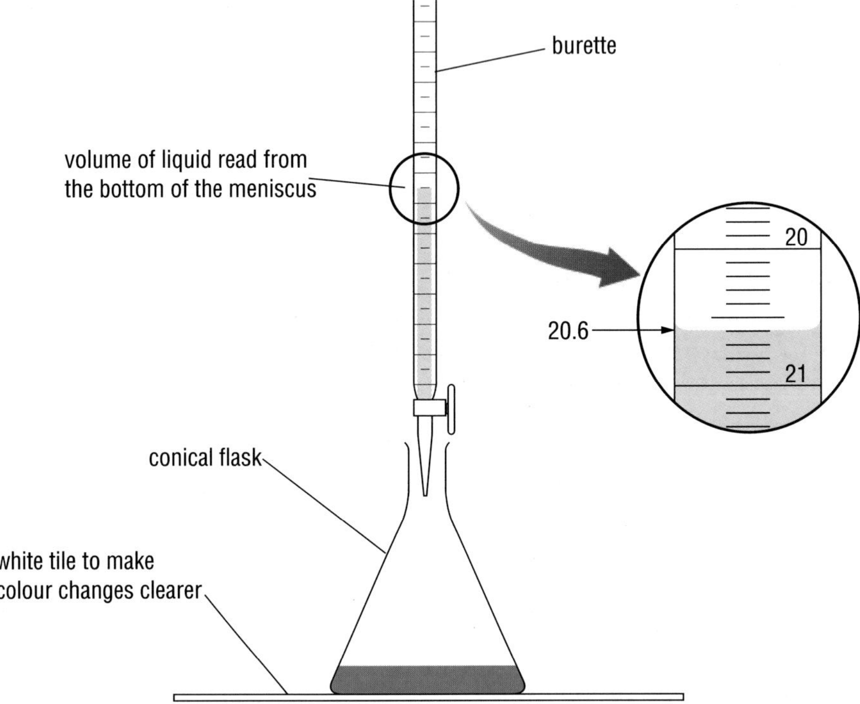

Figure 2.3.16 *The apparatus for a titration. Burette readings are taken from the position of the bottom of the meniscus.*

The end-point is when the solution permanently changes colour. Stand the conical flask on a white tile so that you can see this clearly. Carry out a rough titration (that is do not worry if you slightly overshoot the end-point). Repeat with another volume measured by pipette (the same conical flask can be used provided it has been thoroughly rinsed with distilled water). Add the acid or alkali from the burette 1 cm^3 at a time until 1–2 cm^3 from the end point. The solution in the burette should then be added drop by drop, mixing the contents of the flask thoroughly by swirling it between additions.

3 Recording the results

Here is a suitable way to record the results of a titration.

Titration of 20.0 cm^3 portions of sodium hydroxide solution against 0.100 mol dm^{-3} hydrochloric acid

Titration:	1	2	3
1st burette reading	1.0	22.1	0.0 cm^3
2nd burette reading	22.2	43.0	20.7 cm^3
difference	21.2	20.9	20.7 cm^3
	(rough)		

Average (of 2 and 3) titration $= \dfrac{20.9 + 20.7}{2} = 20.8\ cm^3$

Calculations for acid-base titrations

From the balanced chemical equation for the reaction you can identify the number of moles of acid and alkali involved:

number of moles of acid = n_a
number of moles of alkali = n_b

Suppose that the following data are obtained from a titration:

V_a cm^3 of m_a mol dm^{-3} *acid* reacts with V_b cm^3 of m_b mol dm^{-3} *alkali*

You will know three of these four values. Your aim will be to work out the concentration of either the acid or the alkali, whichever is the unknown.

The formula you need for your calculations is

$$\frac{m_a V_a}{n_a} = \frac{m_b V_b}{n_b}$$

1 mole of acid reacts with 1 mole of alkali

For example, 20.0 cm^3 of *a* mol dm^{-3} hydrochloric acid reacted with 25.6 cm^3 of 0.100 mol dm^{-3} sodium hydroxide.

Equation for the reaction:

$$HCl(aq) + NaOH(aq) \rightarrow NaCl(aq) + H_2O(l)$$

Therefore, 1 mole of hydrochloric acid reacts with 1 mole of sodium hydroxide.

Using

$$\frac{m_a V_a}{n_a} = \frac{m_b V_b}{n_b}$$

$n_a = 1$
$n_b = 1$
$V_a = 20.0$ cm^3
$V_b = 25.6$ cm^3
$m_b = 0.100$ mol dm^{-3}

Substituting in the formula:

$$\frac{m_a \times 20.0}{1} = \frac{0.100 \times 25.6}{1}$$

Therefore, $m_a = 0.128$ mol dm^{-3}
Concentration of hydrochloric acid is 0.128 mol dm^{-3}

1 mole of acid reacts with 2 moles of alkali

For example, 20.0 cm^3 of m_a mol dm^{-3} sulphuric acid reacted with 24.2 cm^3 of 0.200 mol dm^{-3} sodium hydroxide.

Equation for the reaction:

$$H_2SO_4(aq) + 2NaOH(aq) \rightarrow Na_2SO_4(aq) + 2H_2O(l)$$

Therefore, 1 mole of sulphuric acid reacts with 2 moles of sodium hydroxide.

Using

$$\frac{m_a V_a}{n_a} = \frac{m_b V_b}{n_b}$$

$n_a = 1$
$n_b = 2$
$V_a = 20.0\ cm^3$
$V_b = 24.2\ cm^3$
$m_b = 0.200\ mol\ dm^{-3}$

Substituting in the formula:

$$\frac{m_a \times 20.0}{1} = \frac{0.200 \times 24.2}{2}$$

Therefore, $m_a = 0.121\ mol\ dm^{-3}$
Concentration of sulphuric acid is $0.121\ mol\ dm^{-3}$

2 moles of acid reacts with 1 mole of alkali

For example, $20.0\ cm^3$ of a mol dm^{-3} nitric acid reacted with $12.8\ cm^3$ of $0.150\ mol\ dm^{-3}$ calcium hydroxide.

Equation for the reaction:

$$2HNO_3(aq) + Ca(OH)_2(aq) \rightarrow Ca(NO_3)_2(aq) + 2H_2O(l)$$

Therefore, 2 moles of nitric acid reacts with 1 mole of calcium hydroxide.
Using

$$\frac{m_a V_a}{n_a} = \frac{m_b V_b}{n_b}$$

$n_a = 2$
$n_b = 1$
$V_a = 20.0\ cm^3$
$V_b = 12.8\ cm^3$
$m_b = 0.150\ mol\ dm^{-3}$

Substituting in the formula:

$$\frac{m_a \times 20.0}{2} = \frac{0.150 \times 12.8}{1}$$

Therefore, $m_a = 0.192\ mol\ dm^{-3}$
Concentration of nitric acid is $0.192\ mol\ dm^{-3}$

Once you have found the concentration of an acid by titration against an alkali of known concentration, the quantity of acid present in the sample can be determined as follows:

Volume of sample containing the acid = $x\ cm^3$
Concentration of acid = $m_a\ mol\ dm^{-3}$

Mass of 1 mole of acid = M g

Then mass of acid in $x\ cm^3$ of the sample = $x \times \frac{m_a}{1000} \times M$

Don't forget that you may have diluted your sample of acid before analysis. You must take this into account.

Similarly for an alkali:

Volume of sample containing the alkali = x cm^3
Concentration of alkali = m_b mol dm^{-3}

Mass of 1 mole of alkali = M g
Then mass of alkali in x cm^3 of the sample = $x \times \frac{m_b}{1000} \times M$

Again, do not forget that you may have diluted your sample before analysis. You must take this into account.

Case study

MONITORING AIR POLLUTION

Analysts are employed to monitor the quality of the air we breathe. Their job is to measure the amounts of unwanted substances in the atmosphere. These substances are often harmful to health or have a damaging effect on our environment. They may be the result of human activity or a natural event such as a volcanic eruption. It has been said that pollution of the atmosphere is one of the most serious threats to our future. To control pollution we must be able to monitor it. The role of the analyst is vital.

There are two types of pollutants: primary and secondary. Primary pollutants are formed as a direct result of some activity on Earth, e.g. smoke from a forest fire. Secondary pollutants are often formed as a result of complex chemical reactions occurring in the atmosphere, e.g. various oxides of nitrogen.

Illustration 1 *This analyst is determining air quality in the field.*

One cause for concern in recent years has been so-called 'acid rain'. We depend upon sources of energy which are plentiful, reliable and flexible. Stored reserves of energy are called fuels. These are dominated by fossil fuels (such as oil and coal) and nuclear fuels. Both of these are non-renewable, finite sources. In other words, supplies will run out eventually.

Coal-fired power stations provide electricity for the National Grid. Petrol, which is obtained from oil, is the fuel used in cars and lorries. The incomplete combustion of these fossil fuels pollutes the atmosphere. Carbon monoxide and soot (particles of carbon) are formed. Also, due to small amounts of sulphur compounds and nitrogen compounds in coal and crude oil, sulphur dioxide and oxides of nitrogen are produced when these fossil fuels are burnt. These gases dissolve in moisture in the atmosphere and return to the surface as acid rain.

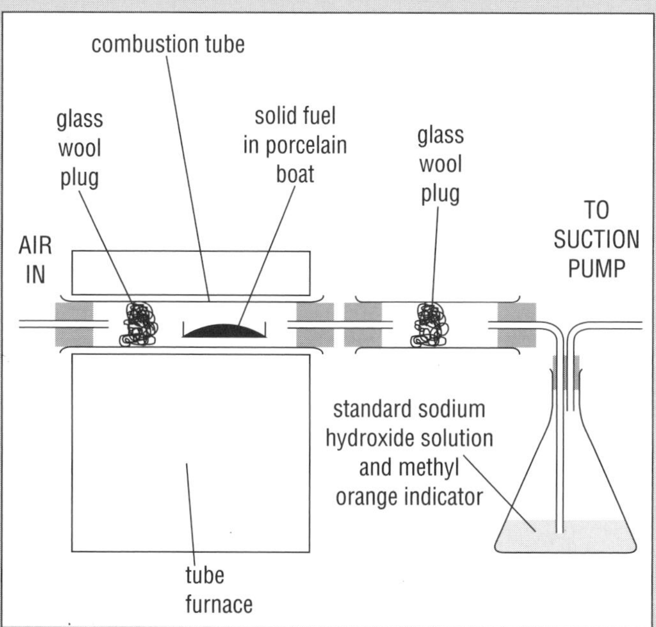

Illustration 2 *Apparatus for measuring pollutants.*

The apparatus in Illustration 2 can be used to compare the possible pollution resulting from burning different solid fuels. The acidity of the combustion products can be determined as follows:

1 An accurately measured volume of standard sodium hydroxide solution is placed in the conical flask. Add 2–3 drops of methyl orange indicator.
2 Draw air over the heated solid fuel at a known rate.
3 Measure the time taken for the methyl orange to change colour form yellow to red.
4 Measure the rate of flow of gas and calculate the volume of combustion gases that is required to neutralise the sodium hydroxide solution.

Questions

1 What is a 'pollutant'?

2 What is 'acid rain' and what are its effects on our environment?

3 If you were determining the quantities of pollutants in the atmosphere, would you take a single sample of air or representative samples? Explain your answer.

4 For the experiment to compare the possible pollution resulting from burning different solid fuels:

(a) What variables must be controlled in order to make a valid comparison of different fuels?

(b) How could you measure the volume of air that has been used?

(c) How could you measure the temperature at which the combustion was occurring?

(d) Draw a piece of apparatus that could be used to measure the rate of flow of air.

(e) How could you measure the quantity of soot that is produced?

(f) What is a standard solution?

(g) How would you measure the volume of the sodium hydroxide solution to be used?

(h) It might be difficult to see the end-point, i.e. when the methyl orange just changes colour. How could you modify the experiment to avoid this problem? *Hint:* Look at the procedure for the 'Quantitative analysis of antacid tablets containing calcium carbonate'.

Note: This case study could be turned into an interesting practical assignment. Think about how you might do this. It is essential that you discuss this with your supervisor before embarking upon any practical work.

Assignment

AN INVESTIGATION OF ANTACID MEDICINES

Setting the scene

Indigestion, and the associated discomfort, is caused by excess acid in the stomach. This can be treated by taking an antacid, a substance which neutralises an acid by chemical reaction. Active ingredients in antacid medicines include magnesium hydroxide, aluminium hydroxide and sodium hydrogencarbonate.

The antacid present in many medicines is calcium carbonate. The medicines usually come in tablet form, each tablet containing 0.5 g calcium carbonate. Calcium carbonate reacts with acids to give the appropriate calcium salt, carbon dioxide and water. For example,

calcium carbonate + nitric acid → calcium nitrate + carbon dioxide + water

The chemical equation is:

$$CaCO_3(s) + 2HNO_3(aq) \rightarrow Ca(NO_3)_2(aq) + CO_2(g) + H_2O(l)$$

The antacid present in Milk of Magnesia (also sold as Cream of Magnesia) is magnesium hydroxide. Typically 5 cm^3 contains 0.415 g magnesium hydroxide. Magnesium hydroxide reacts with acids to give the appropriate magnesium salt and water. For example,

magnesium hydroxide + sulphuric acid → magnesium sulphate + water

The chemical equation is:

$$Mg(OH)_2(s) + H_2SO_4(aq) \rightarrow MgSO_4(aq) + 2H_2O(l)$$

The assignment

Ideally you should work in a team of three. Read through what is required and decide how your team will divide the work between its members.

1 Carry out a survey of antacid medicines.

(a) In each case, write down the brand name, list of ingredients and cost. Summarise your findings in a table, putting the antacids in groups according to their active ingredients.

(b) For each active ingredient found in antacids, write a word equation and a balanced chemical equation for the neutralisation of hydrochloric acid.

Each member should record their own findings. The team should work together to present their combined results on an A1 poster which it will be asked to present to other members of the group.

2 Determine the quantity of magnesium hydroxide in 5 cm^3 of Milk of Magnesia and compare this with the quantity stated on the bottle. Calculate the volume of 2 mol dm^{-3} hydrochloric acid that can be neutralised by the contents of a bottle of Milk of Magnesia.

Each member should carry out their own analysis. Your written account should describe how the analysis was carried out and contain all relevant calculations.

3 Chose an antacid which contains calcium carbonate.

(a) Carry out tests to confirm that the tablets contain calcium ions and carbonate ions.

(b) Determine the quantity of calcium carbonate in a tablet and compare this with the quantity stated on the box.

Each member should carry out an analysis of a brand name antacid containing calcium carbonate. Each team member's account should describe how the analysis was carried out and contain all relevant calculations. In addition it should contain the results of other group members' analyses on other brand name antacids.

Presenting your assignment

Each member of the team will produce

- a table summarising the survey of antacid medicines
- written reports for the two analyses carried out.

Each group will give:

- a five-minute presentation on the survey, followed by time for questions.

Additional information

The following procedures are available

(a) Qualitative chemical tests, page 104

(b) Carrying out an acid-base titration, page 107

(c) Quantitative analysis of liquid antacids containing magnesium hydroxide, page 114

(d) Quantitative analysis of antacid tablets containing calcium carbonate, page 115.

Opportunity to collect evidence
In completing this task you will have the opportunity to meet the following requirements for GNVQ Intermediate Science:

Science units
Unit 1:
Element 1.2 PCs 1, 2, 3, 4, 5
Unit 2:
Element 2, 3 PCs 1, 2, 3

Core skill units

Application of number:
Elements 2.1, 2.2

Communication:
Elements 2.1, 2.2, 2.3, 2.4

Eye protection must be worn

IRRITANT dilute hydrochloric acid

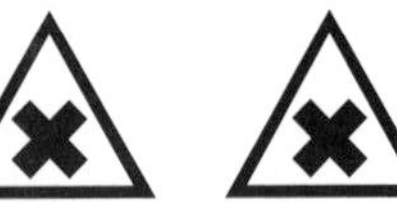
IRRITANT magnesium hydroxide

Requirements

- ❐ Dilute hydrochloric acid – irritant
- ❐ A liquid antacid containing magnesium hydroxide
- ❐ 0.150 mol dm^{-3} hydrochloric acid
- ❐ Methyl red (an acid-base indicator which is red in acid and yellow in alkali)
- ❐ 1 cm^3 pipette
- ❐ The usual titration apparatus.

Grading

This assignment gives you the opportunity to meet merit or distinction criteria. All four themes are covered: Planning; Information Seeking and Information Handling; Evaluation; Quality of Outcomes.

Read through the grading criteria carefully and make sure you know what must be done to gain evidence that you are worthy of a merit or distinction.

You may need help with some of the science in this assignment, so don't be afraid to ask.

Procedure

Quantitative analysis of liquid antacids containing magnesium hydroxide

SAFETY: Wear eye protection

Method

Pipette 1.0 cm^3 of the antacid into a 250 cm^3 conical flask. Add about 30 cm^3 distilled water and 2–3 drops of methyl red. Titrate against 0.150 mol dm^{-3} hydrochloric acid until the colour changes from yellow to red. Repeat the analysis with at least one more sample of the antacid.

Treatment of results

The balanced chemical equation for the reaction is

$$Mg(OH)_2(aq) + 2HCl(aq) \rightarrow MgCl_2(aq) + 2H_2O(l)$$

This tells us that 2 moles of acid react with 1 mole of alkali.
If V_a cm^3 of 0.150 mol dm^{-3} hydrochloric acid is required to neutralise 1 cm^3 of the antacid containing magnesium hydroxide:

1. Calculate the concentration of magnesium hydroxide.
2. Calculate the number of moles of magnesium hydroxide in 1 cm^3 of the antacid.
3. Calculate the number of moles of magnesium hydroxide in 5 cm^3 of the antacid.
4. If 1 mol $Mg(OH)_2$ has a mass of 58.3 g, calculate the mass of magnesium hydroxide in 5 cm^3 of the antacid.

Procedure

Quantitative analysis of antacid tablets containing calcium carbonate

SAFETY: Wear eye protection

Method

Weigh one tablet and put it in a 250 cm^3 conical flask. Pipette 20.0 cm^3 1.000 mol dm^{-3} of hydrochloric acid into the flask. Use a measuring cylinder to add about 30 cm^3 distilled water. Swirl the contents of the flask until the tablet has completely dissolved.

Place the conical flask on a wire gauze supported by a tripod. Put a glass filter funnel in the neck of the flask. Heat with a Bunsen burner so that the solution boils gently for about five minutes. The volume of the solution should be kept roughly constant by adding distilled water.

Allow the solution to cool. Add 2–3 drops of phenolphthalein and titrate against 0.500 mol dm^{-3} sodium hydroxide until a permanent pink tinge to the solution is seen.

Repeat the analysis with at least one more tablet.

Treatment of results

The mass of calcium carbonate in a tablet is given by the formula:

$$\text{mass of calcium carbonate} = \frac{(40 - V_b)}{40}\ \text{g}$$

where V_b = the average volume of 0.500 mol dm^{-3} sodium hydroxide solution required for one tablet.

Eye protection must be worn

IRRITANT dilute hydrochloric acid

CORROSIVE dilute sodium hydroxide

Requirements

- ❐ Three antacid tablets containing calcium carbonate
- ❐ 1.000 mol dm^{-3} hydrochloric acid
- ❐ 0.500 mol dm^{-3} sodium hydroxide
- ❐ Phenolphthalein (an acid-base indicator which is colourless in acid and pink in alkali)
- ❐ The usual titration apparatus.

Questions

1 What type of sample would you take for
(a) a pure substance,
(b) a mixture?

2 Describe a chemical test to identify each of the following ions:
(a) chloride, Cl^-;
(b) sulphate, SO_4^{2-};
(c) carbonate, CO_3^{2-};
(d) copper(II), Cu^{2+};
(e)iron(III), Fe^{3+}.

In each case, list the chemicals you would use and the change you would expect to observe if any of these ions are present.

3 Describe how you would carry out a flame test. What colour flame would you expect to see for each of the following ions:
copper(II), Cu^{2+};
(a) sodium, Na^+;
(b) potassium, K^+;
(c) calcium, Ca^{2+}?

4 Describe a chemical test to identify each of the following gases:
(a) oxygen, O_2;
(b) carbon dioxide, CO_2;
(c) hydrogen, H_2.

In each case, list the chemicals you would use and the change you would expect to observe if any of these gases are present.

5 Write word and balanced chemical equations for the following reactions:
(a) hydrochloric acid and sodium hydroxide
(b) nitric acid and sodium hydroxide
(c) hydrochloric acid and calcium hydroxide
(d) sulphuric acid and sodium hydroxide
(e) sulphuric acid and ammonia.

6 Calculate the concentration of the acid in each of the following titrations:
(a) 20.0 cm^3 of hydrochloric acid reacted with 25.0 cm^3 of 0.100 mol dm^{-3} potassium hydroxide
(b) 25.0 cm^3 of ethanoic acid reacted with 22.1 cm^3 of 0.200 mol dm^{-3} sodium hydroxide
(c) 20.0 cm^3 of sulphuric acid reacted with 30.4 cm^3 of 0.150 mol dm^{-3} sodium hydroxide.

7 Calculate the concentration of the alkali in each of the following titrations:
(a) 20.0 cm^3 of sodium hydroxide reacted with 30.0 cm^3 of 0.500 mol dm^{-3} hydrochloric acid
(b) 20.0 cm^3 of ammonia reacted with 26.8 cm^3 of 0.100 mol dm^{-3} hydrochloric acid
(c) 25.0 cm^3 of potassium hydroxide reacted with 15.5 cm^3 of 0.200 mol dm^{-3} sulphuric acid.

3 Making useful products

Our environment is an invaluable reservoir of raw materials. Not all of the materials which go to make up our world are useful. Many scientists are engaged in the business of turning them into useful products. Naturally-occurring materials such as rocks, plants and even the air we breathe can be converted into clothing, food, medicines and other important substances. Scientists also make devices such as CD players, computers, engines and medical equipment.

Plants provide us with food. They are also sources of many other useful materials such as clothing and medicines. Scientists need to understand how the type of cultivar, growing medium, conditions, pests and diseases affect efficient production.

Figure 3.0.1 *Fibres for clothing can come from plants or from chemical reactions. Looking at this photograph, can you tell which clothing is made from natural fibres and which is made from synthetic fibres?*

Vast numbers of useful substances are made by chemical reactions, using raw materials from our environment. These substances are used in agriculture, health, food production, construction and many other areas. Scientists' knowledge of chemical reactions enables them to obtain these useful substances, whether in the laboratory or on a large industrial scale.

We are dependent on electrical and electronic devices to help us move things, communicate, measure and control situations. These devices must be reliable, accurate, effective and of suitable sensitivity. Often they need to be portable. Scientists design and test these devices.

Figure 3.0.2 Metals are immensely useful for all sorts of reasons. Many are obtained from ores by chemical reactions.

The Elements

Element 3.1 Obtain products from cultivated plants

You will need to show that you can:

- identify the required product
- identify the conditions necessary for successful cultivation of the plant from which it will be obtained
- grow the plant and process it to obtain the required product
- assess the economic efficiency of the process.

Obtain products from cultivated plants, page 120

Element 3.2 Obtain pure substances by chemical reactions

You will need to show that you can:

- describe the chemical reactions involved in making a substance
- prepare the substance and isolate it from the reaction mixture
- determine the yield and the cost of production.

Obtaining pure substances by chemical reactions, page 162

Element 3.3 Make and test devices

You will need to show that you can:

- describe what the device is to be used for
- describe the functions of the various parts of the device
- assemble the device, test and evaluate it.

Make and test devices, page 162

Obtain products from cultivated plants

You will need to show that you can:

- identify the required product
- identify the conditions necessary for successful cultivation of the plant from which it will be obtained
- grow the plant and process it to obtain the required product
- assess the economic efficiency of the process.

What useful products are obtained from plants?

Living things obtain energy, page 58
Characteristic activities of living things, page 58

Plants are all around us. They form a large part of the world of living organisms. Humans benefit from plants in many ways:

- As a result of photosynthesis, plants release oxygen, O_2, into the atmosphere. Without plants, there would be no oxygen for us to breathe.
- Plants affect the weather. They also prevent soil erosion. Forests often act as natural sponges, absorbing rain and then slowly releasing it. If forests are cut down, floods and soil erosion may result (see Figure 3.1.1).
- Plants provide food for domestic herbivores such as sheep, cattle, horses and goats. We obtain wool, leather and food from such animals and may use them for transport.
- We obtain useful products, such as food and medicines from plants. It is this sort of benefit that we shall consider in more detail here. We shall concentrate on **cultivated plants**, that is, plants such as wheat, chrysanthemums and poppies that are grown specially for their products.

FOCUS
Cultivated plants are plants that are grown specially for their products.

Figure 3.1.1 The destruction of forests can lead to massive soil erosion as water floods onto land instead of being released gradually.

The products we obtain from plants can be divided into two main categories:

- natural products
- derived products.

Natural plant products

FOCUS
Natural plant products are obtained directly from plants and require little or no processing. Examples include fruits, vegetables and nuts.

Natural products are obtained directly from the plant and require little or no processing. Examples of natural products, with the parts of a plant from which they are obtained, are given in Table 3.1.1. Most, but not all, of the natural products obtained from plants are edible products.

Table 3.1.1 Examples of natural plant products and their sources

Plant product	Source
Rice	Seeds of rice
Corn	Kernels of maize
Apples	Fruits of apple tree
Strawberries	Fruits of strawberry
Bananas	Fruits of banana tree
Parsley	Leaves of parsley
Rosemary	Leaves of rosemary
Cauliflowers	Flowers of cauliflower
Onions	Bulbs of onion
Carrots	Roots of carrot
Wood	E.g. mahogany, pine, beech trees
Potato	Tuber of potato
Asparagus	Young stems of asparagus
Brussels sprouts	Buds of plant

Derived plant products

Derived products require some degree of processing before they can be used. Some of the major categories of derived products obtained from plants are listed in Table 3.1.2 (page 122). We shall now look briefly at two examples of derived products obtained from cultivated plants. A third example is considered as a case study.

FOCUS

Derived plant products require some degree of processing before they can be used. Examples include paper, sugar, cotton, coffee and certain medicines.

Cotton

Cotton is the most important natural fibre in the world. The fibres come from the seeds of the cotton plant (see Figure 3.1.2). There are some 30 species of cotton, but most of the world's production comes from just one of these – *Gossypium hirsutum* (*hirsutum* means 'hairy'). Cotton was probably first used as early as 12 000 BP (Before Present) by people living on the coasts of Peru. Over time, the cotton plant has been greatly changed, so that today's yields of cotton are far greater than those obtained from the original wild plants.

Cotton is grown in many countries, including China, USA, Russia, India and Pakistan. In tropical countries cotton bushes live for years and may grow into small trees. In other countries, cotton seed is typically sown each year. In the USA chemicals are used to cause the cotton plants to drop their leaves and the cotton is then gathered by machine. With the growth of the 'green movement', there has been an explosion of interest in natural, un-dyed cottons. Plant breeders are trying to introduce colour genes into cotton. This would allow natural cottons to vary in colour more than at present. Blue jeans from blue genes, perhaps?

Figure 3.1.2 *Cotton is obtained from the fibres of the cotton plant,* Gossypium hirsutum. *What do you think might be the natural function of cotton fibres? (Hint: how do you think the seeds of cotton are dispersed?)*

Table 3.1.2 Categories of derived plant products with some examples

Category of derived plant product	Examples
Food	Sugar, jams, flour
Beverage (drink)	Coffee, tea
Clothing	Cotton, linen
Medicine	Digitalis from the foxglove
Lubricant oils	Oils from the coconut and castor bean are used in racing car and aeroplane engines
Paper	Conifer or eucalyptus trees
Dyes	Woad (blue), madder (red)
Rubber	Rubber ball

Coffee

About a third of the world's population drinks coffee. Twenty-five million people owe their jobs to it. Coffee is big business. It comes from the coffee bush, a small tropical tree with glossy, evergreen leaves that develops red berries. Inside each berry there are usually two seeds – or 'beans' as they are also called. Once extracted, the beans are roast and then ground.

In the UK, 90% of the coffee we drink is 'instant'. Coarsely ground beans are put into huge, stainless steel percolators and brewed in water under pressure for several hours. This liquid is then sprayed through fine nozzles into a very high tower. As it falls, the liquid dries into a powder or granules.

Coffee owes its popularity to its taste and to the caffeine it contains. Caffeine is a stimulant. It makes us feel more alert, though it does not help with a hangover.

Decaffeinated coffee is currently made from normal coffee that has had about a half or two-thirds of the caffeine removed. There are, however, wild coffee plants in Madagascar that are completely free of caffeine, so it is possible that plant breeders will one day be able to produce caffeine-free varieties.

What factors affect the successful cultivation of plants?

How can plants be grown?, page 123

How can plant material be processed to a product?, page 130

What is the economic efficiency of producing products from plants?, page 131

The successful cultivation of a plant involves the following steps:

- selecting an appropriate cultivar
- providing the right growing medium
- maintaining the right conditions for plant growth
- protecting from pests and diseases
- harvesting
- processing
- packaging
- selling the final product at a reasonable profit margin.

Selection of an appropriate cultivar

A **cultivar** is a commercial variety of a crop plant. For example, there are dozens of different wheat cultivars and thousands of different rose cultivars (see Figure 3.1.3). The cultivar grown must be suitable for the conditions. The factors that affect the choice of a particular cultivar include:

- the expected yield
- the length of the growing season
- fertiliser and water requirements
- susceptibility to diseases
- consumer preferences.

> **FOCUS**
> **The successful cultivation of a plant involves carrying out a whole string of activities, from choosing the right cultivar through to pricing the product appropriately.**

Figure 3.1.3 *Commercial success for a horticulturist involves choosing the right cultivar. How might a person who grows roses for the cut flower trade decide what varieties to grow?*

For example, it's no good a farmer growing a potentially high-yielding wheat cultivar if that particular cultivar requires a long, hot summer while the farmer farms in the west of Scotland. Consumer preferences are especially important in the horticultural trade where fashions may change rapidly. One year yellow roses may be in fashion, the next, orange ones.

How can plants be grown?

Many factors affect the **growth of plants**. The main ones are:

- characteristics of the growing medium
- climate and weather
- pests and diseases.

> **FOCUS**
> **The main factors affecting the growth of plants are:**
> - **characteristics of the growing medium**
> - **climate and weather**
> - **pests and diseases.**

Characteristics of the growing medium

There are a number of characteristics of the **growing medium** that are important for plants. Chief among these are:

- soil structure
- moisture content
- pH
- mineral nutrients
- organic matter.

> **FOCUS**
> **The principal features of the growing medium that are important for plants are:**
> - **soil structure**
> - **moisture content**
> - **pH**
> - **mineral nutrients**
> - **organic matter.**

Soil structure

Soils are composed mainly of inorganic particles. In a **sandy** soil, these particles are quite large; in a **clay** soil they are very small. A **silty** soil is in between. A **loam** is a soil made of particles with a range of sizes (see Figure 3.1.4).

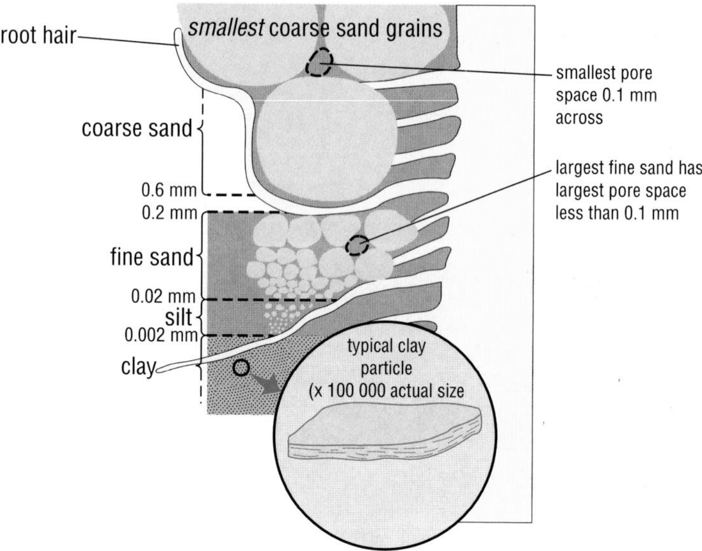

Figure 3.1.4 The sizes of coarse sand, fine sand, silt and clay drawn alongside root hairs for comparison. Water held in pores smaller than 0.1 mm in diameter does not drain away under the influence of gravity. Instead it is available for plants. As shown, clay particles are usually plate-like in structure. Why do sands tend to become cold at night and hot during the day?

Mineral nutrients, page 125

FOCUS

Soils are composed mainly of inorganic particles. In a sandy soil, these particles are quite large; in a clay soil they are very small. A silty soil is in between. A loam is a soil made of particles with a range of sizes.

Clay soils differ from sandy soils in all sorts of ways. For example, sands dry out much more quickly. They also tend to be very low in minerals. This is because they drain rapidly and water washes the soluble nutrients out, a process known as *leaching*. They tend to become hot during the day and cold at night.

Moisture content

The moisture content of a growing medium is very important for the plants and is often related to the soil structure. For example, a compacted soil is more likely to become waterlogged. This excludes air from the soil. Waterlogging is bad for most plants so farmers and gardeners often drain soils and plough or dig them up. Good drainage encourages root growth (see Figure 3.1.5). In addition to drainage and soil compaction, the moisture content of a soil is also affected by:

- whether the soil is sandy or has a lot of clay
- the amount of rainfall
- whether or not there is irrigation
- the crops being grown – some crops take up a lot of water from the soil.

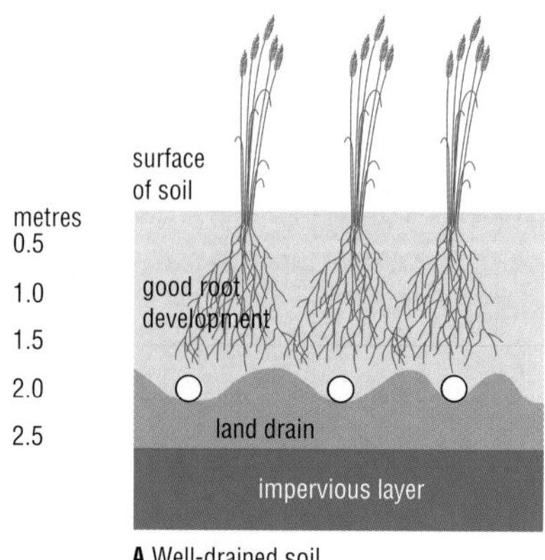

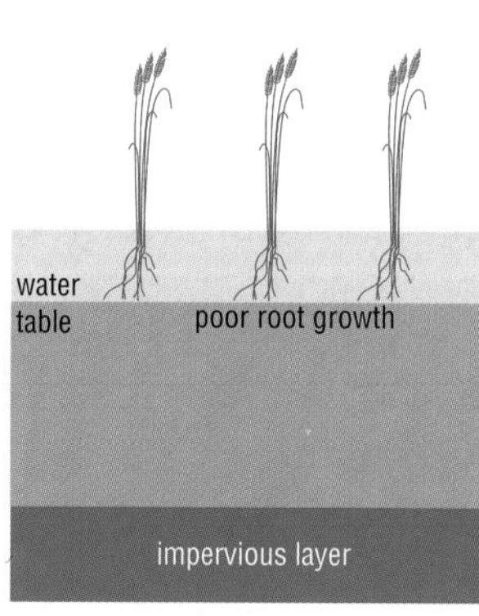

Figure 3.1.5 A well-drained soil usually results in crops with better roots. Such crops go on to have greater yields. It may make economic sense for a farmer to pay to put in drainage pipes if the field would otherwise get waterlogged.

pH

Many plants are affected by the *pH* of their growing medium. Suppose you are a forester, wanting to grow trees. The acidity of the soil makes a difference to which trees will grow well. A soil with a low pH, round about pH 3, is an acid soil. Sitka spruce and birch grow well on such soils (see Figure 3.1.6). A soil with a lot of chalk in it may have a pH of about 7.5. Corsican pine and beech grow well on such soils (see Figure 3.1.7).

Figure 3.1.6 *A forest planted with Sitka spruce. This tree is often planted on acid soils. Sitka spruce grows very quickly. It is used for many building jobs and for chip-board, but rarely for furniture.*

Figure 3.1.7 *A beech wood. Beech grows best on a chalky soil that is slightly alkaline. Beech is widely used in furniture. It is also a good wood for charcoal making.*

Mineral nutrients

Plants need sufficient *mineral nutrients* (inorganic ions) for healthy growth. These minerals are absorbed by the root hairs of the plant (see Figure 3.1.8). Those needed in quite large amounts are: calcium (Ca^{2+}), magnesium (Mg^{2+}), nitrate (NO_3^-), phosphate (PO_4^{3-}), potassium (K^+) and sulphate (SO_4^{2-}). Those needed in smaller amounts include: cobalt (Co^{2+}), iron (Fe^{2+} or Fe^{3+}) and molybdate (MoO_4^{2-}).

Fertilisers are used by farmers and gardeners to improve the growth of plants. Most fertilisers contain large quantities of nitrate ions, phosphate ions and potassium ions. They are called NPK fertilisers (see Figure 3.1.9).

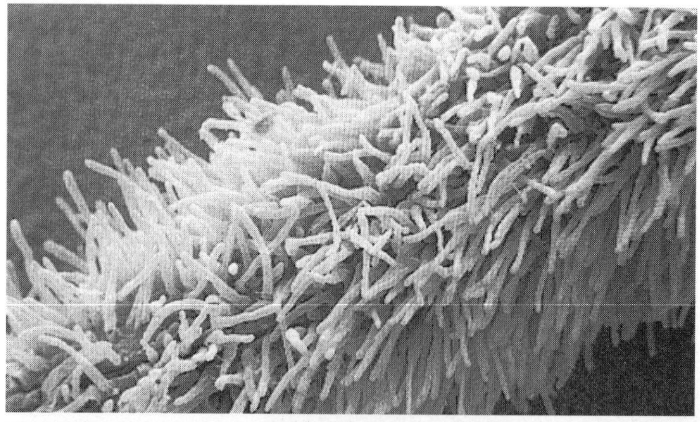

Figure 3.1.8 A scanning electron micrograph of a plant root showing large numbers of root hairs. Root hairs increase the surface area of the root, so helping it to take up water and mineral ions.

N.P.K. FERTILIZER 10–30–30

NITROGEN (N) 10%	**IRON (Fe)** 168 mg/kg.
PHOSPHORUS PENTOXIDE (P_2O_5) Soluble in neutral ammonium citrate and water 30% (P13.1%)	**MANGANESE (Mn)** 85 mg/kg. **COPPER (Cu)** 85 mg/kg.
POTASSIUM OXIDE (K_2O) Soluble in water 30%(K24.9%)	**ZINC (Zn)** 30 mg/kg. **BORON (B)** 44 mg/kg.
MAGNESIUM OXIDE (MgO) 375 mg/kg (Mg 225 mg/kg).	**MOLYBDENUM (Mo)** 1.1 mg/kg.

DIRECTIONS

Using the enclosed spoon dissolve one level measure of fertilizer in two pints of water. Feed this to your Bonsai Trees once a week during the growing season and occasionally at other times.

Figure 3.1.9 Information taken from the side of a Bonsai tree fertiliser packet. Explain why fertilisers containing nitrate ions, phosphate ions and potassium ions are called NPK fertilisers. Why do you think this fertiliser is described as a 10-30-30 fertiliser?

Figure 3.1.10 These mushrooms and toadstools are the fruiting bodies of soil fungi. Soil fungi play a vital role in the breakdown of organic matter in the soil.

Organic matter

Three main categories of soil organic matter can be identified:

- living organisms
- the remains of organisms that have recently died
- humus.

Living organisms in a soil include plants (especially their roots), bacteria, fungi, earthworms and other soil animals such as insects and nematodes (round worms). These organisms play a vital role in the cycling of carbon, nitrogen and other elements in the soil. Without them there would be no decomposition; indeed, no soil. We rarely notice soil organisms unless we spot a bird pulling an earthworm from the soil, or see a crop of mushrooms and toadstools (see Figure 3.1.10).

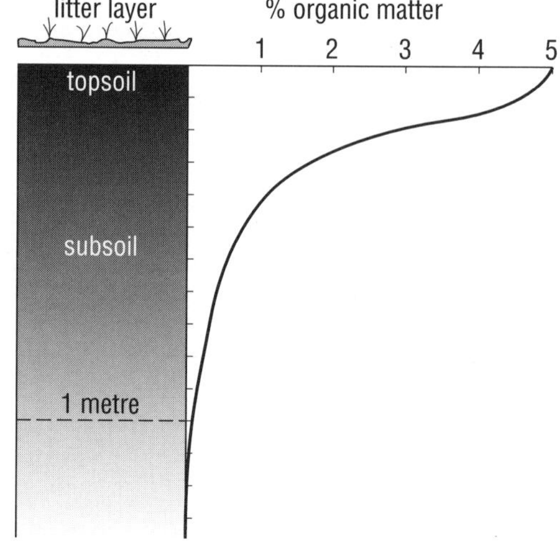

Figure 3.1.11 Organic matter tends to be concentrated nearer the tops of soils. The presence of humus makes topsoils dark in colour. Can you name a soil that has an extremely high percentage of organic matter?

In time soil organisms die. The dead organic matter of a soil is gradually broken down by living soil organisms. The result is a black material which is still organic and is known as *humus*. Humus gives topsoil its characteristic dark colour (see Figure 3.1.11). Eventually, it is completely broken down to carbon dioxide, water and inorganic ions. However, this may take years and, in the meantime, the humus acts as an important reservoir of mineral nutrients.

Figure 3.1.12 *Composts are widely used both by gardeners and by horticulturists.*

What is a compost?

In horticulture, growing media for plants are generally referred to as **composts** (see Figure 3.1.12). For example, the John Innes seed compost consists of 2 parts loam, 1 part peat and 1 part sand. Great care is taken by companies making this compost to ensure it is of a uniform, high quality. The loam used must have a pH of between 5.8 and 6.5, and the peat used has a pH of between 3.5 and 5.0. In addition, 1200 g of a compound containing phosphate and 600 g of calcium carbonate are added to each cubic metre of the compost. Various other John Innes composts are available. For example, they make a special compost for growing plants such as rhododendrons and heathers which require an acid soil.

FOCUS

A compost is a growing medium for plants, as used in the horticultural trade.

Investigation

The effect of different composts on germination and early growth of a crop

SAFETY: Wash your hands after handling soil.
Some commercially available seeds have been treated with pesticides.

1 Obtain two different commercial composts and some garden soil.
2 Set up a total of 15 plant pots – five with one compost, five with the other compost and five with the garden soil.
3 Obtain a packet of fresh seeds (e.g. lettuce). Read the instructions and sow the same number of seeds in each of the 15 pots.
4 Follow the instructions for watering the seeds. Keep the pots in a warm place.
5 Each day for two weeks record the number of seeds that have germinated in each plant pot.
6 At the end of the two weeks, harvest the plants and record their weights.
- Are there any differences in the final percentages of seeds that have germinated in the three different growing media?
- Are there any differences in the rate at which the seeds germinated in the three different growing media?
- Are there any differences in the yields from the three different growing media at the end of the three weeks?

BIOHAZARD
soil

Requirements

- Plant pots, 15
- Two different composts
- Garden soil
- Seed (no dormancy)

Climate and weather

We are all familiar with day-to-day changes in the weather. One day it may be warm and sunny, the next cool and rainy. By **climate** we mean the more regular changes from season to season in such things as:

- **rainfall**
- **temperature**
- **wind**
- **hours of sunlight.**

So, for example, the climate in Cornwall and the Scilly Isles is dominated by the Atlantic Ocean. Compared with the east of England, it is more rainy,

FOCUS

The climate of a region consists of the regular seasonal changes in such things as rainfall, temperature, wind and hours of sunlight. Both the temperature range and average temperature are important.

Light levels, page 62
Temperature, page 64

more windy and there are fewer extremes of temperature during the year. This makes a big difference to the plants that can be cultivated there (see Figure 3.1.13). For example, the rarity of severe frosts means that plants can be grown out-of-doors in Cornwall even if they would be damaged or killed by frosts. Extremes of temperature (indicated by the **range of temperature variation**) can be just as important for plants as the average temperature. Hours of sunlight are also important, and in temperate countries these are obviously greater in the summer than in the winter.

Figure 3.1.13 *The mild winters and early springs that occur in the Scilly Isles mean that considerable sums of money can be made from harvesting plants for the cut-flower trade weeks before such plants can be harvested on the mainland. Explain the reason for the differences between the climate of the south-west and the east of England.*

Pests and diseases

There are many pests and diseases that can reduce the yields of plants grown in cultivation. Weeds, fungi, insects and other animals may be involved.

Weeds

A *weed* is a plant that grows where it is not wanted. For example, wild oats are a weed of cereal crops. Some common UK weeds are shown in Figure 3.1.14.

Figure 3.1.14 *Some common UK weeds. Weeds can usually be controlled on farms by the use of herbicides. Before herbicides were developed, many farm labourers spent several weeks each year removing weeds by hand.*

Fungi

Examples of fungi that attack crops are mildews and rusts. One of the most important diseases of potatoes is caused by an organism usually classified as a fungus. It causes the disease potato blight. Its life cycle is shown in Figure 3.1.15.

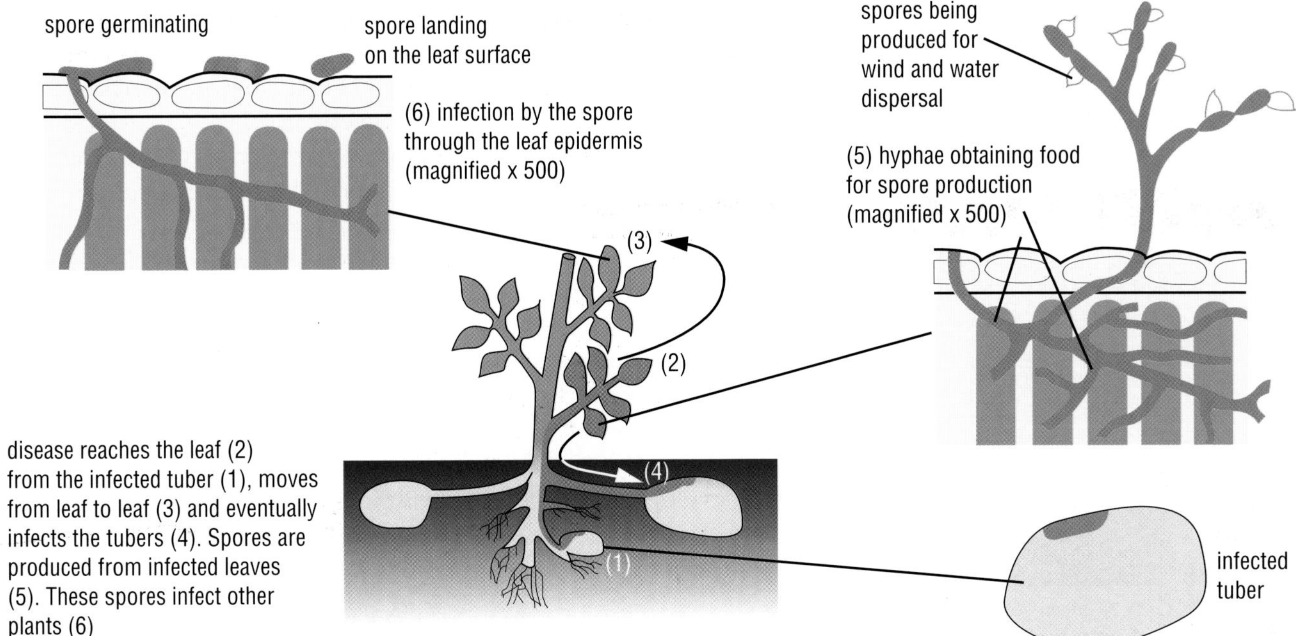

Figure 3.1.15 *The life cycle of the potato blight fungus.*

Insects

Many insects attack crops. For example, cabbages may be damaged by larvae of the large white butterfly (see Figure 3.1.16). Aphids, too, damage many plants.

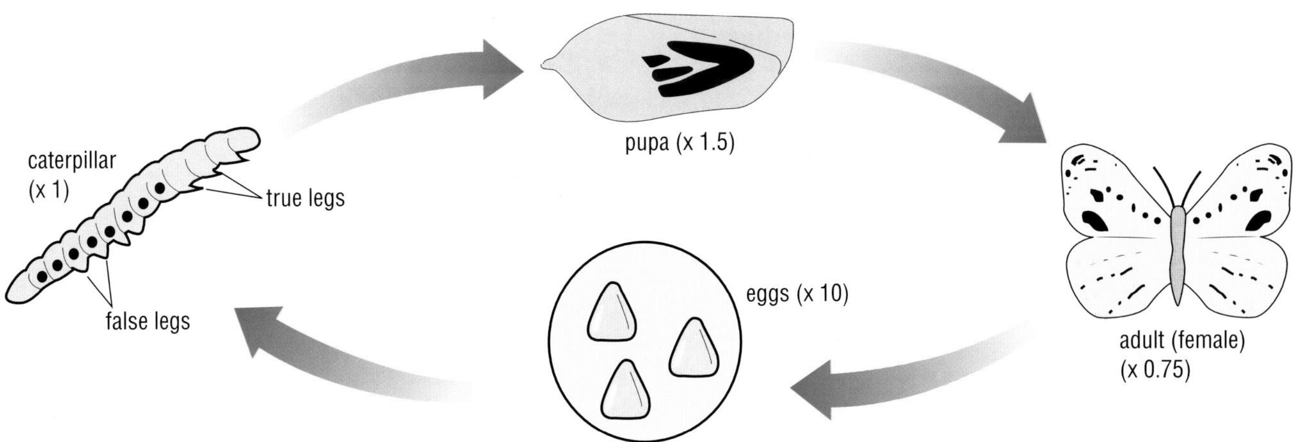

Figure 3.1.16 *The life cycle of the large white butterfly.*

Other animals

Many other animals damage crops. Some of these animals may be quite large. For example, in the UK young trees are often damaged by grey squirrels (see Figure 3.1.17). Grey squirrels are not native to the UK. They were introduced here from north America in the nineteenth century. They are larger than our native species, the red squirrel, and are especially fond of broad-leaved trees. Red squirrels are now found mainly in coniferous woodlands.

How can crops be protected from pests and diseases?

There are a range of ways in which crops can be protected from **pests and diseases.** Measures include:

- **Soil sterilisation**. This is only feasible for greenhouse crops. It is useful against pests that live in the soil, such as certain nematodes (round worms).
- **Herbicides**. These are used to kill weeds.

> **FOCUS**
> **Measures to protect crops against pests and diseases include:**
> - **soil sterilisation**
> - **herbicides**
> - **insecticides**
> - **fungicides**
> - **biological control**
> - **traditional plant breeding**
> - **genetic engineering.**

Figure 3.1.17 Grey squirrels look pretty but cause millions of pounds worth of damage to young trees each year.

- **Insecticides.** These are generally sprayed onto crops when insect numbers build up. One disadvantage is that insecticides are rarely selective. This means that they usually kill a range of useful insects such as predators as well as the pest species.
- **Fungicides.** Sometimes these are sprayed onto crops when weather conditions suggest that a fungal outbreak is about to happen. Sometimes they are put onto the seeds as a seed dressing.
- **Biological control.** Increasingly, predators such as lacewings (carnivorous insects) and parasitic wasps are being used in greenhouses to control pests such as aphids and caterpillars.
- **Traditional plant breeding.** This can result in new varieties resistant to certain pests and diseases. However, each new variety typically takes 10–12 years to develop, and the pest may soon develop resistance.
- **Genetic engineering.** This is increasingly being used to enable a more rapid development of varieties resistant to pests and diseases. For example, a gene for disease-resistance can be moved rapidly from one crop to another.

FOCUS

Four stages may be involved in the processing of crop material:
- **harvesting**
- **grading**
- **conversion to product**
- **packaging.**

How can plant material be processed to a product?

Once a crop has been grown, it is ready for **processing**. In the case of a natural product, the following stages are involved:
- **harvesting**
- **grading**
- **packaging.**

In the case of a derived product, the above three stages are needed and one additional one:
- **conversion to product.**

Figure 3.1.18 The fruit of an entire apple tree can be harvested mechanically in just a few minutes. Why has harvesting become increasingly mechanised in many countries? Are there any undesirable consequences of this?

Harvesting

Harvesting is the act of removing a crop from its growth medium. In recent decades harvesting has become increasingly mechanised in the UK and many other countries. We are all used to seeing combine harvesters harvesting cereal crops. Nowadays, though, even raspberries and apples are frequently harvested mechanically (see Figure 3.1.18).

Grading

Once a crop has been harvested, it is generally *graded* into a number of categories. For instance, the best apples may be sold for eating, while bruised ones may go for apple juice. Consumers (that is, the general public) often want *uniform* plant products. Many people will not buy a 5 kg bag of potatoes if it contains a range of sizes. They want to buy potatoes that are the right size for chipping *or* for boiling *or* for baking, not a mixture of all three.

FOCUS

Plant products are frequently graded according to size and quality.

Conversion to product

In the case of a derived product, such as cotton or sugar, the harvested and graded material needs to be *converted to the product*. Dozens of stages may be involved and large factories may be needed (see Figure 3.1.19).

Packaging

The final stage in the processing of plant material to a product is packaging. Packaging is needed for three main reasons:

- to protect the product if it needs to be stored
- to protect the product as it is transported
- to appeal to the customer.

Most of us are influenced by packaging in powerful ways of which we may not be aware. We come to rely on brand names, and may subconsciously assume that an inexpensively packaged product is sub-standard. Why do you think this is?

Figure 3.1.19 The production of reels of cotton from picked cotton requires a large capital investment.

What is the economic efficiency of producing products from plants?

Successful processing needs to be followed by two further stages:

- transport of the product to market
- sale of product.

Only when the plant product is sold is a farmer or horticulturist in a position to calculate the **economic efficiency** of the whole process. Three main stages are involved:

- determining the total input cost of cultivating the plant product
- determining the output value of the plant product
- calculating the profit or economic efficiency of the entire process.

Determining the total input cost of cultivating the plant product

The main **input costs** of cultivating a plant product are those that relate to the costs of:

- seeds and growth medium
- labour
- chemicals (e.g. fertilisers and pesticides)
- energy (e.g. petrol for tractors, heating for glasshouses)
- capital investment (replacement machinery, glasshouses, etc.).

FOCUS

Calculating the profit or economic efficiency of cultivating a plant product requires knowledge of the total input costs and of the output value.

Determining the output value of the plant product

The **output value** of a plant product depends on two things:

- the *yield* (often measured in units of mass, e.g. kg)
- the *value* of the product per unit yield (e.g. pounds sterling per kg).

From a commercial grower's point of view it is important to realise how unpredictable the output value frequently is. You may be fortunate and have a bumper crop, or the opposite may happen. To some extent, variation in yield is compensated for by variation in the value of the product per unit yield. Suppose it is a bad year for strawberries; strawberries will cost more per punnet. On the other hand, a glut of strawberries means that the unit price (the price per punnet) falls.

Calculating the profit or economic efficiency of the entire process

Finally a commercial grower can calculate whether it's all been worth while from an economic point of view (see Figure 3.1.20). Two related measures can be used:

- profit (or loss)
- economic efficiency.

Figure 3.1.20 *A farmer may need to be as familiar with business administration as with agriculture. Assume you run a small business supplying cut flowers to the retail trade. Your total input costs for the year are £80 000. Calculate your profit (or loss) and the economic efficiency of your business if your output value for the year is:*
(a) £65 000; (b) £80 000; (c) £105 000.

The **profit** (or **loss**) is simply equal to the output value minus the input costs. In a good year the output value will be considerably in excess of the input costs and a profit is made.

The **economic efficiency** is given by the following formula:

$$\text{economic efficiency} = \frac{(\text{output value} - \text{input costs})}{\text{input costs}} \times 100\%$$

Putting this into words, the economic efficiency equals the profit expressed as a percentage of the input costs. Most large businesses would expect profits to be around 10% of the input costs: many farmers do little more than break even.

Case study

THE WORLD OF SUGAR

All plants make sugars as a result of photosynthesis. The most common plant sugar is *sucrose*, and table sugar is almost pure sucrose. Each molecule of sucrose contains 12 atoms of carbon, 22 atoms of hydrogen and 11 atoms of oxygen. Table sugar is obtained almost entirely from sugar beet (a plant related to beetroot) or sugar cane (a tropical grass). Another sugar found in plants is glucose. One form of glucose, known as dextrose, can be bought as an alternative to sucrose.

The commercial use of sugar beet as a source of sugar dates only from the beginning of the nineteenth century, when a German chemist found that 6% of the mass of the root of sugar beet could be extracted as sucrose. That figure is now 20%, thanks partly to the

Illustration 1 *Each of these commercial sugars is almost 100% sucrose. Demerara is raw cane sugar before it is processed.*

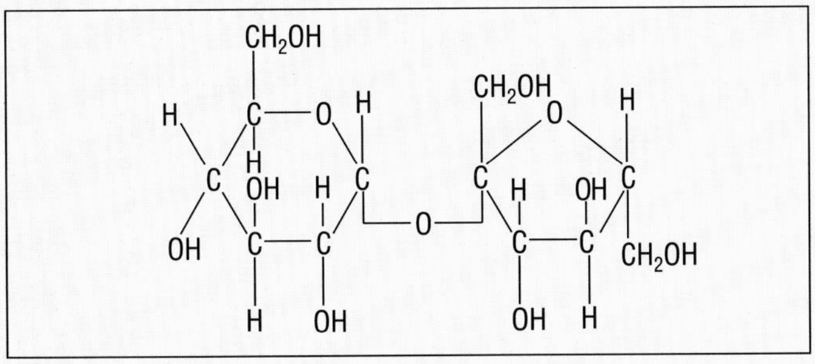

Illustration 2 *The structure of sucrose.*

breeding of superior varieties and partly to better methods of extracting the sugar.

The sugar in sugar beet comes from the swollen roots of the plant. Each harvested root has a mass of about 1 kg. The roots are shredded and then heated in running water. Impurities are removed and the resulting liquid is concentrated and crystallised. The pulp that remains after the sugar has been extracted, together with the leaves, is fed to cattle.

Illustration 4 *Most of the world's sugar comes from sugar beet nowadays. The plants are harvested and the sugar extracted.*

There are now a number of artificial sweeteners available on the market. The best known is saccharine which is made from crude oil. A few years ago it was thought that sales of saccharine might be banned in the USA as tests showed that rats fed saccharine were more likely to develop cancers. However, when the general public found out that this was only because the rats were being forced to eat huge amounts of saccharine, the study was brought into question and its findings have been largely ignored.

Other artificial sweeteners include aspartame, which is a substance formed from two amino acids, and a number of products still actively being researched. One of these is from a plant with the scientific name *Lippia dulcis*. It comes from Mexico and was known to the Aztecs. Scientists at the University of Chicago have isolated a substance from it that is said to be 1000 times sweeter than sucrose.

In many countries, sugar is a luxury. However, in western countries it is very cheap and each of us consumes around 40 kg a year on average. Health experts agree that this is too much for us.

Questions

1. By approximately what factor has the percentage yield of sugar from sugar beet increased over the last 200 years?
2. How does glucose differ from sucrose in chemical structure?
3. Which is sweeter – glucose or sucrose?
4. It is sometimes claimed that dextrose tablets provide a more rapid source of energy for athletes than does sucrose. How might this idea be tested?
5. List those chemical techniques which you think might be involved in the extraction of sucrose from sugar beet.
6. Do you think the sale of saccharine should be permitted or banned, given the finding that high doses can cause cancers in rats? Defend your answer.
7. Do you think the use of rats for studies such as these is:
   (a) useful
   (b) right?
   Explain your answers.
8. What does it mean to say that something is a thousand times sweeter than sucrose'?
9. Suppose a commercially viable sweetener is isolated from *Lippia dulcis*. Do you think the profits from its sale should go to Mexico or the University of Chicago? Defend your answer.
10. Give at least two health risks associated with the intake of large amounts of sugar.

Assignment

MONEY DOESN'T GROW ON TREES – OR DOES IT?

Setting the scene

We all eat vegetables. Vegetables can be grown in gardens by gardeners, or in glasshouses or in fields by farmers. A farmer must ensure that a reasonable profit is made. In this assignment it is suggested that you grow radishes under a range of conditions. You will then be able to see:

- which condition produces the biggest radishes
- which condition produces the greatest yield of radishes
- which condition is best for the farmer.

As we shall see, these three are not necessarily the same!

The assignment

You should work on this assignment in a group of three or four. That way you can share out the work and help each other by exchanging ideas. Each of the four suggested tasks below takes about four weeks. It will probably be best to carry out Task 1 and one or two of the others. The tasks can be carried out one after another or at the same time.

Task 1

Investigate the effect of light intensity on the growth of radishes. Use one variety of radish (e.g. Suttons 'Short top forcing'). Sow it in pots or trays in a laboratory or glasshouse at the density recommended on the packet (density means the number of plants per unit area.) Use a good compost and water the plants so that the soil is moist, but not waterlogged. Make sure you treat all the plants in the same way except that some are kept at average light intensity (e.g. near a window-sill), some at low light intensity (e.g. in the corner of a laboratory) and some at high light intensity (e.g. under fluorescent light banks).

Note: There may be temperature differences due to the treatments. Can you monitor these and reduce their importance?

Electrical hazard

SAFETY: *Ensure any fluorescent light banks are wired up safely by someone with appropriate training.*

After about three or four weeks, harvest the radishes. You will need to decide how to work out the yield. For example, will you include the leaves? Will you include the thin, fibrous roots at the bottom of the red, swollen tap root? Will you use wet mass, or dry the radishes at 110 °C for 24 hours to get dry mass?

Now work out the *economic value* of your radishes. How much would you be able to get for them if you sold them?

Next, carefully work out the cost of growing the radishes. Some of your costs are one-offs (e.g. the cost of trays or pots) as you would be able to re-use such items many times. Other costs, the running costs, will have to be met every time you grow the radishes (e.g. cost of the seed and cost of the compost). Find out how to cost any electricity used to improve the lighting.

Try to cost your own time. How many hours did you spend on the project? How much is an hour of your time worth? Finally, for each of the treatments, work out:

- the profit (or loss), i.e. the running costs minus value of the crop
- the economic efficiency, i.e. the profit from the crop divided by running costs × 100%.

Task 2

Investigate the effect of sowing radishes at different densities on:

- the size of individual radishes
- the yield per pot or tray
- the profit or economic efficiency.

You will need to think about the same sorts of questions as those listed under Task 1. You should vary only density, and keep other factors, including light intensity, the same.

Task 3

Compare the yields from three different varieties of radish. You will need to think about the same sorts of questions as those listed under Task 1. Does one variety appear to be the best yielding? Why do you think there are a number of different radish varieties available on the market?

Task 4

Compare the yields obtained when different composts are used or when fertilisers are added to the growing medium. You will need to think about the same sorts of question as those listed under Task 1. Work out whether the extra cost of certain composts and fertilisers makes economic sense.

Presenting your assignment

You should:

- write a report explaining what your group did
- include a recommendation in your report about the best conditions for growing radishes
- present your report, together with samples of radishes, to show the yields you obtained.

Additional information

The following Investigation is available:

- the effect of different composts on germination and early growth of a crop, page 127.

A detailed account of investigations involving radish growing is given by John Hewitson and Richard Price (1994) 'Plant mineral nutrition in the classroom: the radish, *Raphanus sativus L* is a good plant for such studies', *School Science Review*, 76(274), pages 45–55. Information about growing plants and about how, safely, to make a fluorescent light bank can be obtained from Mr Richard Price, Science and Plants for Schools (SAPS), Homerton College, Cambridge CB2 2PH.

Grading

This assignment gives you ample opportunity to meet merit or distinction criteria. All four themes are covered: Planning, Information Seeking and Information Handling, Evaluation, Quality of Outcomes.

Opportunity to collect evidence

In completing this assignment you will have the opportunity to meet the following requirements for Intermediate GNVQ Science:

Science units

Unit 1:
Element 1.3, PCs 1, 2, 3, 4
Unit 2:
Element 2.1, PCs 2, 3, 4
Unit 3:
Element 3.1, PCs 1, 2, 3, 4, 5

Core skill units

Application of number:
Elements 2.1, 2.2, 2.3

Communication:
Elements 2.1, 2.2

Questions

1 Distinguish between natural and derived plant products. Give three examples of each.

2 What characterises a growing medium as a:
(a) sand
(b) loam
(c) clay
(d) compost?

3 Briefly outline how each of the following characteristics of a growth medium may affect plant growth:
(a) pH
(b) moisture content
(c) mineral nutrient content.

4 Describe how both the average temperature and the range of temperature variation can affect cultivation.

5 Describe how the hours of sunlight and rainfall can affect cultivation.

6 Describe two ways in which plants can be protected from pests and diseases.

7 Under what circumstances might soil sterilisation be of commercial value?

8 Give one advantage and one disadvantage of using chemicals to protect plants from pests and diseases.

9 (a) State the main stages involved in the processing of a derived plant product.
(b) How does the processing of a natural plant product differ?

10 Explain the importance of input costs and output value to the commercial success of a plant grower.

11 Distinguish between profit and economic efficiency.

12 Suppose the business of a commercial grower has, over the course of a year, an output value of £210 000 and input costs of £195 000. Calculate:
(a) the profit (or loss)
(b) the economic efficiency.

Obtaining pure substances by chemical reaction

You will need to show that you can:

- describe the chemical reactions involved in making a substance
- prepare the substance and isolate it from the reaction mixture
- determine the yield and the cost of production.

The importance of obtaining pure substances

The Earth is a vast reservoir of chemical and energy resources. The work of many chemists revolves around using these natural resources to make materials which benefit human beings. For example, coal, crude oil and natural gas are changed into medicines, plastics, pesticides, fibres, detergents, dyes, perfumes and fuels. Rocks and minerals, and even the air we breathe, are the starting point for, amongst other things, the manufacture of metals, glass, fertilisers and superconductors. All of these involve converting materials into the desired product by *chemical reaction*.

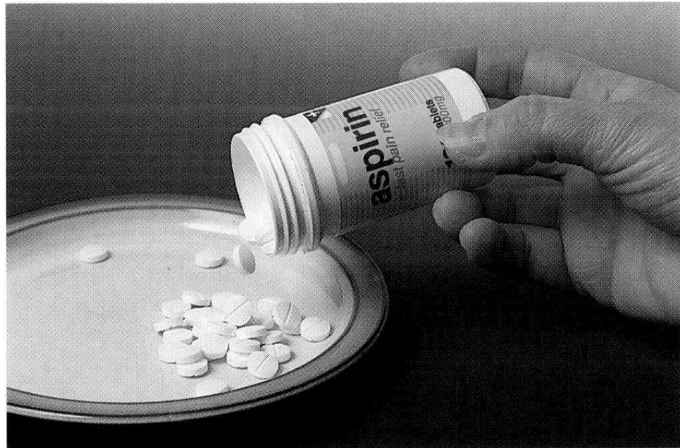

Figure 3.2.1 These tablets, and the plastic bottle which contains them, are made by a series of chemical reactions. The bottle is made from crude oil. Where does crude oil come from? What other household products are made from crude oil?

Over ten million different chemical substances are known. Nearly half a million new ones are obtained each year. The goal of the chemist is *customised synthesis*. This means being able to make new substances with required properties, not by a hit-or-miss process, but by design. This will become increasingly feasible as chemists combine their imagination with their ever-growing knowledge and understanding of how substances behave and react with one another.

Figure 3.2.2 The Earth is a fragile resource. We must manage this resource so that we can provide health, comfort and a suitable environment for all its inhabitants. We must also protect and preserve it for future generations.

Types of reaction

There are four useful types of reaction which can be used to make chemicals in the laboratory:

- redox (e.g. to obtain metals from their compounds)
- acid-base (e.g. to make insoluble salts)
- precipitation (e.g. to make insoluble salts)
- esterification (to make esters).

There are other types, but you need to know about these four in particular.

FOCUS
Redox reactions may be defined as those in which there is a:
- **loss (reduction) or gain (oxidation) of oxygen**
- **gain (reduction) or loss (oxidation) of electrons.**

Redox reactions

In a **redox reaction, oxidation** and **reduction** reactions occur simultaneously. The term *redox* comes from *red*uction-*ox*idation.

There are two useful definitions of oxidation and reduction:

(a) gain or loss of oxygen
(b) loss or gain of electrons.

Gain or loss of oxygen

A simple definition of oxidation is 'gain of oxygen'. Reduction is 'loss of oxygen'.

Most metals react with oxygen to give the metal oxide. They are said to have been oxidised. An example is the rusting of iron:

iron + oxygen → iron(III) oxide
$4Fe(s) + 3O_2(g) \rightarrow 2Fe_2O_3(s)$

Figure 3.2.3 *A redox reaction occurs when iron(III) oxide is converted to iron in this blast furnace.*

The oxygen can be removed from metal oxides, leaving the metal. These reactions can be used to obtain metals. Here are some examples:

iron(III) oxide + carbon → iron + carbon dioxide
$2Fe_2O_3(s) + 3C(s) \rightarrow 4Fe(s) + 3CO_2(g)$

iron(III) oxide + carbon monoxide → iron + carbon dioxide
$Fe_2O_3(s) + 3CO(g) \rightarrow 2Fe(s) + 3CO_2(g)$

(Both of these reactions occur in a blast furnace during the industrial production of iron.)

copper(II) oxide + hydrogen → copper + water
$CuO(s) + H_2(g) \rightarrow Cu(s) + H_2O(l)$

In each case, the metal oxide has been reduced (oxygen has been lost). The substance which brings this about is called a *reducing agent*. So, carbon, carbon monoxide and hydrogen are all acting as reducing agents. These substances gain oxygen and, therefore, have been oxidised.

FOCUS
Metals can be obtained from their compounds by redox reactions. The compounds are said to be reduced to give the metal.

Electron transfer

Redox reactions may be defined in terms of the transfer of electrons. A substance which loses electrons is oxidised. One which gains electrons is **reduced**.

One example of this is the displacement of a metal from a solution containing its ions. For example, when zinc is placed in an aqueous solution of copper(II) sulphate, it dissolves to give a solution of zinc sulphate, and copper forms.

zinc + copper(II) sulphate → zinc sulphate + copper
$Zn(s) + CuSO_4(aq) \rightarrow ZnSO_4(aq) + Cu(s)$

Let's look more closely at what is happening in this reaction.

When salts dissolve in water they break up to give solutions containing their ions. Copper(II) sulphate dissolves to give a solution of copper(II) ions, $Cu^{2+}(aq)$, and sulphate ions, $SO_4^{2-}(aq)$. This means that we can write the equation rather differently:

$$Zn(s) + Cu^{2+}(aq) + SO_4^{2-}(aq) \rightarrow Zn^{2+}(aq) + Cu(s) + SO_4^{2-}(aq)$$

We see that the sulphate ions, SO_4^{2-} (aq), are present in solution before and after the reaction. They take no part and are said to be *spectator ions*. The *ionic equation* for the displacement reaction becomes:

$$Zn(s) + Cu^{2+}(aq) \rightarrow Zn^{2+}(aq) + Cu(s)$$

This type of equation is known as an ionic equation. Its use here has the advantage that it represents the displacement of copper from a solution of any of its soluble salts by zinc.

Electrons are transferred from zinc to copper(II) ions. This can be represented with *two half-equations:*

$Zn(s) \rightarrow Zn^{2+}(aq) + 2e^-$ zinc is being oxidised (loss of electrons)

$Cu^{2+}(aq) + 2e^- \rightarrow Cu(s)$ copper(II) ions are being reduced (gain of electrons)

The ionic equation for the reaction is obtained by 'adding' these two half reactions. The electrons (e^-) cancel out.

$$\begin{array}{ll} Zn(s) & \rightarrow Zn^{2+}(aq)^- \\ Cu^{2+}(aq) & \rightarrow Cu(s) \\ \hline Zn(s) + Cu^{2+} & \rightarrow Zn^{2+}(aq) + Cu(s) \end{array}$$

The *electrochemical series* places metals in order of their reactivity. A metal which is above another in the electrochemical series (Table 3.2.1) will displace it from a solution of its salts. However, the metals above zinc will not precipitate from solutions of their salts. This is because they are so reactive that they react with water.

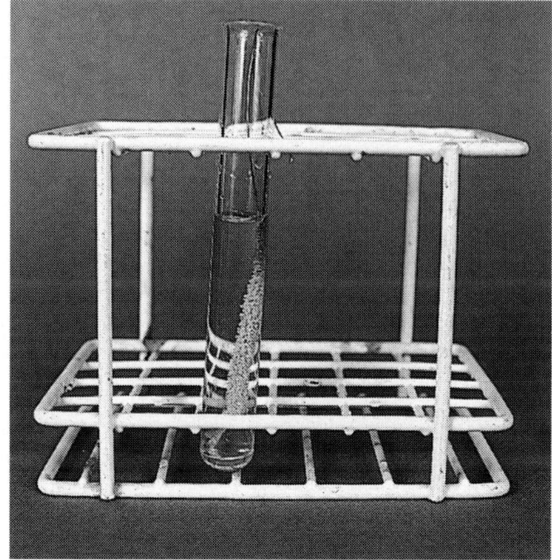

Figure 3.2.4 *Beautiful crystals of silver 'grow' on a piece of copper wire placed in a solution of silver nitrate. In fact, the copper dissolves as it is oxidised to copper(II) ions, while the silver ions are reduced to give metallic silver. Which is the more reactive metal: copper or silver?*

Table 3.2.1 The electrochemical series

Metal	Reactivity
potassium	highly reactive
calcium	↓
sodium	
magnesium	
aluminium	
zinc	decreasing reactivity
iron	
tin	
lead	
copper	
silver	↓
gold	unreactive

FOCUS
An acid and a base react to give a salt and water only.

Acid-base reactions

Acids are *neutralised* by **bases** to give solutions of salts, with water being the only other product of reaction:

acid + base → salt + water only

Here are two examples:

hydrochloric acid + magnesium oxide → magnesium chloride + water
$2HCl(aq) + MgO(s) \rightarrow MgCl_2(aq) + H_2O(l)$

nitric acid + sodium hydroxide → sodium nitrate + water
$HNO_3(aq) + NaOH(aq) \rightarrow NaNO_3(aq) + H_2O(l)$

Salts, page 103

Figure 3.2.5 The effect of adding zinc to copper(II) sulphate solution. Why does copper(II) sulphate solution lose its blue colour when powdered zinc is added to it?

Precipitation

Soluble salts dissolve in water to give solutions of their ions. For example, magnesium sulphate ($MgSO_4$) dissolves in water to give a solution of magnesium ions, $Mg^{2+}(aq)$, and sulphate ions, $SO_4^{2-}(aq)$. An insoluble salt such as barium sulphate, $BaSO_4$, will precipitate if two solutions containing barium ions and sulphate ions are mixed.

An example will help you to understand this process.

Silver chloride is insoluble in water. It can be prepared by mixing solutions containing silver ions, $Ag^+(aq)$, and chloride ions, $Cl^-(aq)$.

Silver nitrate is a silver salt which is soluble in water. It dissolves to give a solution containing silver ions, $Ag^+(aq)$, and nitrate ions, $NO_3^-(aq)$.

Sodium chloride is a soluble chloride. It dissolves in water to give a solution containing sodium ions, $Na^+(aq)$, and chloride ions, $Cl^-(aq)$.

When these solutions are mixed, silver chloride precipitates but the other ions remain in solution since sodium nitrate is soluble.

silver nitrate + sodium chloride → silver chloride + sodium nitrate
$AgNO_3(aq) + NaCl(aq) \rightarrow AgCl(s) + NaNO_3(aq)$

We can show this in terms of ions as follows:

$$Ag^+(aq) + NO_3^-(aq) + Na^+(aq) + Cl^-(aq) \rightarrow AgCl(s) + Na^+(aq) + NO_3^-(aq)$$

We can see that the sodium ions and nitrate ions are present in solution before and after the reaction. They are *spectator ions*. The equation simplifies to the following ionic equation:

$$Ag^+(aq) + Cl^-(aq) \rightarrow AgCl(s)$$

This has the advantage that it can be used to show the formation of silver chloride from any solution containing silver ions and chloride ions.

Esterification

An ester is formed when a *carboxylic acid* reacts with an *alcohol*. This type of reaction is called an esterification. The general word equation is

carboxylic acid + alcohol → ester + water

Here are two examples:

ethanoic acid + ethanol → ethyl ethanoate + water
$CH_3COOH + C_2H_5OH \rightarrow CH_3COOC_2H_5 + H_2O$

propanoic acid + methanol → methyl propanoate + water
$C_2H_5COOH + CH_3OH \rightarrow C_2H_5COOCH_3 + H_2O$

Be careful not to become confused. Looking at the equations may tempt you to think that this is an acid reacting with a base to give a salt and water. However, alcohols are not bases. They have none of the characteristic reactions of bases. So, esterification is not an acid-base reaction. Esters are not salts and do *not* consist of ions.

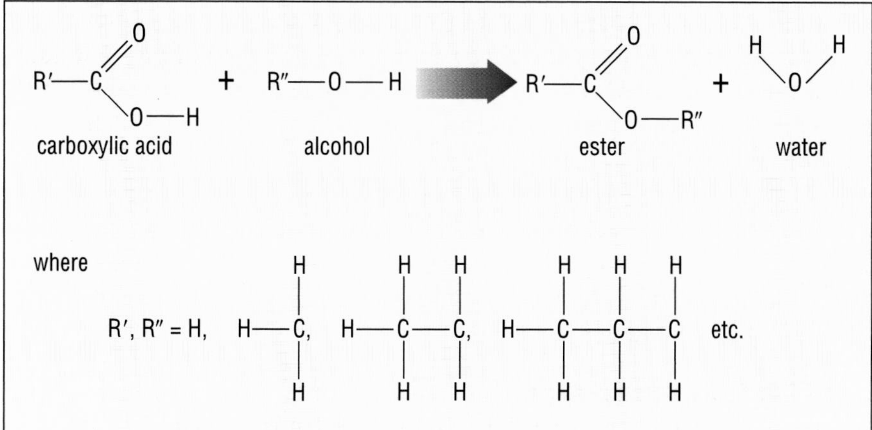

Figure 3.2.6 *The structures of carboxylic acids, alcohols and esters. Can you draw the structure of methyl propanoate?*

Table 3.2.2 Some simple carboxylic acids, alcohols and esters

Carboxylic acid	Alcohol	Ester
methanoic acid, $HCOOH$	methanol, CH_3OH	methyl methanoate, $HCOOCH_3$
methanoic acid, $HCOOH$	ethanol, C_2H_5OH	ethyl methanoate, $HCOOC_2H_5$
methanoic acid, $HCOOH$	propan-1-ol, C_3H_7OH	propyl methanoate, $HCOOC_3H_7$
ethanoic acid, CH_3COOH	methanol, CH_3OH	methyl ethanoate, CH_3COOCH_3
ethanoic acid, CH_3COOH	ethanol, C_2H_5OH	ethyl ethanoate, $CH_3COOC_2H_5$
ethanoic acid, CH_3COOH	propan-1-ol, C_3H_7OH	propyl ethanoate, $CH_3COOC_3H_7$
propanoic acid, C_2H_5COOH	methanol, CH_3OH	methyl propanoate, $C_2H_5COOCH_3$
propanoic acid, C_2H_5COOH	ethanol, C_2H_5OH	ethyl propanoate, $C_2H_5COOC_2H_5$
propanoic acid, C_2H_5COOH	propan-1-ol, C_3H_7OH	propyl propanoate, $C_2H_5COOC_3H_7$

Handling chemical substances during laboratory preparations

Measuring mass, page 18

Measuring out solids and liquids

Solids are measured out using an *electronic balance*. Usually you will need to weigh out reactants and products to the nearest 0.01 g.

Various pieces of glassware can be used to measure the volume of liquids. The glassware has a mark or marks on the side to indicate the volume. These marks are called *graduations*. The glassware to choose depends on the precision you require.

Some *beakers* have marks on the side to indicate rough volumes. These are very approximate and beakers should not be used to measure volumes of liquids. Volumes are usually best measured using a *measuring cylinder*. Various sizes are available and you should use the smallest one available that can hold the volume you need.

Transferring chemicals

Solids are handled using a spatula. They can be transferred a little at a time by gently tapping the spatula (see Figure 3.2.7). Remember:

- do not try to carry too much at a time
- keep the the two containers, between which the solid is being transferred, as close together as possible
- wash the spatula before putting it down on the laboratory bench (it is a good idea to lay a sheet of paper towel on part of the bench surface and to put freshly-washed apparatus on it).

Figure 3.2.7 Transferring a powder. Be careful not to touch the chemical with your hand and not to raise any dust which you might inhale.

Small quantities of a *liquid* may be transferred using a dropping pipette. Remember:

- do not try to transfer too much at a time
- keep the the two containers, between which the liquid is being transferred, as close as possible
- always keep the dropping pipette upright to avoid liquid going into the rubber bulb (this is not a problem if all-in-one polythene pipettes are used)
- wash the dropping pipette with distilled water before putting it into a test tube for storage.

Liquids are often poured from one container to another. To avoid the liquid going down the outside of the beaker it is sometimes useful to pour it down a glass rod (see Figure 3.2.8).

Reaction vessels

For many reactions which occur in aqueous solution, test tubes (for small quantities), beakers or conical flasks are suitable. Sizes depend on the

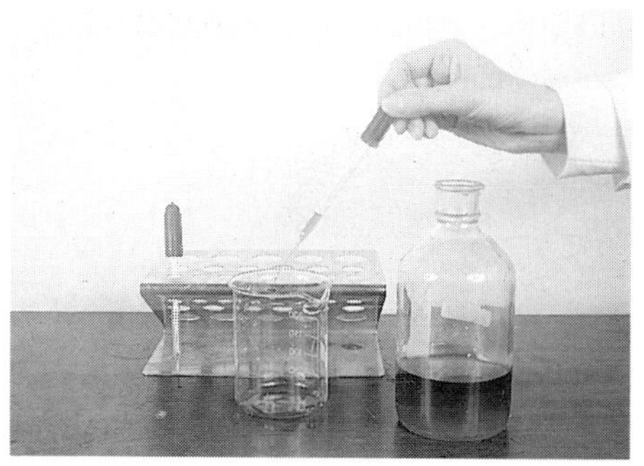

Figure 3.2.8 Using a dropping pipette and pouring a liquid from a beaker. Why should the dropping pipette be kept upright?

quantities being used. If the reaction mixture is to be heated, heat-resistant glassware must be used. This is marked 'Pyrex' or an equivalent trade name. Reaction vessels should not be more than a half to two-thirds full. Bear this in mind when choosing your apparatus.

Some reactions involve chemicals which we do not want to escape into the atmosphere. They may be flammable or hazardous in some other way. Apparatus with ground glass joints (*Quickfit glassware*) is useful here. They allow apparatus to be assembled and dismantled easily.

All Quickfit joints must be clean before assembly. Smear the clean joints with a very small quantity of vaseline before assembly. If joints stick together, do not panic – a gentle tap with a spatula often enables the joint to be worked free. If not, ask your supervisor for help.

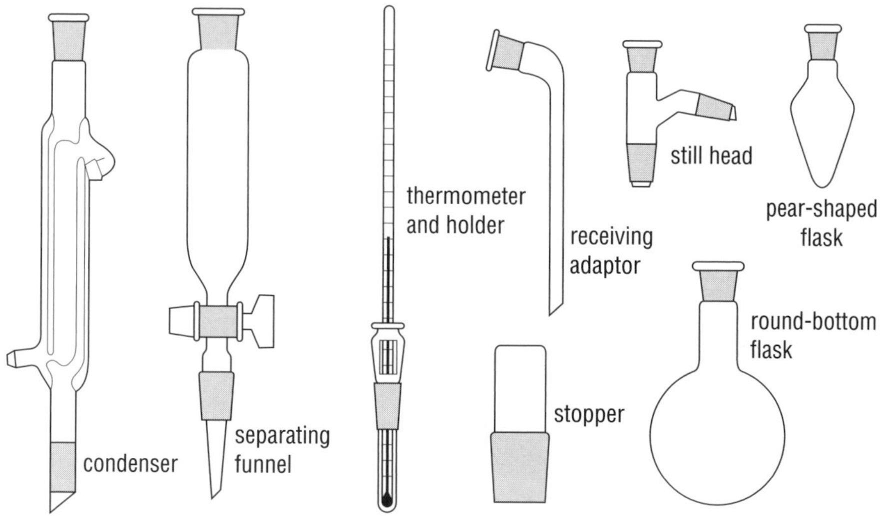

Figure 3.2.9 Some Quickfit apparatus which can be assembled in different ways to suit a particular purpose. Look at Figure 3.2.12. Which pieces of Quickfit are needed for this reflux?

It is often necessary to stir a reaction mixture. This can be done:

- manually (e.g. using a glass stirring rod)
- with a paddle stirrer driven by a motor (often useful if the liquid to be stirred is quite viscous)
- with a magnetic flea (a small magnet covered in a plastic sheath) driven by a rotating magnet outside the reaction vessel.

Figure 3.2.10 A magnetic flea is being used to stir this solution as dilute hydrochloric acid is added to a solution of lead nitrate. What precipitate is being produced? Write an ionic equation for the reaction.

Heating reaction mixtures

Test tubes containing aqueous solutions can be heated directly with a Bunsen burner.

The test tube should be held with a test tube holder and not with your fingers!

Small Bunsen burners, often called microburners, are available and should be used if possible. The test tube should be gently shaken while being heated. Beakers and conical flasks can be placed on a wire gauze supported by a tripod and heated with a Bunsen burner. A glass rod placed in the reaction mixture will help to avoid uneven boiling which can cause the mixture to 'bump'.

SAFETY: You should take these precautions:

- *wear eye protection*
- *do not fill test tubes more than one-fifth full*
- *use wide diameter boiling tubes in preference*
- *never heat a mixture in a sealed apparatus (unless very special precautions are taken). Sealed apparatus may explode if heated.*

Eye protection must be worn

WARNING

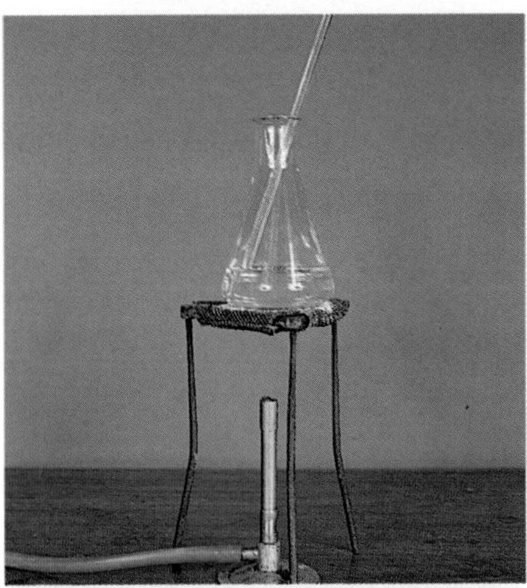

Figure 3.2.11 *Aqueous reaction mixtures in Pyrex conical flasks can be heated with a Bunsen burner. The flask should be placed on a gauze on top of a tripod. Use a glass rod to prevent bumping. How else could bumping be avoided?*

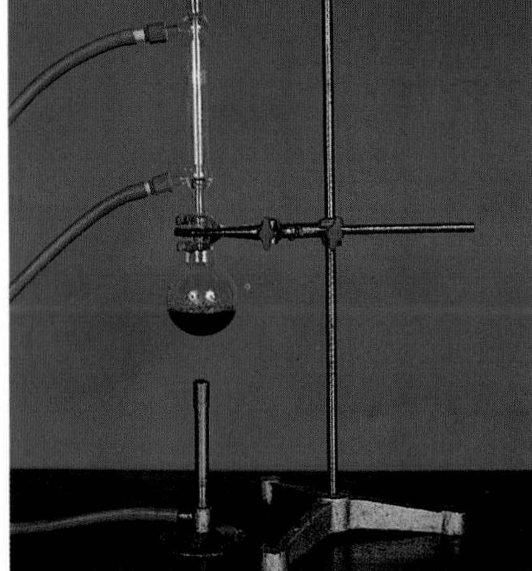

Figure 3.2.12 *Heating a reaction mixture in Quickfit glassware. Vapour from the boiling liquid condenses and is returned to the reaction vessel (the round-bottom flask). This process is called reflux. Anti-bumping granules should be used. What would happen if a condenser was not used?*

Separating and purifying products from reaction mixtures

The product of a chemical reaction must be separated from a reaction mixture and then purified. There are a number of important techniques that you need to know about:

- crystallisation
- decantation
- filtration and centrifuging
- distillation.

Figure 3.2.13 *Blue copper(II) sulphate crystallises from solution when water is removed by evaporation. How could you best obtain large crystals?*

FOCUS

A solution consists of a solute dissolved in a solvent. A solution of a solute, such as a salt, in water is called an aqueous solution.

Crystallisation

A dissolved solid (e.g. a soluble salt) can be obtained from **aqueous solution** by crystallisation. The solution is heated gently to evaporate water. When crystals begin to appear, heating should be stopped. As the mixture cools, crystals will continue to form. This is because solid compounds are usually less soluble in cold water than in hot water. The crystals can be isolated by filtration.

If you are not in a hurry, the solution can be left to evaporate slowly at room temperature. The slower the rate of evaporation, the larger the crystals that form.

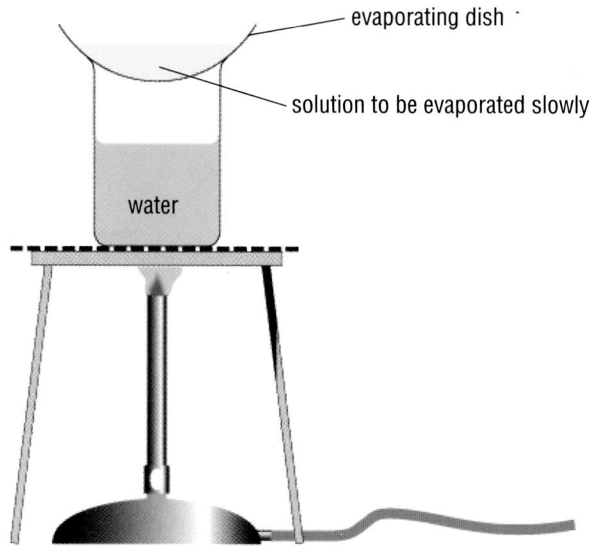

Figure 3.2.14 *A solution can be evaporated slowly using this apparatus.*

Decantation

Sometimes a solid settles to the bottom of a reaction mixture. In this case, the bulk of the liquid can be poured off, taking care not to disturb the solid. This process of separation is called **decantation**. Alternatively, a dropping pipette can be used to remove the liquid from above the solid that has settled out. You need to be careful not to put the pipette in too far and disturb the solid.

> FOCUS
>
> **A mixture of a solid and a liquid is called a suspension. Allow the solid to settle before trying to separate the mixture (e.g. by decantation or filtration).**

Filtration and centrifuging

A solid (e.g. a precipitate which forms, or excess unreacted solid) can be separated from a reaction mixture by **filtration**. A filter funnel and filter paper are used. (See Figure 3.2.15 below)

Filtration of very finely divided solids can be very slow. Suction filtration can be the answer (see Figure 3.2.17 on following page). Alternatively, a centrifuge can be used. The mixture is placed in a centrifuge tube which is placed in the centrifuge. The tube is spun round very fast, forcing the solid to the bottom of the tube. The liquid can then be decanted or removed using a dropping pipette.

> FOCUS
>
> **The liquid which passes through a filter paper is the filtrate. The solid which remains on the filter paper is the residue.**

Figure 3.2.15 *Filtration. Fold a filter paper and place in a funnel. Pour the contents of the beaker into the folded filter paper. Wash through using a squeezy bottle containing distilled water.*

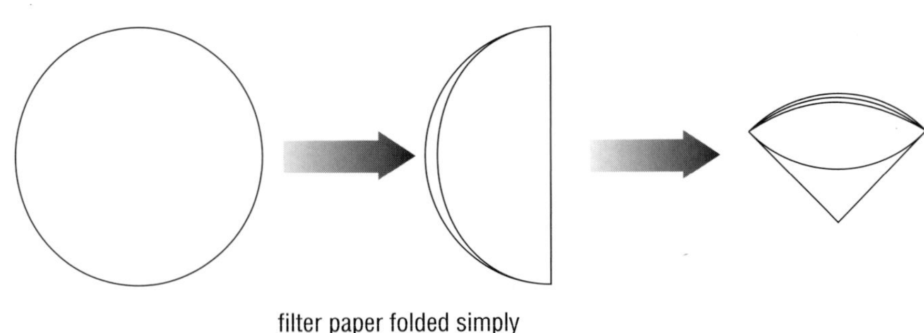

folding a fluted filter paper

Figure 3.2.16 Faster filtration can be achieved using a fluted filter paper rather than one which has been folded simply. Why do you think this is?

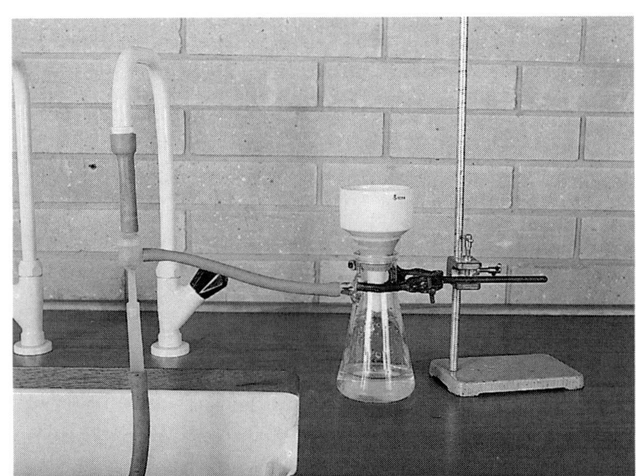

Figure 3.2.17 Suction filtration. Connect the filtration flask to a water pump. Place a piece of filter paper in the funnel. Wet it to bed it down. Turn the pump on to draw the liquid through the filter paper.

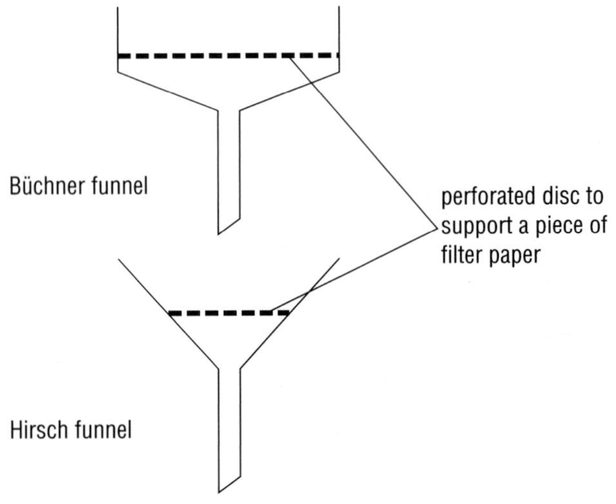

Figure 3.2.18 Büchner and Hirsch funnels for use in suction filtration. When do you think it is preferable to use a Hirsch funnel rather than a Büchner?

Distillation
A liquid can be obtained from a reaction mixture by distillation. Aqueous solutions can be heated with a Bunsen burner to obtain the water. However, a heating mantle or water bath should be used where flammable liquids are involved.

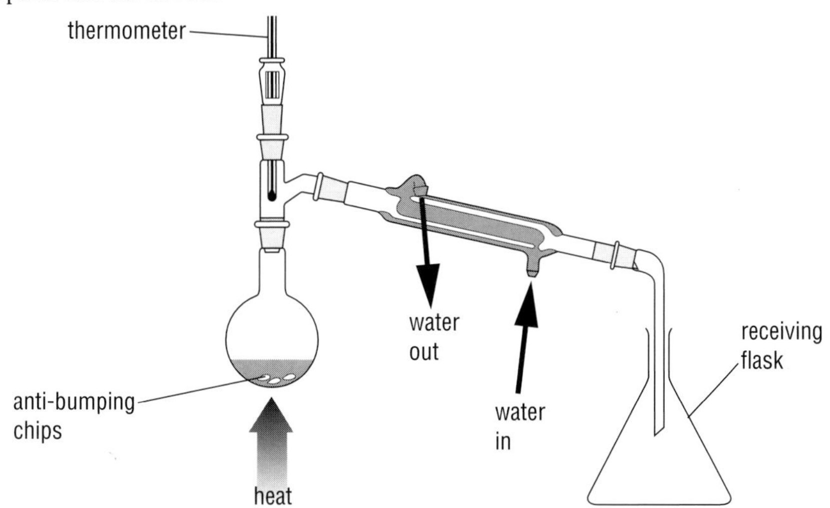

Figure 3.2.19 Simple distillation. Place the mixture in a flask with a few anti-bumping chips. Heat gently to raise the temperature slowly. Keep the liquid boiling smoothly and collect the liquid as it distils over.

Obtaining metals from their compounds

Metals are obtained from their compounds by redox reactions. Two types are useful:

- the reduction of metal oxides, that is, the removal of oxygen from the oxide to leave the metal
- the displacement of one metal from a solution of its ions by another metal which is more reactive, that is, the transfer of electrons from the reactive metal to the ions of the less reactive metal.

Redox reactions, page 138

Reduction of metal oxides

The oxygen can be removed from some metal oxides by heating the oxide with carbon. Carbon dioxide forms as well as the metal. This reaction is used industrially to extract iron, zinc and lead from their ores. Hydrogen and carbon monoxide are also capable of removing the oxygen, as water and carbon dioxide respectively. However, these are more difficult to use in the laboratory: hydrogen forms an explosive mixture with air; carbon monoxide is poisonous.

The procedure for reducing a metal oxide with carbon is given below. The reduction using hydrogen or carbon monoxide is described *but you are advised not to try this in the laboratory*.

Procedure

Obtaining metals: reduction of a metal oxide by carbon

Mix a powdered sample of the metal oxide and carbon thoroughly. Place in a Pyrex glass test tube. Heat strongly with a Bunsen burner, beginning at one end of the mixture and slowly working along as the reaction proceeds. Determine the actual yield of the metal obtained by weighing the product. However, this may not be possible unless you have been able to remove any unreacted metal oxide or carbon, and this is not always straightforward.

Eye protection must be worn

HARMFUL many metal oxides

Requirements

- ❒ Pyrex test tube
- ❒ Bunsen burner suitable for media used
- ❒ Heat-resistant mat

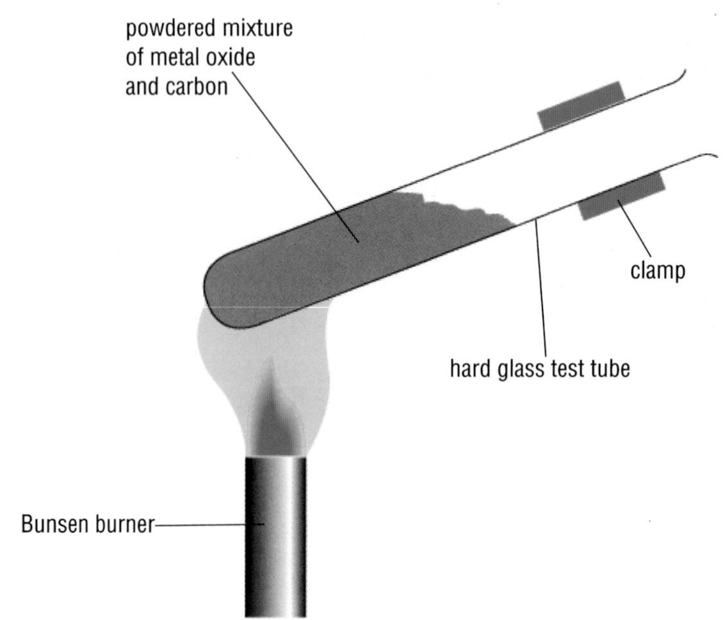

Figure 3.2.20 *Reducing a metal oxide with carbon.*

Reduction of a metal oxide by hydrogen or carbon monoxide

SAFETY: *Do not carry out this practical.*

The metal oxide is put in a porcelain boat which is placed in a thick-walled glass tube. The gas (hydrogen or carbon monoxide) is passed through the tube. A Bunsen burner is used to heat the tube and its contents strongly, beginning at one end of the mixture in the boat and slowly working along as the reaction proceeds. The tube is allowed to cool before turning off the gas supply. The actual yield of the metal obtained is determined by weighing the product.

Figure 3.2.21 *Some metal oxides can be reduced (oxygen removed) by hydrogen or carbon monoxide. Why would you expect to see water droplets forming at the cool end of the reaction tube when hydrogen is used as the reducing agent?*

Displacement reactions

This involves one metal (X) being displaced from a solution of one of its salts by a more reactive metal (Y).

Procedure

Obtaining metals: displacement reactions from solution of salts

1. Dissolve a salt of X in distilled water. Add the required quantity of metal Y. This quantity is calculated so that it is just less than that needed to completely displace metal X.
2. Stir the reaction mixture for 10 minutes or so. Some mixtures may need warming (check with your supervisor).
3. Separate metal X from the reaction mixture by filtration. Wash well with distilled water.
4. Dry in an oven at about 110°C for 2 hours.
5. Determine the actual yield of the metal obtained by weighing the product.

Requirements

- ❒ Test tube or small beaker
- ❒ Glass stirring rod
- ❒ Filtration apparatus (either normal or suction filtration)
- ❒ Oven

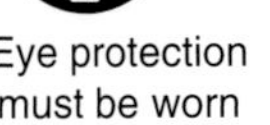

Eye protection must be worn

TOXIC
lead nitrate
silver

OXIDISING
lead nitrate
silver nitrate
zinc nitrate

HARMFUL
copper(II) sulphate
copper(II) nitrate

Table 3.2.3 Quantities for some displacement reactions

(a) Lead from reaction of lead nitrate with zinc:
lead nitrate 3.3 g, zinc 0.6 g

(b) Copper from copper(II) sulphate and zinc:
copper(II) sulphate 2.5 g, zinc 0.6 g

(c) Silver from silver nitrate and copper:
silver nitrate 1.7 g, copper 0.6 g

Other quantities can be used provided they are in the same proportions.

Preparing salts

The method to use depends on whether or not the salt is soluble in water (Table 3.2.4).

Table 3.2.4 The solubility of acids, bases and salts

	Soluble	Insoluble
Acids	all common acids	
Bases	sodium hydroxide, potassium hydroxide, calcium hydroxide (slightly soluble), ammonia	all other metal oxides and hydroxides
Salts	all nitrates	
	all chlorides, except	silver chloride, lead chloride
	all sulphates, except	barium sulphate, lead sulphate, calcium sulphate (slightly soluble)
	sodium carbonate, potassium carbonate	all other carbonates

Making salts by acid-base reactions

If the salt you want to make is soluble, there is a choice of three general reactions which can be used to prepare it. The correct acid (e.g. sulphuric acid if you want to make a sulphate, nitric acid if you want a nitrate, and so on) can be reacted with:

- a reactive metal (e.g. magnesium, zinc, iron) to give a salt + hydrogen
- a carbonate to give a salt + carbon dioxide + water
- a base to give a salt + water only (called an *acid-base* reaction).

Acid-base reactions, page 140

The procedure for the preparation of a salt from an acid and an insoluble base is given below. This procedure can be used to prepare a salt from any of these reactions provided the metal, oxide or carbonate being used does not react with water.

When reacting an acid with an insoluble base, you should use excess of the base. Since the salt is soluble, the excess base can be removed by filtration and the salt crystallised from the filtrate.

When reacting an acid with an alkali (a soluble base), an indicator is used to identify when just sufficient quantity of the acid has been used.

Procedure

Preparation of salts by an acid-base reaction

1 Acid and insoluble base

1. Place the dilute acid in a suitable-sized beaker, together with a glass rod to prevent the solution from 'bumping' when it is heated.
2. Put the beaker on a wire gauze supported by a tripod. Heat gently with a Bunsen burner.
3. Add the insoluble base a little at a time, stirring between additions, until no more solid dissolves (you will be able to see the excess).
4. Filter the hot solution through a folded filter paper and collect the filtrate in an evaporating dish.
5. Place the dish on a wire gauze supported on a tripod. Heat gently with a Bunsen burner until the crystals begin to appear. Put the dish to one side and allow to cool. The salt will crystallise.
6. Separate the crystals by filtration under reduced pressure and place in a desiccator for at least 24 hours to dry.
7. Determine the actual yield of the salt obtained by weighing the product.

Requirements

- ❒ Beaker
- ❒ Glass stirring rod
- ❒ Tripod, gauze, Bunsen burner, heat-resistant mat
- ❒ Evaporating basin
- ❒ Filtration apparatus (either normal or suction filtration)
- ❒ Oven

Eye protection must be worn

HARMFUL copper(II) chloride

IRRITANT dilute hydrochloric acid

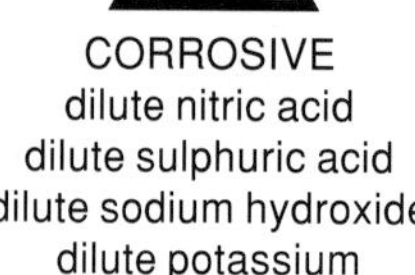

CORROSIVE dilute nitric acid dilute sulphuric acid dilute sodium hydroxide dilute potassium hydroxide

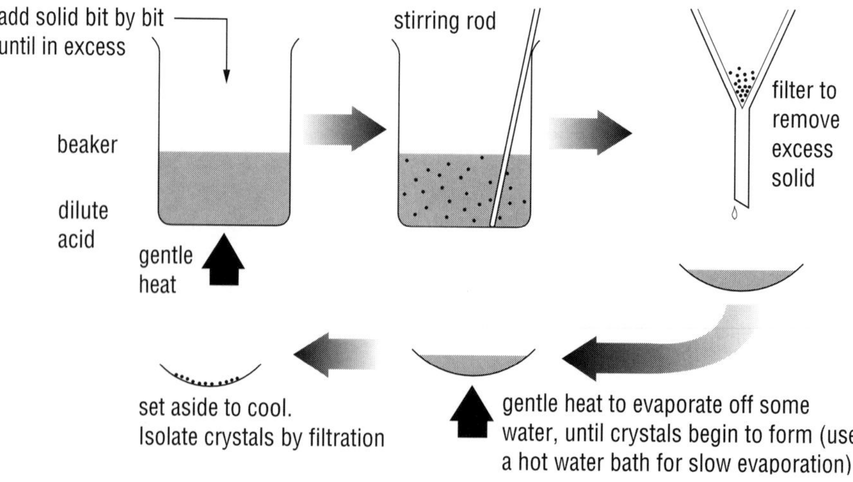

Figure 3.2.22 *Preparing a salt.*

Table 3.2.5 Details for the preparation of some salts using insoluble oxides

The quantity of oxide is a little more than is required for complete reaction; it does not matter if rather more then the quantities given here is used.

Name of oxide	Mass of oxide	Name of acid	Quantity of acid
magnesium oxide	2.8 g	hydrochloric acid	20 cm^3
magnesium oxide	2.8 g	nitric acid	20 cm^3
magnesium oxide	2.8 g	sulphuric acid	10 cm^3
copper(II) oxide	4.9 g	hydrochloric acid	20 cm^3
copper(II) oxide	4.9 g	nitric acid	20 cm^3
copper(II) oxide	4.9 g	sulphuric acid	10 cm^3
zinc oxide	5 g	hydrochloric acid	20 cm^3
zinc oxide	5 g	nitric acid	20 cm^3
zinc oxide	5 g	sulphuric acid	10 cm^3

Note. In each case the concentration of the acid is 2 mol dm^{-3}.

2 Acid and alkali (soluble base)

1 Place the dilute acid in a burette and the alkali in a conical flask (use a safety filler if a pipette is used).
2 Add the acid a little at a time, mixing the contents of the flask thoroughly between additions. After each addition use the glass rod to put a drop of solution on a piece of Universal indicator paper. Initially the paper turns blue. When nearly enough acid has been added the paper will turn green. At this stage add the acid more slowly, a few drops at a time. Stop when the paper turns yellow.
3 Pour the solution from the conical flask into an evaporating dish. Place the dish on a wire gauze supported on a tripod. Heat gently with a Bunsen burner until the crystals begin to appear. Put the dish to one side and allow to cool. The salt will crystallise.
4 Separate the crystals by filtration under reduced pressure and place in a desiccator for at least 24 hours to dry.
5 Determine the actual yield of the salt obtained by weighing the product.

Requirements

- ❒ Burette
- ❒ Conical flask
- ❒ Pipette and safety filler
- ❒ Glass rod
- ❒ Evaporating basin
- ❒ Tripod, gauze, Bunsen burner, heat-resistant mat
- ❒ Suction filtration apparatus
- ❒ Desiccator

Eye protection must be worn

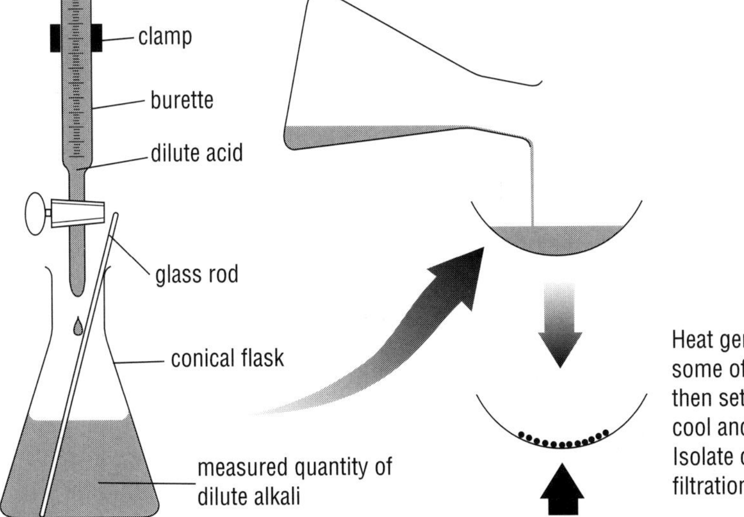

Figure 3.2.23 Preparing a salt with an acid and a soluble base.

Table 3.2.6 Salt preparations from dilute acids and dilute alkalis

All laboratory 'dilute' acids and alkalis are 2 mol dm^{-3}
10 cm^3 hydrochloric acid reacts with about 10 cm^3 sodium hydroxide; 10 cm^3 potassium hydroxide; 10 cm^3 ammonia
10 cm^3 nitric acid reacts with about 10 cm^3 sodium hydroxide; 10 cm^3 potassium hydroxide; 10 cm^3 ammonia
10 cm^3 sulphuric acid reacts with about 20 cm^3 sodium hydroxide; 20 cm^3 potassium hydroxide; 20 cm^3 ammonia

Making salts by precipitation reactions

Precipitation, page140

Insoluble salts can be prepared by precipitation reactions. Aqueous solutions of two soluble salts are mixed. One contains the appropriate metal ion and the other contains the appropriate anion. The insoluble salt forms as a precipitate.

Table 3.2.7 Insoluble salts and their reactants

Insoluble salt	Reactants
Silver chloride Silver bromide Silver iodide	silver nitrate + any soluble chloride silver nitrate + any soluble bromide silver nitrate + any soluble iodide
Lead chloride Lead bromide Lead iodide	lead nitrate + any soluble chloride lead nitrate + any soluble bromide lead nitrate + any soluble iodide
Barium sulphate Lead sulphate	barium chloride + any soluble sulphate lead nitrate + any soluble sulphate
Metal carbonates	soluble metal salt + sodium carbonate or sodium hydrogencarbonate (**Note.** This is not always straightforward as sometimes a 'basic carbonate' – a mixed carbonate and hydroxide – is precipitated; this is less likely with sodium hydrogencarbonate.)

Requirements

- ❒ Test tube
- ❒ Dropping pipette
- ❒ Glass rod
- ❒ Centrifuge
- ❒ Oven

Eye protection must be worn

CORROSIVE silver nitrate

IRRITANT silver nitrate

TOXIC lead nitrate

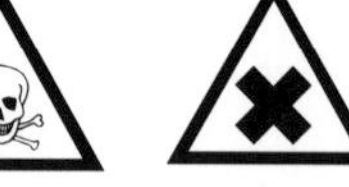

HARMFUL barium chloride

Procedure

Preparation of insoluble salts by precipitation reactions

1. Place a solution of the salt containing the required metal ion in a test tube.
2. Use a dropping pipette to add a solution of the salt containing the required anion (e.g. $SO_4^{2-}(aq)$, $NO_3^-(aq)$, $Cl^-(aq)$). Continue adding until no more precipitate appears to be forming.
3. Centrifuge the mixture. Now add 1 drop of the solution of the salt containing the required anion to check that precipitation is complete. If a precipitate forms, continue to add the solution until no more appears. Centrifuge and test again.
4. When all the insoluble salt has precipitated, centrifuge once more. Carefully remove the clear solution above the precipitate using a dropping pipette. Now add half a test tube of water, stir well and centrifuge. Repeat this process one more time to ensure that the solid has been thoroughly washed.

5 Place the test tube in an oven at 110°C for 2-3 hours to dry. Remove from the oven, using tongs, and place in a desiccator to cool.
6 Determine the actual yield of the salt obtained by weighing the product.

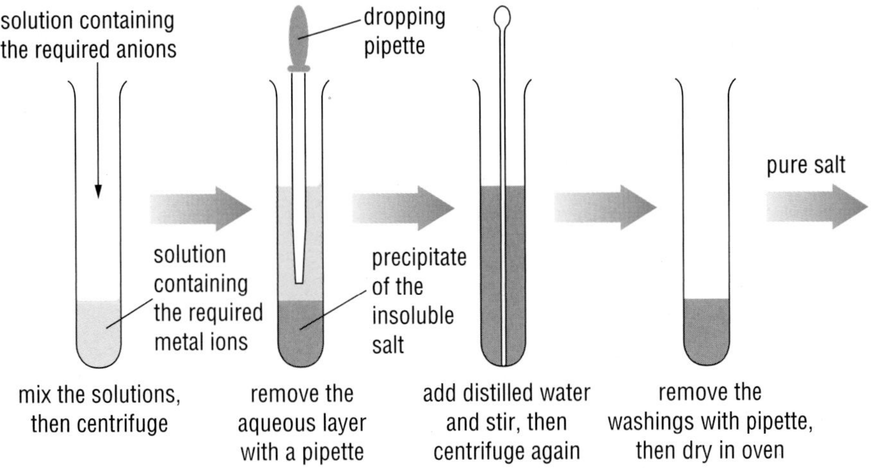

Figure 3.2.24 *Preparation of an insoluble salt.*

Preparing esters

Esters are made by reacting a carboxylic acid with an alcohol. Concentrated sulphuric acid is needed to speed up the reaction.

 Esterification, page 140

Procedure

Preparation of an ester

1 Place *x* cm^3 of the alcohol and *y* cm^3 of the carboxylic acid in a 50 cm^3 round-bottom Quickfit flask. Mix well and add a few anti-bumping granules.
2 Set up the apparatus for reflux (Figure 3.2.25). Use a dropping pipette to add 5 cm^3 concentrated sulphuric acid a little at a time through the condenser. Swirl the contents of the flask to mix them. Keep the flask cool by occasionally running cold water over it.
3 Reflux the mixture gently for 30 minutes using a water bath.
4 Allow to cool and then rearrange the apparatus for distillation (see Figure 3.2.19). Heat the flask on a gauze using a small bunsen burner flame. Continue until the thermometer is reading 85 °C.
5 Place the distillate in a separating funnel. Add 5 cm^3 sodium carbonate solution to remove acid remaining in the reaction mixture. Swirl the contents of the funnel until any effervescence stops. Stopper the funnel, shake and allow the mixture to settle. When shaking, periodically invert the separating funnel and hold the stopper in place with the palm of your hand (Figure 3.2.26). Then open the tap to reduce the pressure. The ester is the top layer. Remove the stopper and run out the bottom layer. Repeat the process using firstly 5 cm^3 of concentrated calcium chloride solution and, secondly, 5 cm^3 of distilled water. Each time, discard the lower layer.
6 Put the 'clean' sample of ester in a small flask and add 2–3 pieces of anhydrous calcium chloride. Stopper the flask and leave overnight.
7 Decant the dried ester into a 50 cm^3 pear shaped Quickfit flask and distil. Collect the liquid which distils at a particular temperature range (check with your supervisor) in a weighed sample tube.
8 Determine the yield of ester.

Requirements

- ❒ 50 cm^3 round bottom Quickfit flask
- ❒ Apparatus for reflux
- ❒ Separating funnel
- ❒ 50 cm^3 pear-shaped Quickfit flask
- ❒ Apparatus for simple distillation

Eye protection must be worn

HIGHLY FLAMMABLE
ethanol
ethyl ethanoate

FLAMMABLE
all alcohols
all esters

CORROSIVE
conc. sulphuric acid
all carboxylic acids

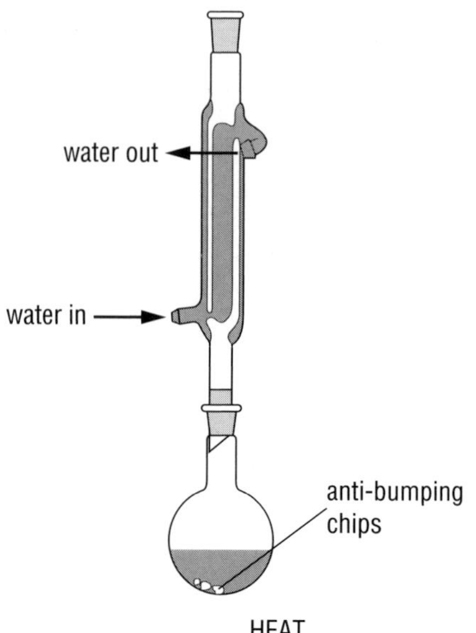

Figure 3.2.25 Apparatus for reflux.

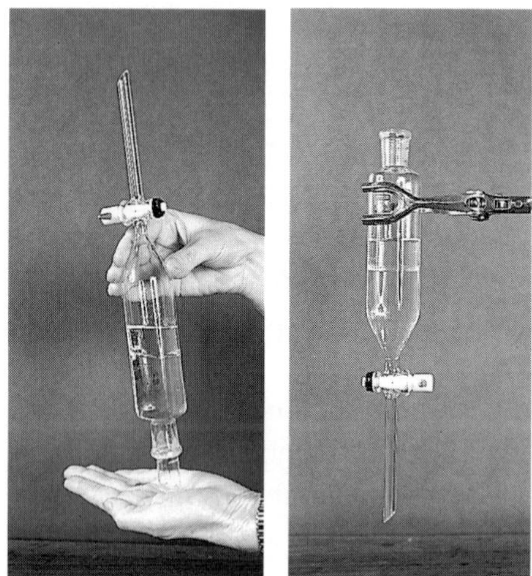

Figure 3.2.26 Using a separating funnel.

The mole: the scientist's counting unit, page 12

FOCUS

Converting quantities and amounts:
***n* = amount of substance / mol**
***m* = mass of substance / g**
***M* = molar mass / g mol^{-1}**

$n = \frac{m}{M}$ $m = nM$

Table 3.2.8 Quantities to be used in the preparation of esters

Ester	Alcohol	x/cm^3	Carboxylic acid	y/cm^3
ethyl ethanoate	ethanol	12	ethanoic acid	8
propyl ethanoate	propan-1-ol	15	ethanoic acid	8
butyl ethanoate	butan-1-ol	18	ethanoic acid	8
methyl propanoate	methanol	8	propanoic acid	10
ethyl propanoate	ethanol	12	propanoic acid	10
propyl propanoate	propan-1-ol	15	propanoic acid	10
butyl propanoate	butan-1-ol	18	propanoic acid	10
methyl butanoate	methanol	8	butanoic acid	13
ethyl butanoate	ethanol	12	butanoic acid	13
propyl butanoate	propan-1-ol	15	butanoic acid	13
butyl butanoate	butan-1-ol	18	butanoic acid	13

Notes:
(a) Methyl methanoate, methyl ethanoate and ethyl ethanoate are too soluble in water to be obtained by this method.
(b) Other esters may be made by this procedure. For quantities, check with your supervisor.

Determining yields

The mass of a product obtained from a chemical reaction is found by weighing it. But how much might you have obtained?

The *theoretical yield* is the maximum quantity of a compound that could be formed in a reaction from known quantities of starting materials. It may be calculated if the balanced chemical equation for the reaction is known. The following sequence can be used:

1. Write the balanced equation for the reaction.
2. **Convert** mass of reactant into amount of substance (moles).
3. Use the balanced chemical equation to work out the amount of product that could be formed.
4. Convert back from amount of product to mass of product.

For example, calculate the mass of copper that could be formed from 7.95 g copper(II) oxide: (A_r[Cu] = 63.5, A_r[O] = 16).

1 Equation for the reaction:

$$CuO(s) + H_2(g) \rightarrow Cu(s) + H_2O(l)$$

2 M[CuO] = 63.5 + 16 = 79.5 g mol^{-1}

Using $n = m/M$, amount of CuO = $\frac{7.95}{79.5}$ = 0.1 mol

3 From the equation, 1 mol CuO gives 1 mol Cu
Therefore, 0.1 mol CuO yields 0.1 mol Cu

4 Using $m = nM$, mass of Cu = 0.1 × 63.5 = 6.35 g
Therefore, 7.95 g of copper(II) oxide can give 6.35 g of copper.

Here is a second example. Calculate the mass of silver chloride that could be obtained from 1.70 g of silver nitrate when an excess of dilute hydrochloric acid is added.

(A_r[Ag] = 108, A_r[S] = 32, A_r[O] = 16, A_r[Cl] = 35.5, A_r[N] = 14)

1 Equation for the reaction:

$AgNO_3(aq) + HCl(aq) \rightarrow AgCl(s) + HNO_3(aq)$

2 M[$AgNO_3$] = 108 + 14 + (3 × 16) = 170 g mol^{-1}

Using $n = m/M$, amount of $AgNO_3 = \frac{1.70}{170} = 0.01$ mol

3 From the equation, 1 mol $AgNO_3$ gives 1 mol AgCl
Therefore, 0.01 mol $AgNO_3$ yields 0.01 mol AgCl

4 M[AgCl] = 108 + 35.5 = 143.5 g mol^{-1}
Using $m = nM$, mass of AgCl = 0.01 × 143.5 = 1.435 g
Therefore, 1.70 g silver nitrate can give 1.435 g silver chloride

You need to be careful when **calculating** the theoretical yield of a soluble salt. This is because they usually crystallise with water of crystallisation. Yet the balanced equation does not show this.
For example,

copper(II) oxide + sulphuric acid → copper(II) sulphate + water
$CuO(s) + H_2SO_4(aq) \rightarrow CuSO_4(aq) + H_2O(l)$

But copper(II) sulphate crystallises as $CuSO_4.5H_2O(s)$. One mole of copper(II) oxide gives one mole of solid copper(II) sulphate-5-water.

Using A_r[Cu] = 63.5, A_r[S] = 32, A_r[O] = 16, A_r[H] = 1:

M[CuO] = 63.5 + 16 = 79.5 g mol^{-1}
M[$CuSO_4.5H_2O$] = 63.5 + 32 + (4 × 16) + 5[(2 × 1) + 16] = 249.5 g mol^{-1}

Therefore, 7.95 copper(II) oxide could give 24.95 g copper(II) sulphate-5-water.

The *actual yield* is the quantity obtained in a preparation. This is found by simply weighing the product obtained. (It is important to be sure that it is dry before weighing.)

The percentage yield is given by the formula:

$$\text{percentage yield} = \frac{\text{actual yield}}{\text{theoretical yield}} \times 100\%$$

For example, suppose that the actual yield of copper from 7.95 g copper(II) oxide was 5.92 g. As we showed above, the theoretical yield is 6.35 g.

Therefore, the percentage yield = $\frac{5.92}{6.35} \times 100 = 93.2\%$

FOCUS

The molar mass, *M*, of a substance can be calculated by adding the relative atomic masses (A_r) of all atoms present. For example:

***M*[KCl] = 39.1 + 35.5 = 74.6 g mol^{-1}**
***M*[$CuCO_3$] = 63.5 + 12 + (3 x 16) = 123.5 g mol^{-1}**
***M*[$Na_2CO_3.10H_2O$] = (2 x 23) + 12 + (3 x 16) + 10[(2 x 1) + 16] = 286 g mol^{-1}**

A_r[K] = 39.1, A_r[Cl] = 35.5, A_r[Cu] = 63.5, A_r[C] = 12, A_r[O] = 16, A_r[H] = 1, A_r[Na] = 23

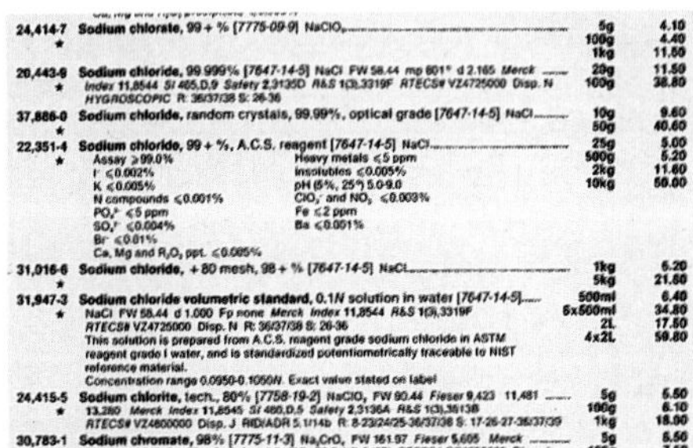

24,414-7 ★	**Sodium chlorate,** 99+% [7775-09-9] $NaClO_3$	5g 100g 1kg	4.10 4.40 11.60
20,443-6 ★	**Sodium chloride,** 99.999% [7647-14-5] NaCl FW 58.44 mp 801° d 2.165 *Merck Index* 11,8544 *SI* 465,D,9 *Safety* 2,3135D *R&S* 1(3),3319F *RTECS#* VZ4725000 Disp. N *HYGROSCOPIC* R: 36/37/38 S: 26-36	20g 100g	11.50 38.80
37,886-0 ★	**Sodium chloride,** random crystals, 99.99%, optical grade [7647-14-5] NaCl	10g 50g	9.60 40.60
22,351-4 ★	**Sodium chloride,** 99+%, A.C.S. reagent [7647-14-5] NaCl Assay ≥99.0%; Heavy metals ≤5 ppm; I^- ≤0.002%; insolubles ≤0.005%; K ≤0.005%; pH (5%, 25°) 5.0-9.0; N compounds ≤0.001%; ClO_3^- and NO_3^- ≤0.003%; PO_4^{3-} ≤5 ppm; Fe ≤2 ppm; SO_4^{2-} ≤0.004%; Ba ≤0.001%; Br^- ≤0.01%; Ca, Mg and R_2O_3 ppt. ≤0.005%	25g 500g 2kg 10kg	5.00 5.20 11.60 50.00
31,016-6 ★	**Sodium chloride,** +80 mesh, 98+% [7647-14-5] NaCl	1kg 5kg	6.20 21.60
31,947-3 ★	**Sodium chloride volumetric standard,** 0.1*N* solution in water [7647-14-5] NaCl FW 58.44 d 1.000 Fp none *Merck Index* 11,8544 *R&S* 1(3),3319F *RTECS#* VZ4725000 Disp. N R: 36/37/38 S: 26-36 This solution is prepared from A.C.S. reagent grade sodium chloride in ASTM reagent grade I water, and is standardized potentiometrically traceable to NIST reference material. Concentration range 0.0950-0.1050*N*. Exact value stated on label	500ml 6x500ml 2L 4x2L	6.40 34.80 17.50 59.80
24,415-5 ★	**Sodium chlorite,** tech., 80% [7758-19-2] $NaClO_2$ FW 90.44 *Fieser* 9,423 11,481 13,280 *Merck Index* 11,8545 *SI* 460,D,5 *Safety* 2,3136A *R&S* 1(3),3613B *RTECS#* VZ4800000 Disp. J RID/ADR 5.1/14b R: 8-23/24/25-36/37/38 S: 17-26-27-36/37/39	5g 100g 1kg	5.50 6.10 18.00
30,783-1 ★	**Sodium chromate,** 98% [7775-11-3] Na_2CrO_4 FW 161.97 *Fieser* 5,605 *Merck Index* 11,8547 *SI* 477,A,9 *Safety* 2,3136B *R&S* 1(3),3467I *RTECS#* GB2955000 Disp. J	5g 100g	5.50 7.50

Figure 3.2.27 *This extract from a chemical supplier's catalogue shows how the cost of a chemical depends on the purity required and the quantity purchased.*

The cost of obtaining pure substances by chemical reaction

You will need to think about each of the following when deciding how much it costs to make a chemical in the laboratory:

- raw materials
- energy
- labour
- equipment.

Raw materials

The raw materials include the starting compound, other reactants and any other chemicals required. When costing a preparation, make a check list of the raw materials and the quantities of each that are used.

To find the costs, look in a chemical supplier's catalogue. The prices vary from one supplier to another. The cost of a chemical depends on its purity and the quantity bought. For example, solid compounds are often available in quantities such as 50 g, 100 g, 250 g, 500 g and 1000 g (1 kg). Similarly, liquids can often be bought in quantities such as 100 cm^3, 500 cm^3, 1000 cm^3 (1 dm^3) and 2 dm^3. You will need to calculate the cost of the actual quantity that you used.

Energy

The major use of energy is for heating. This may be gas or electrical heating. To estimate the cost you will need to find out how much a unit of electricity costs and how many units are consumed in the process. Similar calculations are necessary for any gas used. In your homes, these are recorded on gas and electricity meters.

Labour

Often the most expensive part of any preparation is the labour. Labour will include the time of people undertaking the preparation, as well as the time of support staff such as office workers and cleaners. To estimate the cost you will need to find out about typical wages and salaries.

Equipment

The same procedure applies as for raw materials: look in a supplier's catalogue. Of course, any apparatus will be available for you to use again (provided you don't break it!). Even so it is usual to build in something for depreciation (that is the decrease in value due to wear and tear). The amount that it depreciates depends on how many times it can reasonably be expected to be used. As a rule of thumb you could take this to be 1–2% of the purchase price.

Case study

FOOD ADDITIVES, SALTS AND E NUMBERS

Some chemicals are added to food even though they have little or no nutritional value. They serve two main purposes:

- as preservatives and antioxidants which prevent food from deteriorating
- as additives which enhance the texture, flavour or appearance of food.

Many of these chemicals are salts, most commonly of calcium, magnesium, potassium and sodium. Sodium chloride, NaCl, has been added to food for thousands of years to enhance flavour and to preserve it. The expressions 'salt of the earth' and 'worth his salt' reflect this importance.

The addition of chemicals to food is strictly controlled. The European Community (EC) publishes a list of chemicals which have undergone exhaustive tests and are generally considered to be safe. The list is reviewed regularly with some chemicals being removed and others added. Each approved chemical is given an 'E number'.

Illustration 1 *The label on this packet of soup shows the ingredients.*

In the UK, food manufacturers are required by law to show a list of additives on their products, either by the E numbers or by the actual names. Usually the ingredients are listed in descending order of the quantity present.

E100 to E180 are additives that may be used to colour food. Many of these are substances which occur naturally. For example, chlorophyll (E140) is extracted from nettles and grass. It is used to colour food green. One of the few salts used for colour is white calcium carbonate (E170).

E200 to E290 are preservatives. Three important ones are sodium sulphite (E221), sodium nitrite (E250) and sodium nitrate (E251). All are salts of the so-called mineral acids. Some carboxylic acids and their salts are also used. For example benzoic acid (E210) and its salts sodium benzoate (E211), potassium benzoate (E212) and calcium benzoate (E213). The calcium salt of propanoic acid is also used. It is E282.

E300 to E321 are anti-oxidants. One of the most common is vitamin C (E300) which occurs naturally in fresh fruit and vegetables. Its chemical name is ascorbic acid. Its sodium salt is also used.

Numbers above E321 include the other types of additives such as emulsifiers and stabilisers. Examples which are salts include:

- potassium dihydrogencitrate (E332) – emulsifier
- sodium dihydrogenphosphate(V) (E339) – texture improver
- magnesium carbonate (E504) – anti-caking agent.

Questions

1 Benzoic acid is a white crystalline solid (melting point 122 °C which is insoluble in water. It is a monobasic acid. Design experiments to prepare samples of the food additives E211, E212 and E213. In each case:
(a) describe the type of chemical reaction used
(b) describe the apparatus and chemicals you would use to prepare and isolate the product
(c) write balanced chemical equations to represent the formation of the salt
(d) explain how you would determine the actual, theoretical and percentage yield
(e) find data which would enable you to estimate the cost of the product.

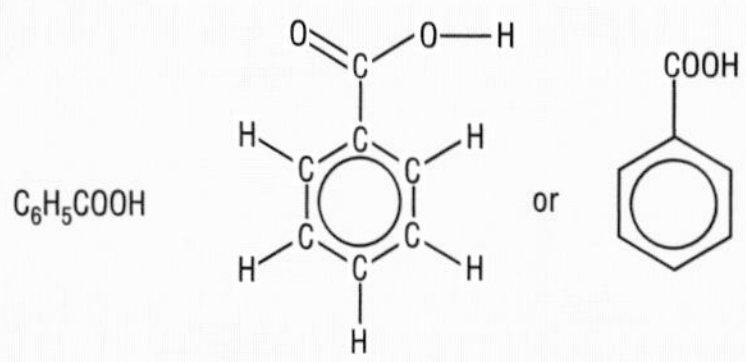

C_6H_5COOH or COOH

Illustration 2 *The structure of benzoic acid.*

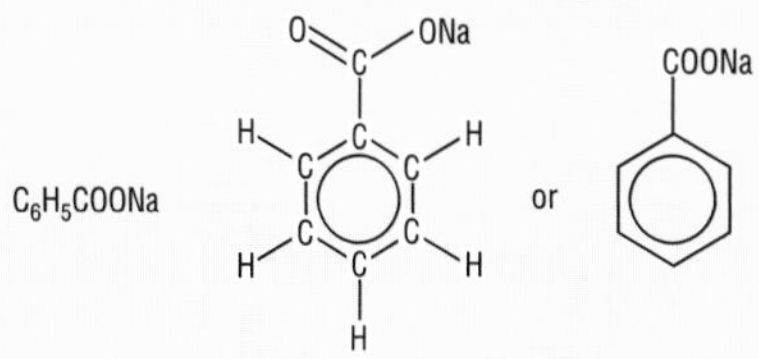

C_6H_5COONa or COONa

Illustration 3 *The structure of sodium benzoate.*

C_2H_5COOH $\quad$ $H{-}C(H)(H){-}C(H)(H){-}C({=}O){-}O{-}H$

Illustration 4 The structure of propanoic acid.

Ester	Odour
$CH_3{-}CH(CH_3){-}CH_2{-}CH_2{-}O{-}C({=}O){-}CH_3$	banana
$CH_3{-}CH(CH_3){-}CH_2{-}CH_2{-}O{-}C({=}O){-}CH_2{-}CH_2{-}CH_2{-}CH_3$	apple
$CH_3{-}CH_2{-}CH_2{-}CH_2{-}O{-}C({=}O){-}CH_2{-}CH_2{-}CH_3$	pineapple
$CH_3{-}CH(CH_3){-}CH_2{-}O{-}C({=}O){-}CH_2{-}CH_3$	rum
$CH_3{-}CH(CH_3){-}CH_2{-}O{-}C({=}O){-}H_2$	raspberry
$C_6H_5{-}CH_2{-}O{-}C({=}O){-}CH_2{-}CH_2{-}CH_3$	roses

Illustration 5 Some esters and their characteristic odours.

2 Propanoic acid is a colourless liquid (boiling point 141 °C) which is soluble in water. It is a monobasic acid. Design an experiment to prepare a sample of E282. You must
 (a) describe the type of chemical reaction used
 (b) describe the apparatus and chemicals you would use to prepare and isolate the product
 (c) write balanced chemical equations to represent the formation of the salt
 (d) explain how you would determine that actual, theoretical and percentage yield
 (e) find data which would enable you to estimate the cost of the product.

3 Esters are also used in the food industry as flavourings. Describe how you could make a series of esters from propanoic acid in order to assess their potential as flavourings.

Note. This case study could be turned into an interesting practical assignment. Think about how you might do this. It is essential that you discuss this with your supervisor before embarking upon any practical work.
Make sure you carry out a risk assessment: identify the hazards and decide upon appropriate action.

Assignment

FERTILISERS AND HEALTHY PLANTS

Setting the scene

The growth of healthy plants depends on an adequate supply of nutrients. The three most important elements are nitrogen (N), phosphorus (P) and potassium (K). If you look in a gardening shop you will find a range of commercial fertilisers which supply 'NPK' to the soil. These elements must be in a form which can be used by the plants. They are usually in the form of salts such as ammonium sulphate, ammonium phosphate and potassium sulphate. These are soluble in water and so can be absorbed through the roots of a plant.

Other elements are required in smaller quantities. These include magnesium, boron, manganese, copper, zinc, molybdenum and iron. Of these, boron, manganese and copper are only added through a fertiliser in emergencies. This is because some trace elements can be harmful to plants if given in too large a quantity. Cobalt and iodine are also added on occasions. They are not necessary for healthy plant growth but are passed on to animals which eat the plants.

Test kits are available to analyse soil samples so that deficiencies in any of these elements can be identified.

Commercial fertilisers may provide a single element or more than one element. This latter type is called a compound fertiliser.

The assignment

You should work on this assignment by yourself. Read through what is required before you prepare a plan of action to tackle the assignment.

SAFETY: *At each stage check with your supervisor before carrying out the practical work.*

1 Find out the effect of deficiencies of each of the following elements on plant growth: nitrogen, phosphorus, potassium, magnesium.

2 You are given a supply of dilute sulphuric acid, dilute potassium hydroxide solution and dilute aqueous ammonia (each approximately 2 mol dm^{-3}). Use these to prepare samples of the fertilisers potassium sulphate and ammonium sulphate. In each case, use 20 cm^3 of dilute sulphuric acid.
   (a) What type of reaction is being used in these preparations?
   (b) Determine the actual yields.
   (c) Calculate the theoretical and percentage yields.
   (d) Estimate the cost of the preparations.

3 You are provided with 6 g magnesium oxide and have access to the usual laboratory chemicals (including the dilute acids) and apparatus. Devise and carry out the preparation of a fertiliser which can provide both magnesium and nitrogen. You should use all the magnesium oxide provided.
   (a) What type of reaction is being used in the preparation?
   (b) Determine the actual yield and calculate the theoretical and percentage yield.

4 A company which makes magnesium compounds for use in fertilisers wants to diversify. The company has decided to manufacture the antacid magnesium carbonate. Magnesium oxide is first converted to magnesium sulphate, which is converted in turn into magnesium carbonate. You have been asked to investigate the feasibility of this preparative route. Devise and carry out the preparation of magnesium carbonate starting with 5 g magnesium oxide. You will need to adapt the procedures described in this book.
   (a) What type of reaction is being used in this two-step preparation?
   (b) How must you adapt the procedures in this book in order to carry out the preparation?
   (c) Determine the actual yield in each step.
   (d) Calculate the theoretical and percentage yield in each step.
   (e) Estimate the total cost of the preparation.

Presenting your assignment

Write a report of your investigation and present it together with samples of the compounds you made. The compounds should be in separate labelled sample tubes.

Additional information

The following Procedures are available:

- preparation of salts by an acid-base reaction, page 150
- preparation of insoluble salts by precipitation reactions, page 152
- preparation of magnesium carbonate, page 160.

Eye protection must be sworn

CORROSIVE
dilute sulphuric acid
dilute potassium hydroxide

Opportunity to collect evidence
In completing this task you will have the opportunity to meet the following requirements for GNVQ Intermediate Science:

Science units
Unit 1:
Element 1.3 PCs 1, 2, 3, 4
Unit 3:
Element 3.2 PCs 1, 2, 3, 4, 5

Core skill units

Application of number:
Element 2.2

Communication:
Element 2.2

Grading

This assignment gives you the opportunity to meet merit or distinction criteria. All four themes are covered: Planning, Information seeking and information handling, Evaluation, Quality of Outcomes.

You will need help with some of the science in this assignment, so don't be afraid to ask.

Read through the grading criteria carefully and make sure you know what must be done to gain evidence that you are worthy of a merit or distinction.

Requirements

- ❒ Weighing boat
- ❒ 2 × 250 cm^3 beakers
- ❒ 100 cm^3 measuring cylinder
- ❒ Glass rod
- ❒ Dropping pipette
- ❒ Suction filtration apparatus or centrifuge
- ❒ Desiccator

Eye protection must be worn

Procedure

Preparation of magnesium carbonate

1. Weigh out about 5 g of magnesium sulphate on a weighing boat and transfer it to a 250 cm^3 beaker.
2. Add 40 cm^3 distilled water using a 100 cm^3 measuring cylinder. Stir the mixture with a glass rod until the solid dissolves. Leave the glass rod in the beaker.
3. Weigh out about 2.5 g of anhydrous sodium carbonate (a slight excess) on a weighing boat. Transfer it into another 250 cm^3 beaker and add 40 cm^3 distilled water using the 100 cm^3 measuring cylinder. Stir the mixture with a glass rod until the solid dissolves.
4. Add the sodium carbonate solution to the magnesium sulphate solution a little at a time using a dropping pipette. Stir between additions and continue adding the sodium carbonate solution until no more white precipitate forms.
5. Collect the white precipitate by filtration under reduced pressure or by centrifuging. Place in a desiccator for at least 24 hours to dry.
6. Determine the yield of magnesium carbonate.

Questions

1 Classify each of the following reactions as redox, acid-base, precipitation or esterification:

(a) ethanoic acid + methanol → methyl ethanoate + water

(b) nitric acid + copper(II) oxide → copper(II) nitrate + water

(c) hydrogen + copper(II) oxide → copper + water

(d) methanoic acid + ethanol → ethyl methanoate + water

(e) iron(III) oxide + carbon → iron + carbon dioxide

(f) sodium chloride + silver nitrate → silver chloride + sodium nitrate

(g) $BaCl_2(aq) + Na_2SO_4(aq) \rightarrow BaSO_4(s) + 2NaCl(aq)$

(h) $CH_3COOH(l) + C_2H_5OH(l) \rightarrow CH_3COOC_2H_5(l) + H_2O(l)$

(i) $PbO(s) + CO(g) \rightarrow Pb(s) + CO_2(g)$

(j) $PbO(s) + 2HNO_3(aq) \rightarrow Pb(NO_3)_2(aq) + H_2O(l)$

(k) $2AgNO_3(aq) + Zn(s) \rightarrow 2Ag(s) + Zn(NO_3)_2(aq)$

2 Metals often occur in nature as their oxides. Why can redox reactions be used to obtain the metal from these oxides?

3 Write a word equation to describe the preparation of a salt by an acid-base reaction.

4 Describe how an insoluble salt, such as lead(II) chloride, can be made by a precipitation reaction.

5 In the preparation of ethyl ethanoate, 6.0 g ethanoic acid was reacted with an excess of ethanol (10 cm^3). The following data come from the experiment:

- mass of collecting flask = 16.24 g
- mass of collecting flask + distillate at 74–79 °C = 21.68 g
- theoretically, 1 mol ethanoic acid (CH_3COOH) gives 1 mol ethyl ethanoate ($CH_3COOC_2H_5$).
- relative atomic masses (A_r): C = 12, H = 1, O = 16.
- costs of chemicals: ethanoic acid, £3.60 for 100 g; ethanol, £2.58 for 500 cm^3.
- other costs: energy, £5; labour, £25; equipment, £5.

Calculate:

(a) the actual yield of ethyl ethanoate

(b) the theoretical yield of ethyl ethanoate

(c) the percentage yield of ethyl ethanoate

(d) the cost of making the sample of ethyl ethanoate.

Making and testing devices

You will need to show that you can:

- describe what the device is to be used for
- describe the functions of the various parts of the device
- assemble the device, test and evaluate it.

There are many devices that you use regularly which employ electricity as their energy source. Hair dryers, calculators, microwave ovens, televisions, computers, torches, personal stereos. These are all examples of **electrical devices.** Your life would very different if they didn't exist!

FOCUS

Electricity can be used to move people and objects. It allows people to communicate over large distances. Electrical devices can monitor situations and warn us when things go wrong. They can make measurements for us. They can automatically control processes for us.

Purpose of electrical devices

This section will help you to understand how a range of electrical devices work. The list is not complete. **Electricity** can do many things which are not listed below.

Movement

Electricity can be used to **move** things. Figure 3.3.1 shows a wheelchair. It uses electric motors to help a disabled person to get around. The motors are controlled by switches. The electricity is supplied by large rechargeable batteries.

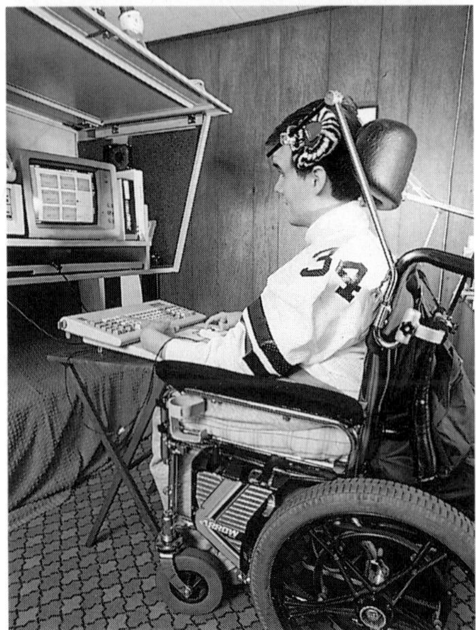

Figure 3.3.1 Electrical systems can get disabled people mobile. They can also help them to communicate.

Communication

Electricity can be used to allow people to **communicate** with each other. The cellular telephone is a good example of this. Telephones allow two-way communication. Radios and televisions allow one-way communication.

Warning

Electrical devices can **warn** people of danger. Burglar alarms tell us about intruders in our homes. Electronic systems are routinely used in hospitals to monitor patients and set off alarm signals if anything goes wrong.

Measuring

Electrical devices can **measure** many things more accurately than people can. Electronic timers are now always used at race meetings. Electronic thermometers are commonplace. The police use electronic sensors to measure the speed of vehicles (see Figure 3.3.2).

Figure 3.3.2 Hand-held electronic systems are often used to measure vehicle speeds.

Controlling

Electronic devices (such as computers) excel at controlling machinery and complex systems. Computers control railway switching networks. They help pilots to control and fly aircraft. They control dishwashers and microwave ovens.

For each purpose listed above, could you give two other examples of electrical systems with that purpose?

Parts of electronic devices

Most electronic devices look very complicated and difficult to understand. Don't worry. Once you have learnt to identify the four main parts of the system, it all becomes much simpler!

Figure 3.3.3 shows how any electronic system can be split up into four main parts. These are the **power supply,** the **input devices**, the **processor** and the **output devices.** The arrowed lines show which way electrical energy flows through the system. Most of the energy flows from the power source to the other parts (shown by thick lines). Smaller amounts of energy, containing information, flow from the input devices to the processor. The processor controls the output devices by feeding energy into them in turn.

FOCUS

All electronic systems can be broken down into four parts. These are:

- **power supply**
- **input devices**
- **processor**
- **output devices**

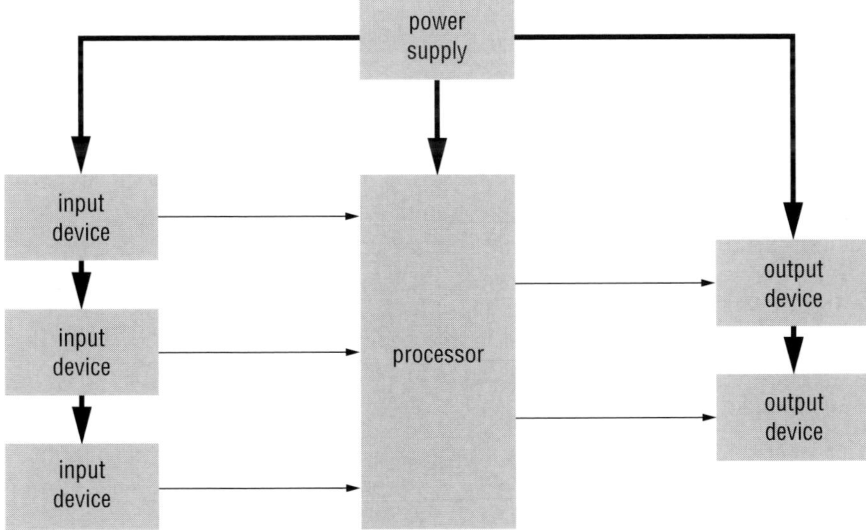

Figure 3.3.3 The four main parts of an electronic system.

In your calculator, for example, the power source is a battery or a solar cell. The keys which you press are the input devices. An integrated circuit inside the calculator processes all the signals from the keys and activates the liquid-crystal display, the output device.

Power supplies

All electronic devices must have a **power supply**. This provides energy for the system. Figure 3.3.4 shows a number of different power supply. *Solar cells* can last a long time, but are expensive, need a source of light and can't provide very much electricity. *Batteries* allow a device to be portable, but are expensive to replace. If large amounts of electricity are needed, the batteries can be large and heavy. *Rechargeable batteries* are available but are expensive to buy. *Mains power supplies* can also be large and heavy. They need a cable connected to the mains power supply and they contain (dangerously) high voltages.

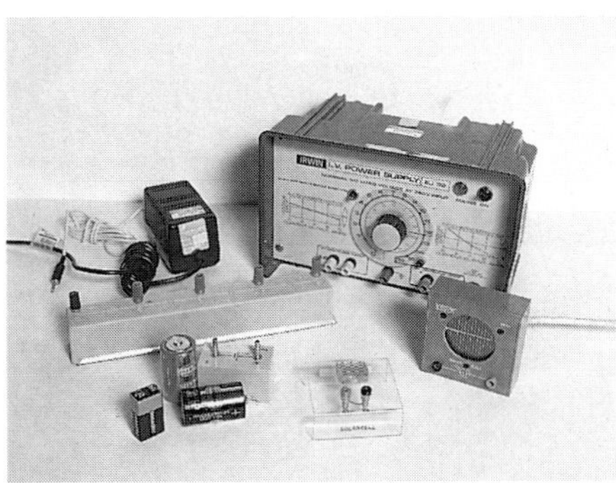

Figure 3.3.4 Power supplies for electrical systems.

Figure 3.3.5 Various input devices.

Input devices

Electronic devices can accomplish many things because they can use input devices to obtain information about the system they are controlling. Figure 3.3.5 illustrates a number of different input devices. Each one responds to a different type of non-electrical signal. Table 3.3.1 lists some of the devices and what they respond to.

Table 3.3.1 Some input devices and what they respond to

Input device	What it senses
switch	pressure
LDR (light-dependent resistor)	light
thermistor	heat
microphone	sound
aerial	radio waves

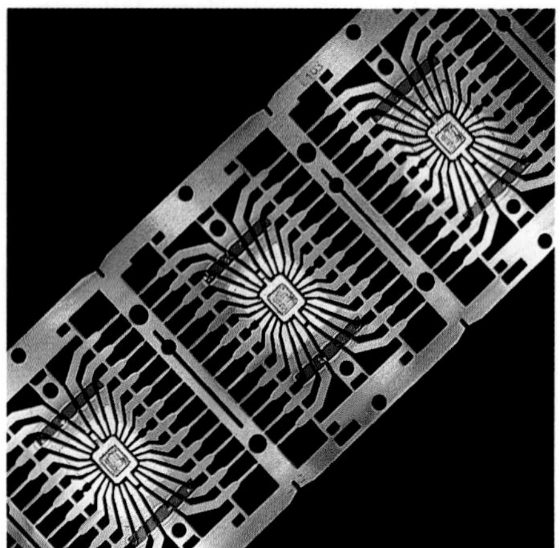
Figure 3.3.6 The silicon chip inside an integrated circuit.

Processors

Electronic devices contain processors. These take in information from the input devices and use it to work out what needs to be done to the output devices.

Processors in modern systems are usually *integrated circuits*. These contain large numbers of electronic switches (called *transistors*) built onto a small piece of silicon (Figure 3.3.6). The integrated circuit is often enclosed in black plastic for protection. Electrical connections are made via metal pins which poke out of the plastic (Figure 3.3.7).

Figure 3.3.7 An integrated circuit package.

Output devices

A number of different output devices are shown in Figure 3.3.8. They all convert electrical energy into other forms of energy. Table 3.3.2 shows what they do.

Table 3.3.2 Some output devices and what they do

Output device	What it does
lamp	emits light
buzzer	makes a noise
motor	spins round
loudspeaker	emits sounds
heater	makes heat energy

Figure 3.3.8 Various output devices.

Examples of electrical and electronic systems

Any electrical system can be made from a set of parts (more properly called components). These components have to be connected to each other by conducting paths. These connections are either copper tracks on a printed circuit board (p.c.b.) or insulated copper wire (Figure 3.3.9).

Each example which follows is an example of a useful electrical system. You will be told what each component does. This should help you to appreciate how the whole system works.

> **FOCUS**
>
> **Electronic systems require a power supply. This can be controlled with switches. When a switch is closed it allows current to flow from the positive terminal of the power supply to the negative terminal.**

Constructing electrical devices, page 173

Example 1: Toy car

Imagine a toy car. It sits on the floor, with an electric motor connected to the back wheels. A pair of wires goes from the motor to the battery pack in your hand. You can make the car go backwards or forwards by altering the switch on the battery pack.

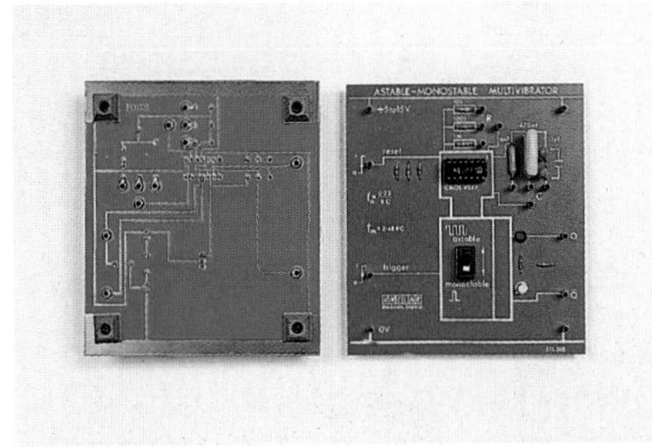

Figure 3.3.9 A printed circuit board holds the components firmly in place and allows metal tracks to make the connections between them.

Block diagram

Figure 3.3.10 is a block diagram of the system. It shows the flow of energy and information through the system. Notice how the switch is placed between the power supply and the motor. This is because it controls the flow of energy to the motor.

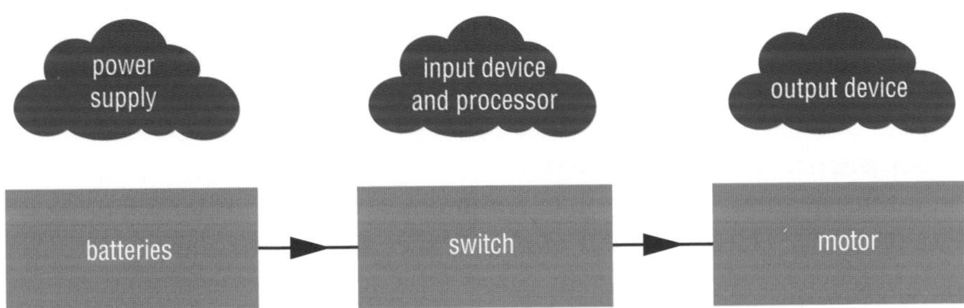

Figure 3.3.10 Block diagram of toy car electrical system.

Circuit diagram

The *circuit diagram* is shown in Figure 3.3.11. It shows how the components (the batteries, the switch and the motor) have to be connected to each other with wire. Details of the connections to the switch are also shown.

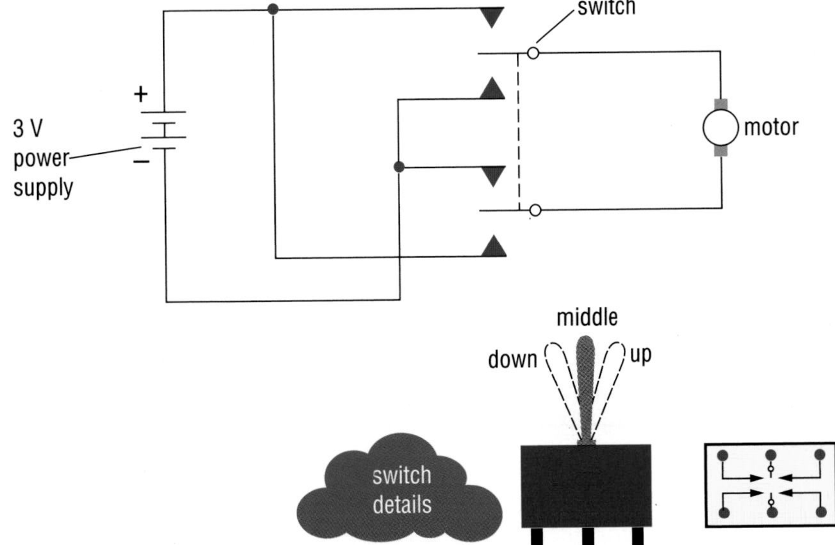

Figure 3.3.11 Circuit diagram for the toy car's electrical system. Only the motor is in the car! The switch has six terminals.

The circuit diagram is *not* a picture of the system. It is a map which shows you how to connect the components together. It can also be used to help you understand how the whole system works.

The switch

There are many types of switch. The one in this circuit is a *double-pole double-throw* switch. It behaves like two separate switches with a single lever. Each switch has a *pole* which can be connected to one or other of the *throws*. The lever has three settings: up, middle or down.

Figure 3.3.11 shows the lever in its middle setting. The motor is not connected to the batteries, so it doesn't spin round. In Figure 3.3.12 the lever is in its top setting. The motor spins clockwise because electric *current* can flow through it from the + terminal of the battery to the – terminal.

When the lever is in its bottom position, the current flows the other way, and the motor spins anticlockwise.

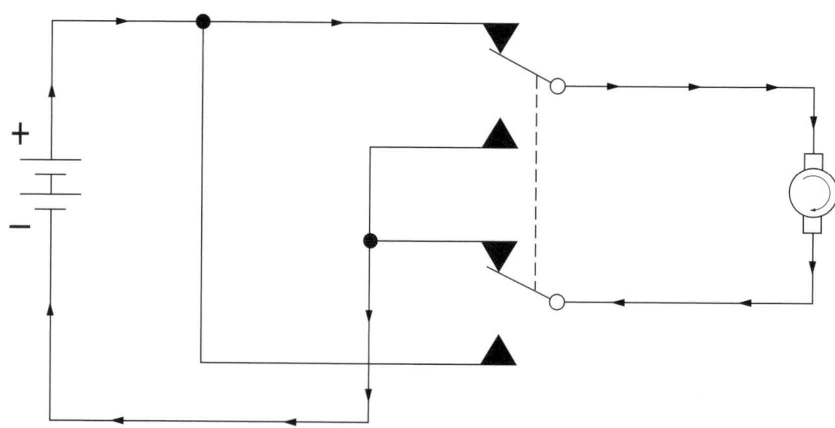

Figure 3.3.12 *The arrows show the flow of current when the switch lever is up. The current always flows from the + terminal of the power supply to its – terminal. Could you redraw the circuit, with the lever down and using arrows to show the path followed by the current?*

Example 2: The intercom

An intercom allows one person to communicate with another some distance away. They are widely used in offices and as baby alarms.

Block diagram

Look at Figure 3.3.13. Each time that the switch is pressed, any sound fed into the microphone appears at the loudspeaker. At the same time, a *light-emitting diode* (LED) comes on next to the microphone.

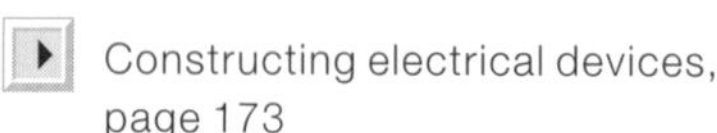
Constructing electrical devices, page 173

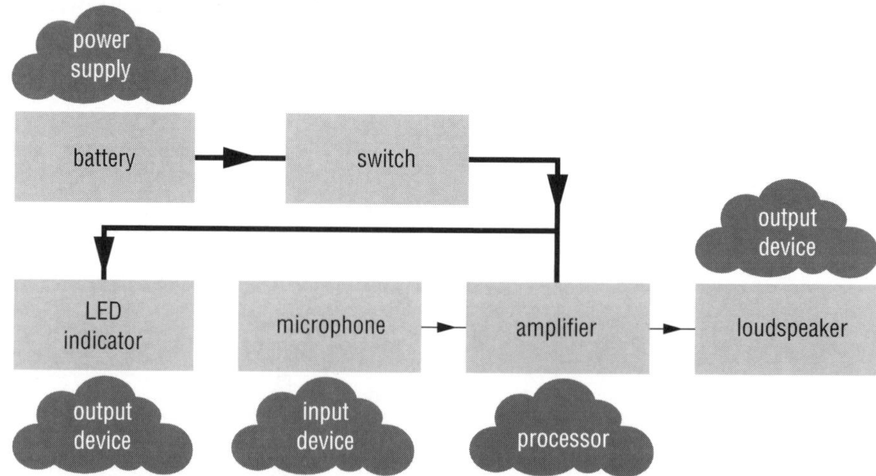

Figure 3.3.13 *Block diagram for an intercom system.*

The block diagram shows the different components needed to make the system. The switch controls the supply of electricity to the rest of the system. The LED is connected *in parallel* with the amplifier, allowing both to operate off the same power supply. The amplifier takes the signal from the microphone and boosts it before sending it out to the loudspeaker along a pair of wires.

Circuit diagram

The circuit diagram in Figure 3.3.14 shows how the components are connected to each other. (The diode protects the circuit from the battery being accidentally connected round the wrong way.)

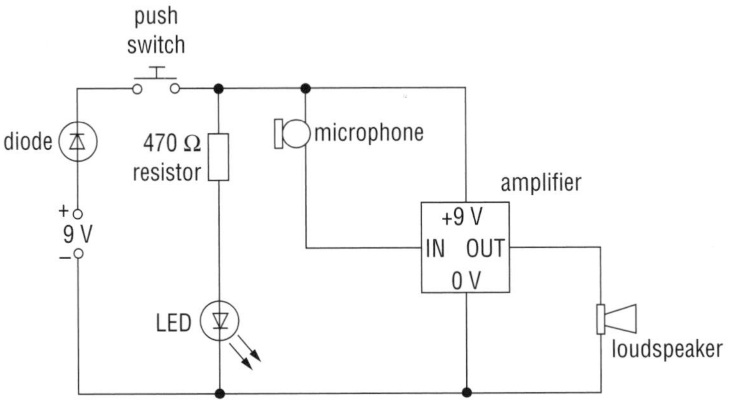

Figure 3.3.14 Circuit diagram for an intercom system.

The LED has a *resistor* in series with it. This is because LEDs are rated at 2 V. Direct connection to a 9 V supply would destroy it.

The *amplifier* has four connections. Two go to the power supply rails at 9 V and 0 V. The third takes in the signal from the microphone. The fourth feeds out a signal to the loudspeaker.

Integrated circuits

There are many ways of putting the amplifier together. Figure 3.3.15 shows you how one particular **integrated circuit** (or IC)can be used.

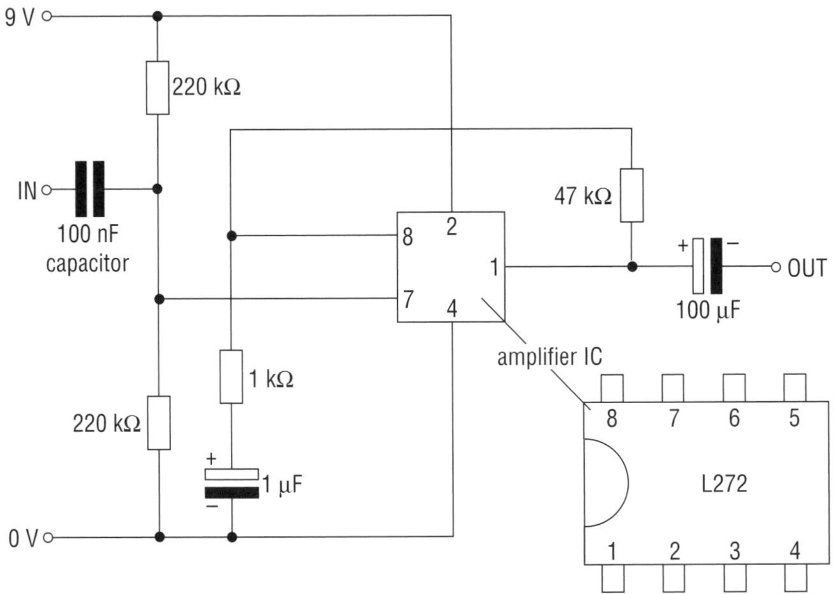

Figure 3.3.15 Using an L272 integrated circuit to make an amplifier.

FOCUS

Integrated circuits process information from input devices. They control the flow of energy from the power supply to the components connected to their outputs.

There are many different types of IC, each with their own special task. This particular IC is the L272. It is a black plastic package with metal pins leading to the silicon chip inside. Some resistors and capacitors have to be connected to the IC to make it work. The pin numbers are shown on the circuit diagram.

Printed circuit boards

Wiring all the components together to make the amplifier can be awkward. A printed circuit board (or p.c.b.) is the best way. The metal pins of the components are pushed through holes in the board. They are then soldered to the copper tracks etched on the underside of the board (Figure 3.3.16).

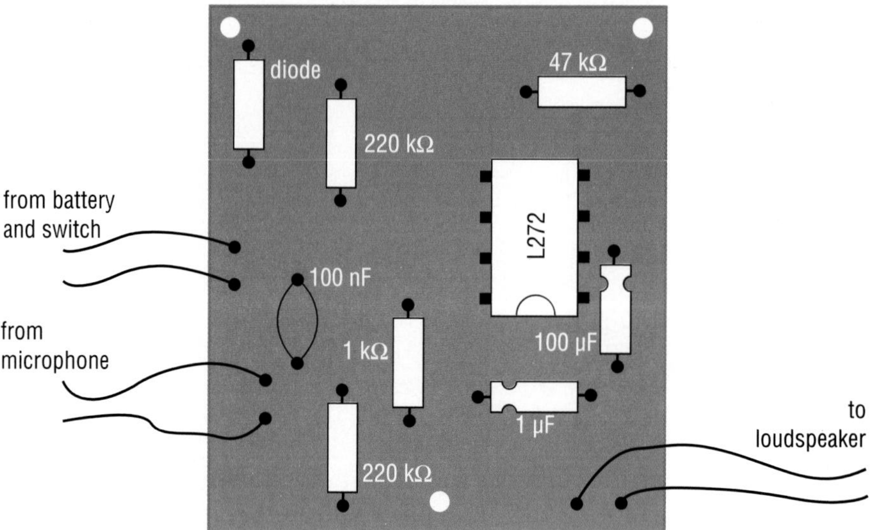

Figure 3.3.16 How the intercom system looks on a p.c.b.

FOCUS

Electronics systems can increase safety by continuously monitoring potentially dangerous situations and giving warnings or providing automatic control.

Example 3: Liquid level warning

Electronic warning systems are widely used in industry. Unlike people, they don't need time off to eat and sleep. Nor do they get tired or lazy. They can be vigilant all the time!

This section describes an electronic system which can be used to set off an alarm automatically if there is too little liquid in a container. The liquid could be oil for lubrication, water for cooling or another chemical for part of an industrial process.

Block diagram

The system shown in Figure 3.3.17 sets off an alarm if the level of liquid in a tank gets too low. The liquid level sensor is a switch connected to a float. When the liquid level drops too far, the switch closes. This activates the *timer* into producing pulses at one second intervals. This series of pulses switches the driver on and off continually. When the *driver is* on, it allows up to 100 mA of current to flow through the *buzzer* and the *lamp*.

As soon as the liquid level drops too low the buzzer and bulb are pulsed on and off.

Figure 3.3.17 Block diagram of a liquid level warning system.

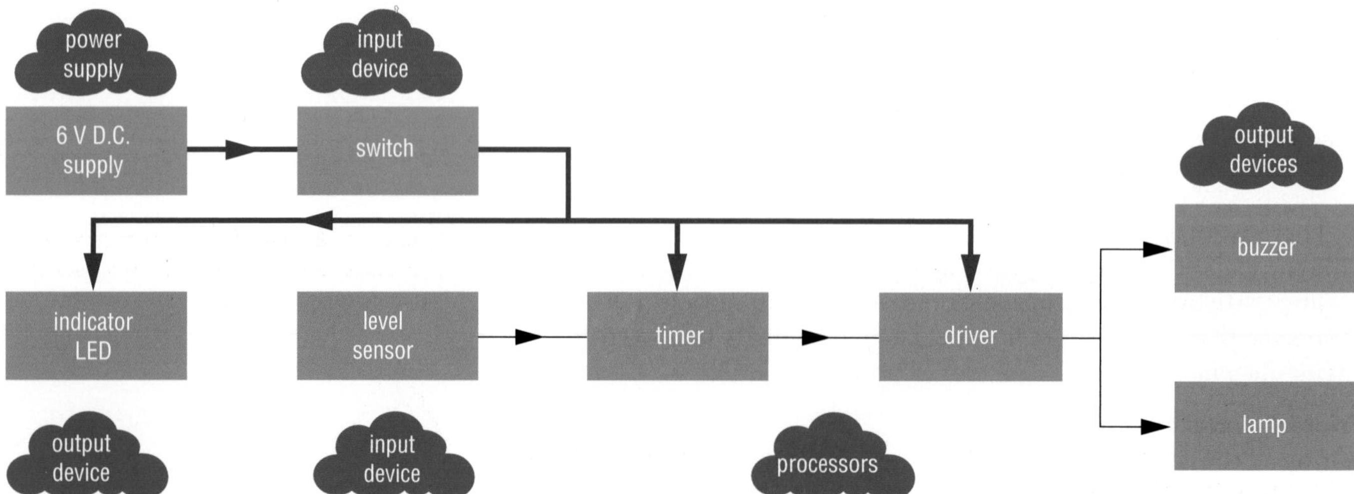

Circuit diagram

The circuit diagram of figure 3.3.18 shows how the lamp and the buzzer have to be connected *in parallel* with each other. Both devices have to be *rated* at 6 V as the whole system has a 6 V supply.

The timer is a 555 IC. The rate at which it turns the lamp and buzzer on and off is fixed by the values of the resistor and capacitor connected around it.

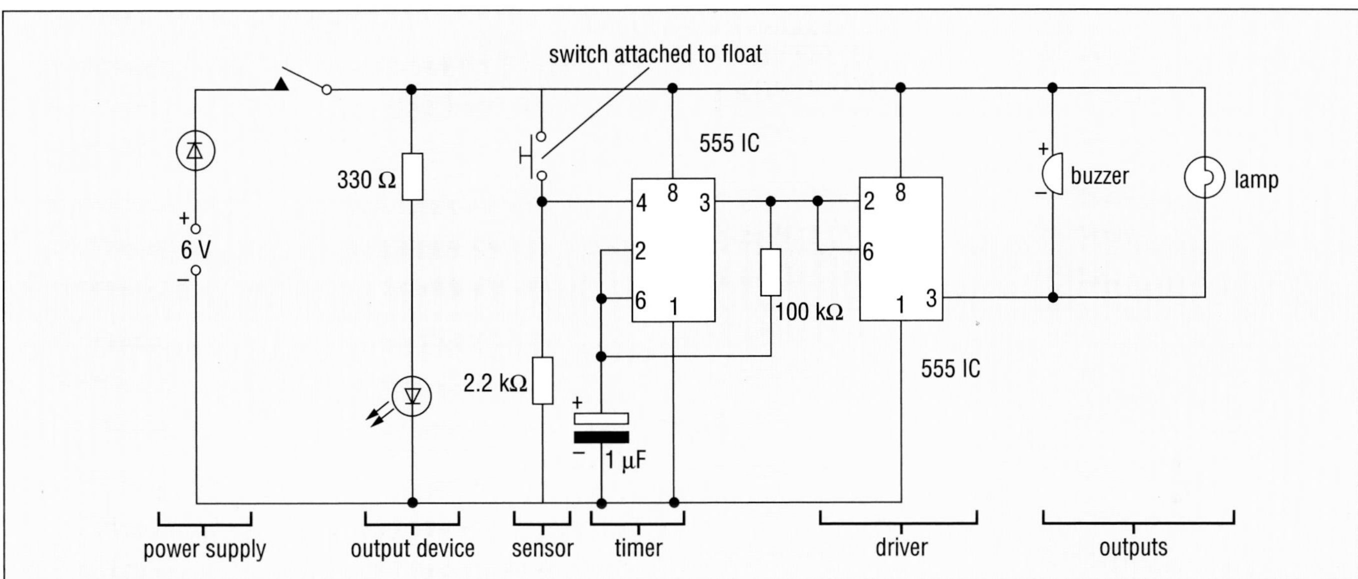

Figure 3.3.18 *Circuit diagram for the liquid level warning system. Could you adapt this diagram so that it is for a system which will set off an alarm if the liquid in the tank gets too hot?*

Mains power supply

The warning circuit contains an LED. This glows whenever the rest of the circuit has been connected to its power supply. This is a good safety feature, because it is very easy to switch off the system and forget about it.

Another way of making the system even safer is to run it off the mains supply. If a 6 V battery were used to run the system, the battery would need replacing at regular intervals. If a battery ran down too quickly, perhaps nobody would notice until it was too late. It is much better to run it off the mains electricity supply via a transformer and regulator (Figure 3.3.19).

Figure 3.3.19 *The transformer and regulator are sealed in an insulating box for safety. The output is a safe low-value d.c. voltage.*

SAFETY: *You should never use the mains electricity supply without completing a risk assessment and consulting your teacher.*

Electrical hazard

Example 4: Light meter

A useful feature of **electronic systems** is their ability to sense a wide variety of things, including light.

Block diagram

Figure 3.3.20 shows that a light level measurement system has just three components. One of them is, of course, the power supply. The other two are a light sensor and a voltmeter.

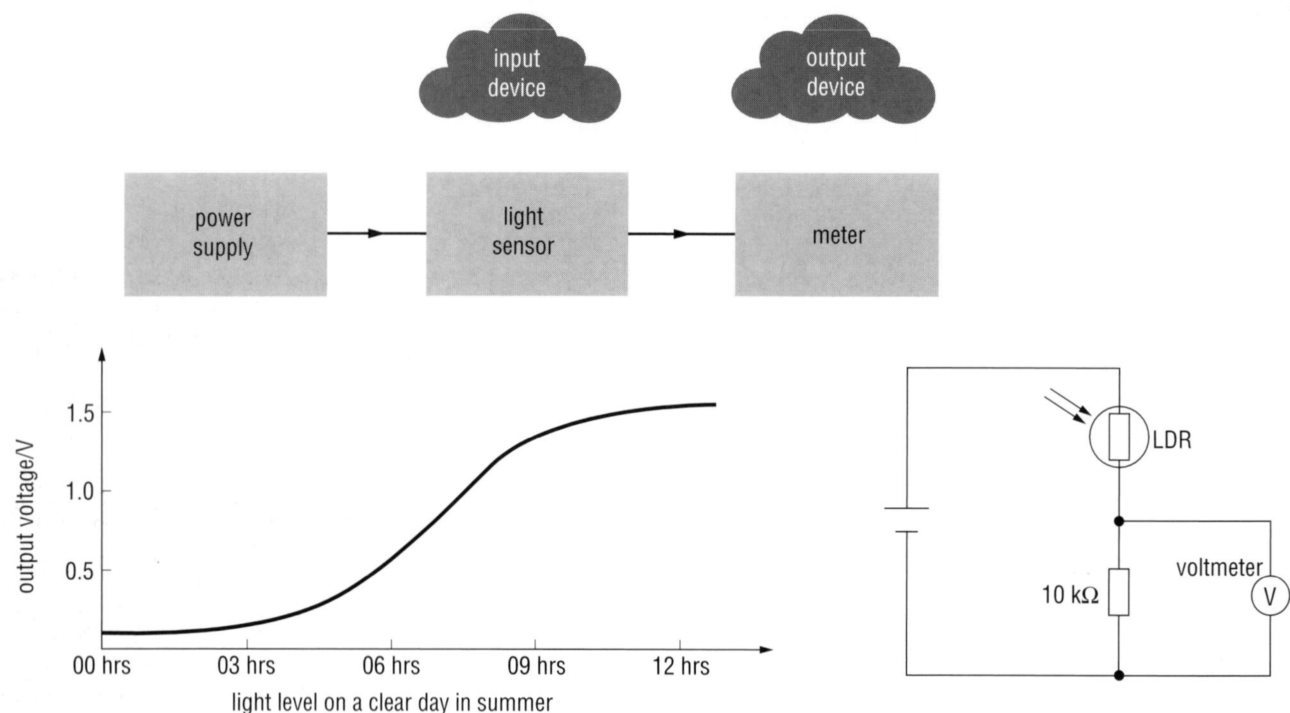

Figure 3.3.20 Block and circuit diagrams for a light meter system. The graph shows how the output changes with light level. How would you adapt the circuit to make an electronic thermometer, using a thermistor as the sensor. How would you calibrate this?

Light sensors

As you can see from Figure 3.3.20, the light sensor is a *light-dependent resistor* (LDR) *in series* with a 10 kΩ resistor. The resistance of an LDR drops dramatically as the light level increases. It changes from about 100 Ω in bright sunlight to 10 MΩ in the dark.

A *voltmeter* measures the voltage drop across the 10 kΩ resistor. As the light level goes up, so does the voltage. A digital voltmeter makes it easier to take precise readings.

Calibration

Before you can use the light meter, you need to *calibrate* it. This involves exposing it to a variety of known light levels and recording the reading on the voltmeter each time. You can then draw a graph to show how the meter reading depends on the light level (Figure 3.3.20). That graph can then be used to convert any meter reading into a light level.

Example 5: Temperature control

Many industrial processes require a steady temperature. Brewing is a good example. Yeast converts sugar to ethanol fastest when it is held at about 22 °C. If it is raised too far above this temperature, it will be killed. If it falls too far below this temperature, the reaction will take place much more slowly. So the brewing industry uses electrical control systems to keep its fermenting vats at the right temperature.

The system shown in Figure 3.3.21 controls the temperature of a greenhouse during the night. If the temperature falls below 0 °C, endangering the plants, an electric heater is switched on.

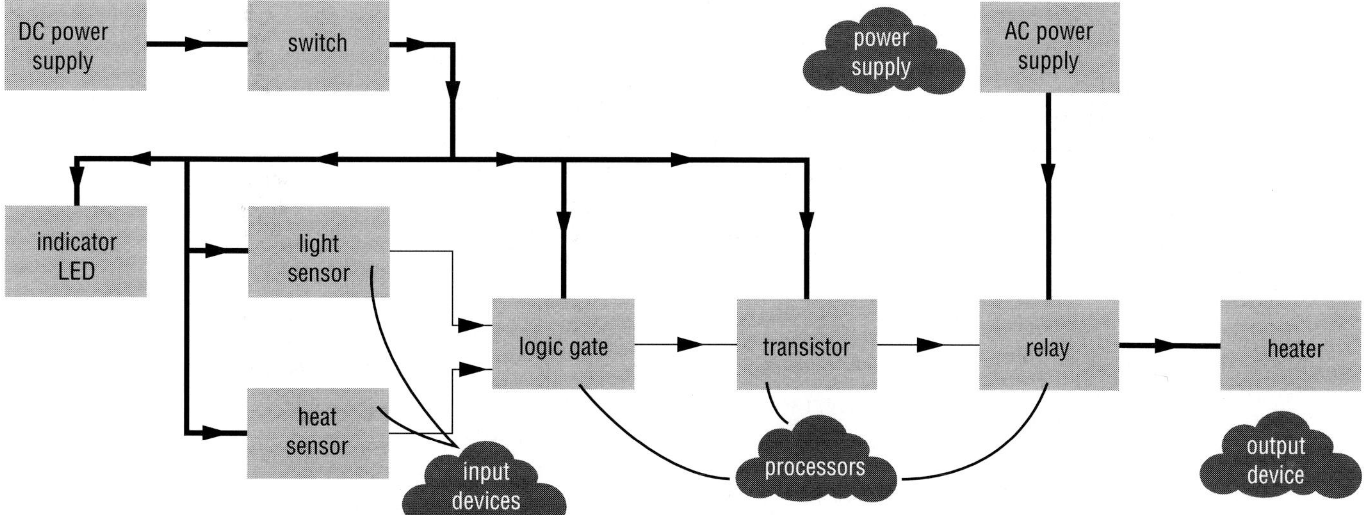

Figure 3.3.21 *Block diagram of a greenhouse temperature controller.*

FOCUS

Logic gates allow electronic devices to combine signals from more than one input device. The output of a logic gate can use a relay to control devices which need large currents or voltages.

Logic gates

This system is more complicated because it has two sensors. The light sensor tells the system when it is night time. The heat sensor tells it when it gets too cold. Both of these signals are *processed* by the **logic gate**. In its turn, the logic gate can turn the heater on and off via the *relay*.

High and low

Logic gates are ICs which use the voltage at their input terminals to set the voltage of their output terminal. They only recognise two types of voltage. Their values are fixed by the power supply. So if the power supply is 6 V, anything between 6 V and 3 V is a *high* voltage. A *low* voltage is between 3 V and 0 V.

There are five different logic gates which you can purchase as ICs. They are called *AND*, *OR*, *EOR*, *NAND* and *NOR* gates. Their names have been chosen to describe what they do. Their behaviour is summarised by *truth tables*.

AND gate

inputs		output
low	low	low
low	high	low
high	low	low
high	high	high

OR gate

inputs		output
low	low	low
low	high	high
high	low	high
high	high	high

EOR gate

inputs		output
low	low	low
low	high	high
high	low	high
high	high	low

NAND gate	inputs		output
	low	low	high
	low	high	high
	high	low	high
	high	high	low

NOR gate	inputs		output
	low	low	high
	low	high	low
	high	low	low
	high	high	low

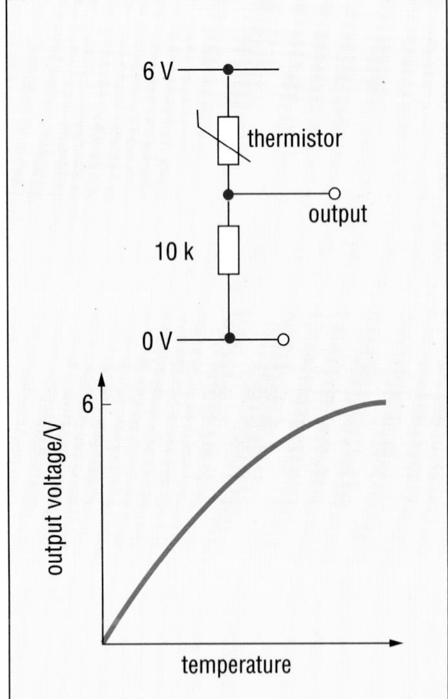

Figure 3.3.22(a) Using a thermistor to make a heat sensor.

There are also devices called *inverters* or *NOT gates*. They are used to convert a high voltage into a low one and vice versa.

inverter	input	output
	low	high
	high	low

Heat sensor

A *thermistor* is used to make the heat sensor. Its resistance falls rapidly as its temperature rises. When combined with a fixed value resistor (Figure 3.3.22(a)), it makes a sensor whose output voltage rises with temperature. When the thermistor has the same resistance as the resistor, the output voltage is exactly half of the supply voltage.

Circuit behaviour

Look at the circuit diagram in Figure 3.3.22(b). A 4001 NOR gate IC combines the signals from the two sensors.

A NOR gate is used because its output will only be high if both of its inputs are low (see the truth tables above). The input from the light sensor will be low at night, and the input from the heat sensor output will be low when it is cold. So the output of the logic gate will *only* be high when it is cold and dark.

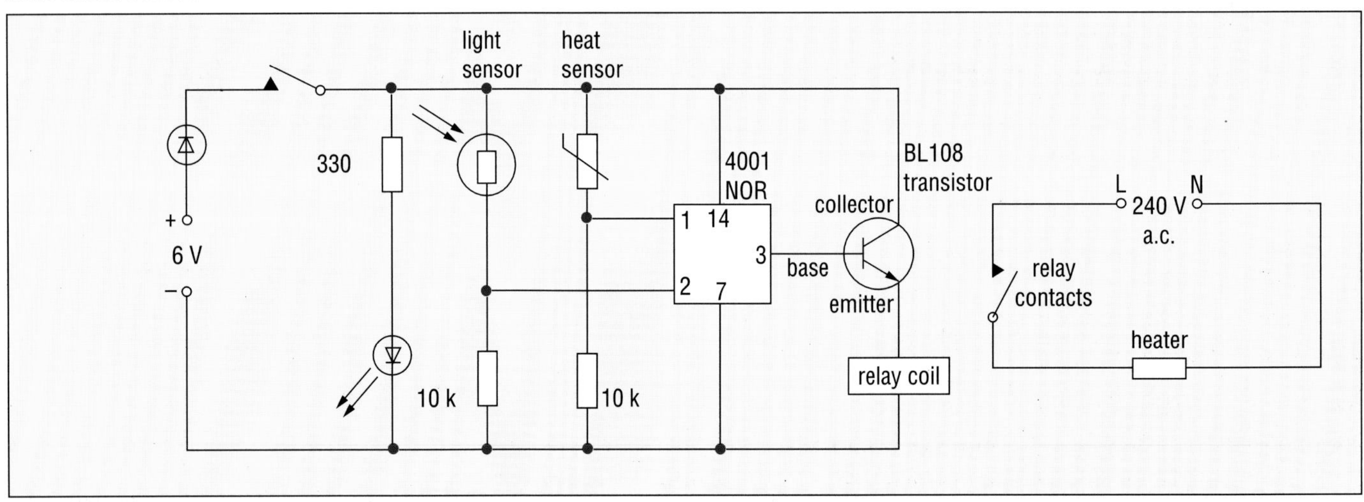

Figure 3.3.22(b) Circuit diagram for the greenhouse system. What would the system do if the NOR gate was replaced by an AND gate?

The relay and transistor

The NOR gate can't supply enough electrical energy to run the heater directly. It can, however, control a *relay* via a *transistor* (Figure 3.3.22).

The transistor is a current amplifier. The current flowing out of the *emitter* is about 100 times larger than the current flowing into the base. That extra current comes from the *collector* connected to the 6 V supply rail.

A relay is a switch controlled by an electromagnet (a coil of wire around some iron). If enough current flows through the *coil*, the relay contacts will close. This happens whenever the NOR gate output is high.

The heater is run off the mains 240 V a.c. supply. For safety, the relay contacts are used as a switch in the (dangerous) live wire of the a.c. supply.

There is no direct electrical connection between the relay contacts and the relay coil. This allows (safe) low voltage systems to turn (dangerous) high voltage ones on and off.

You should never use the mains electricity supply without completing a risk assessment and consulting your teacher.

Electrical hazard

Constructing electrical devices

There are five stages to constructing an electrical device:

1 Select the components.
2 Decide how they must be connected.
3 Sort out how they are going to fit into the container.
4 Construct a p.c.b. (if you need to).
5 Solder all the components together.
6 Ask your teacher to check before testing.

Selecting components

Having studied the circuit diagram, you can write down a list of components. This is a list for the intercom circuit.

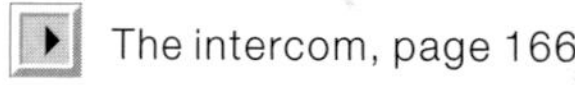

The intercom, page 166

9V battery connector and PP3 battery
microphone insert
small loudspeaker
capacitors: 100 nF, 1μF, 100μF
resistors: 220 kΩ (two), 47 kΩ, 1 kΩ, 470kΩ
LED
1N4001 diode
L272 IC
push switch
2 mm sockets (four)
2 mm plugs (four)
single strand connecting wire
two-core flexible wire

Resistors

Resistors have coloured bands on them (Figure 3.3.23). These tell you, in code, what their resistance is. Each colour represents a number from 0 to 9 (Table 3.3.3).

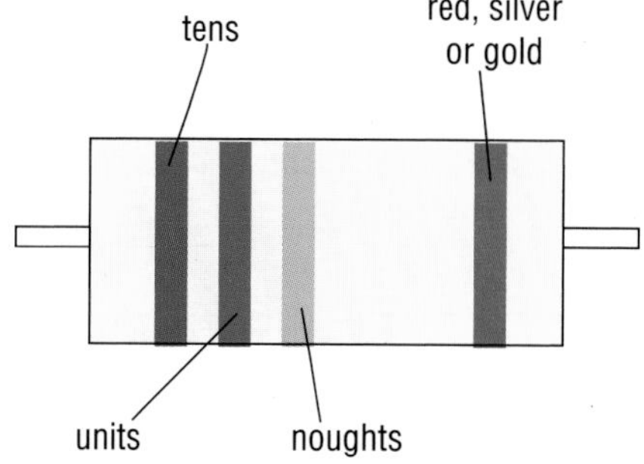

Figure 3.3.23 *Coloured bands on a resistor allow you to work out its value. If a resistor has, brown, green and orange bands, convince yourself that its resistance is 15 kΩ.*

This is how to use the colour code. One of the bands on the end of the resistor will be red, silver or gold. It tells you how accurately the resistor has been manufactured (red is best, silver worst). Turn the resistor so that this band is on the right.

The first two bands on the left give you a number between 10 and 99. The next band tells you how many zeroes to place after this number. The final result is the resistance in ohms.

For example, the sequence red, orange, yellow, gold would be 230 000 Ω or 230 kΩ.

Table 3.3.3 The resistor colour code

Colour	Number
black	0
brown	1
red	2
orange	3
yellow	4
green	5
blue	6
purple	7
grey	8
white	9

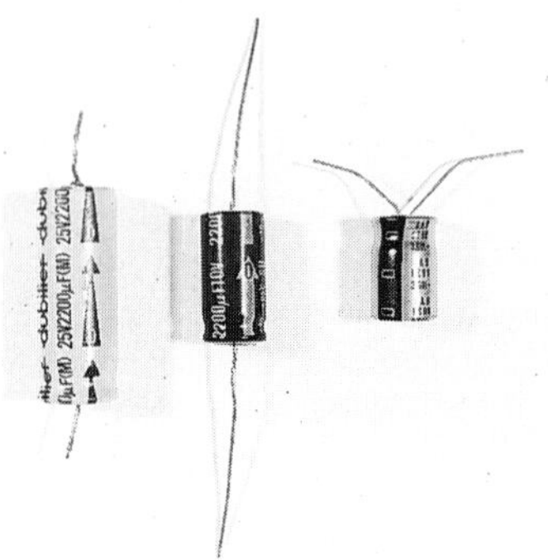

Figure 3.3.24 The polarity of capacitors is clearly marked on them.

Capacitors

Some capacitors are *polarised*. This means that they have positive and negative terminals.

SAFETY: *They must be connected in the circuit the right way round, otherwise they risk exploding.*

Figure 3.3.24 shows how the leads are marked.

Capacitors whose value is less than 1μF are not usually polarised. They can be inserted either way round.

ICs

Figure 3.3.25 shows how the pins on an IC are numbered.

This is how you find pin 1. One end of the IC will have some of the plastic missing; it will have a D-shaped cutout. Place the IC on the table with the pins down and the D-shape on the left. Pin 1 is then on the bottom left-hand corner.

Sometimes there is a dot impressed in the plastic next to pin 1.

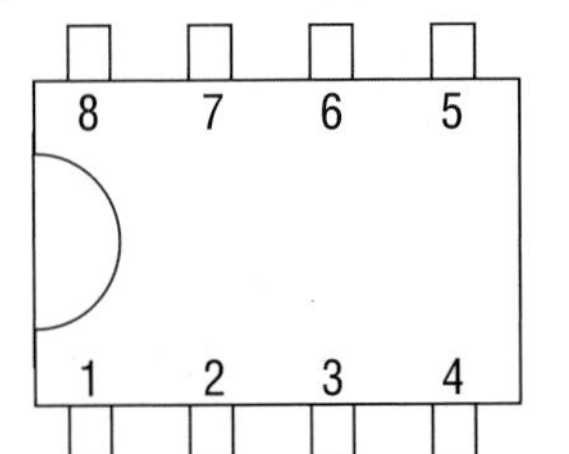

Figure 3.3.25 How to find pin 1 of an IC.

LEDs and diodes

LEDs are polarised. If you insert them the wrong way round, they will be destroyed. The *anode* (positive terminal) must be at a higher voltage than the *cathode* (negative terminal) (Figure 3.3.26(a)).

The diode will only let current flow from its anode to its cathode (Figure 3.3.26(b)).

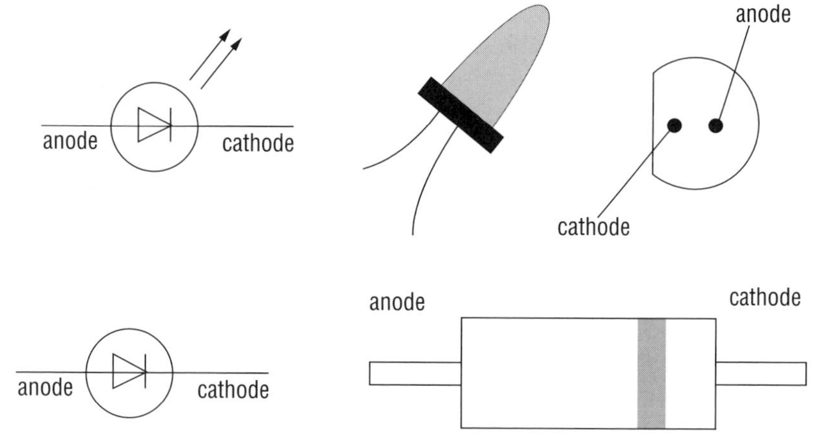

Figure 3.3.26(a) The cathode of an LED is next to the flat part on its rim.

Figure 3.3.26(b) The cathode of a diode is nearest the band painted on its body.

The container

Figure 3.3.27 illustrates the type of box which is easily available for mounting small electronic circuits. It is made from a polymer, so it is tough, light and an electrical insulator. The material is easily drilled and cut with hand tools.

Figure 3.3.27 Boxes which can be used for housing electronic circuits.

Making a p.c.b.

Making a good p.c.b. is an art which comes with practice.

Procedure

Making a p.c.b.

Your p.c.b. will have one face plated with copper. This is covered by a light-sensitive polymer called *photoresist*. It is protected from the light by a black plastic film.

1 Leave the film on while you cut the p.c.b. to shape.
2 Produce a full scale drawing of the copper tracks that you want on the bottom of the p.c.b. This is known as a *mask*. It must be drawn in black on transparent plastic film. Use transfers and black rubber strip if you can.

Requirements

- ❒ One-sided p.c.b.
- ❒ UV exposure box
- ❒ Plastic trays and tongs
- ❒ 0.5 mol dm^{-3} sodium hydroxide
- ❒ 0.5 mol dm^{-3} iron chloride ($FeCl_3$)
- ❒ Plastic film and p.c.b. transfers
- ❒ Drill with 1mm bit

Figure 3.3.28 is a mask for the amplifier circuit of Figure 3.3.15. The black portions show the copper which needs to remain on the p.c.b. It has been enlarged; the IC pins are really separated by 0.10 inches.

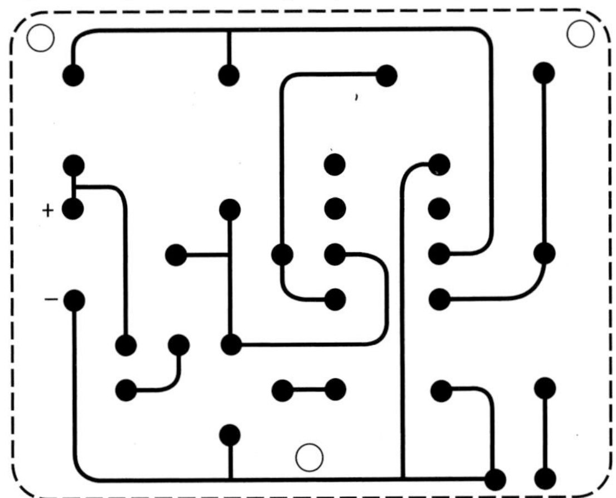

Figure 3.3.28 *P.c.b. mask for the amplifier circuit. The black parts give the pads and tracks needed on the underside of the board, looking through the top of the board.*

Eye protection must be worn UV light chemicals

HAZARD UV light

SAFETY: *Make sure the lid of your UV source is closed when it is switched on.*

3 Remove the black plastic film from the p.c.b.
4 Place the top surface of the mask on the photoresist and put them both in a UV light box (Figure 3.3.29). *The top surface of the mask must touch the photoresist.*
5 Expose the p.c.b. to UV light through the mask for about four minutes. (The exact time will depend on your box and your p.c.b. Some trial and error may be necessary.)

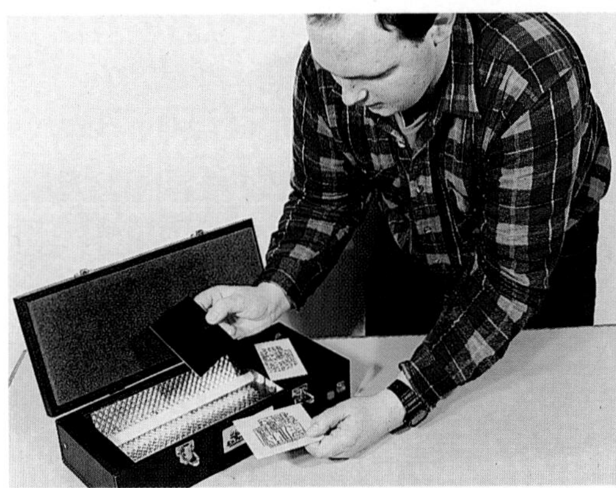

Figure 3.3.29 *A UV light exposure kit.*

CORROSIVE sodium hydroxide

SAFETY: *Use tongs to handle the p.c.b.*

6 Remove the mask from the p.c.b. No marks will be visible, but the UV will have softened some of the polymer film.
7 Immerse the exposed p.c.b. in 0.5 mol dm^{-3} sodium hydroxide solution for a few minutes. A shallow plastic tray is best (Figure 3.3.30). Most of the polymer coating will turn blue and dissolve. What remains will have the pattern on the mask.
8 Rinse the p.c.b. in cold water.
9 Immerse the p.c.b in a warm 0.5 mol dm^{-3} solution of iron(III) chloride. Agitate from time to time. This will slowly remove the exposed copper. Once it has all gone, remove the p.c.b. and rinse in water.
10 Drill all the holes with a 1 mm drill bit, starting from the underside of the board, where the copper tracks are.

IRRITANT iron(III) chloride

Figure 3.3.30 Dissolving photoresist which has been exposed to UV light.

Soldering components

SAFETY: Soldering irons can burn. Handle them with care. Use a proper stand. Be careful not to allow the hot bit to touch the cable.

The fumes from flux in cored solder can trigger asthma attacks. Use a resin-free flux cored solder.

Wear eye protection when trimming the board with side cutters.

The soldering iron must be hot. Clean it at intervals on a damp sponge. Use cored solder. Before using the bit, make sure that its surface is coated with a thin film of fresh solder.

1. Push the pins of the components through the holes (Figure 3.3.16). The pins need soldering to the copper track. This will need two hands.
2. Hold the hot bit of the iron against a pin and the copper (Figure 3.3.31).

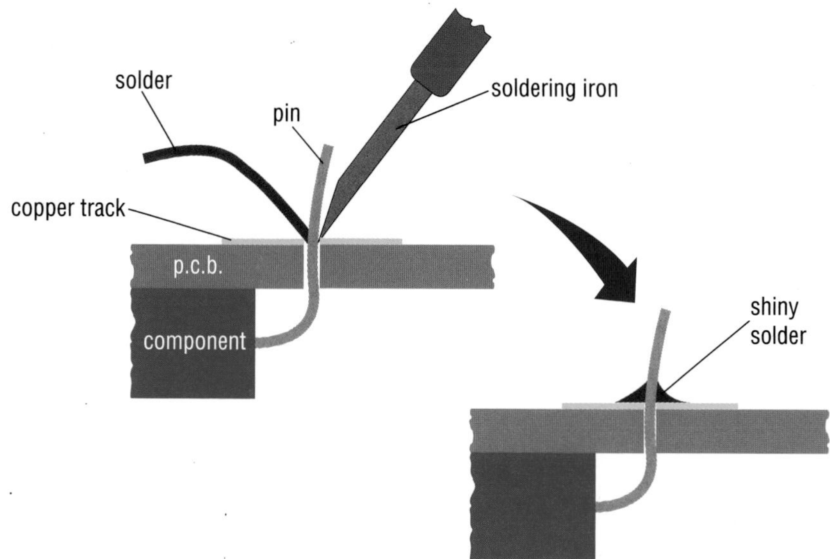

Figure 3.3.31 How to obtain the perfect soldered joint.

3. Push the solder against the pin and let a small amount melt.
4. Remove the bit when the solder has flowed over the pin and the copper track.
5. A good soldered joint is shiny. If it is rough, apply the bit and fresh solder again.
6. Use side cutters to remove surplus copper wire poking through the board.

FOCUS

Electrical devices can be tested and evaluated for their:
- **reliability**
- **accuracy**
- **effectiveness**
- **sensitivity**
- **portability.**

Testing and evaluating electrical devices

No newly built device should be put to work until it has been thoroughly **tested** and evaluated. This is to check that it is able to perform the task for which it was designed and built.

Here are some aspects of the finished device which you should consider. Not all of them are valid for every device. For example, accuracy may not be appropriate for an intercom.

Reliability

Does the device work at all? Does it work every time? Do you have to keep on repairing it? How long will it keep going for? Is it robust enough for the job it has to do?

Accuracy

If the circuit measures some property, how accurately does it do so? If the circuit is supposed to respond to changes at its inputs, does the output change when it is supposed to?

Effectiveness

How well does the circuit accomplish its task? Does it do what it was designed to do? Is it useful? Are its outputs effective? Are they noticed and acted upon?

Sensitivity

How good is the circuit at picking up signals at its input? Can it only respond to strong signals? How weak a signal can it detect?

Portability

How large is the system? How heavy is it? Does it rely on the mains supply? Does it use batteries? Does it have to be connected by wires?

Case study

ELECTRONICS AND SEWAGE

Julie works in a laboratory at a large sewage works in London. Most of her time in the laboratory is spent on routine chemical analysis of sewage and river water samples. Many items of apparatus that she uses are electronic. They allow her to work with an efficiency and accuracy unheard of twenty five years ago.

Illustration 1

Treating sewage

The works treat about half of the sewage generated by London. Most of the work is done by microbes. These are encouraged to digest the organic matter in the sewage. Air is mixed with the sewage to allow aerobic respiration.

Inorganic solid matter is then separated by allowing it to settle to the bottom. The remaining liquid (the effluent) is safe to drink, but inevitably contains many microbes. It is allowed to flow into the River Thames.

Measuring oxygen levels

One of Julie's tasks is to monitor the health of the River Thames. One way that she does this is by measuring the amount of oxygen dissolved in the water. If the sewage works is not careful, the microbes in the effluent can reduce the oxygen content of the river water to below the level needed to sustain fish.

Julie uses a series of oxygen probes at different places, each linked to a data logger. A data logger is a small computer which records the probe measurements over several days. The information can then be transferred into a larger computer. All the information is ultimately stored on magnetic discs, so that it can be analysed at any time in the future.

Calibrating probes

Each probe has to calibrated at regular intervals. Julie does this by measuring the dissolved oxygen of several different water samples, using a chemical technique based on titrations. She can then check that the oxygen probe's electronic measurements agree with her chemical ones, within an acceptable degree of accuracy.

The chemical technique is messy and involves the use of concentrated phosphoric acid. Julie thinks that electronic devices have made the measurement of oxygen levels much safer!

Cooking sludge

The sewage works uses sewage to make its own electricity. Quite often, it produces more electricity than it needs. It sells the surplus to National Power.

Microbes in large tanks are encouraged to digest sewage sludge anaerobically. The organic matter in the sludge is ultimately reduced to methane. Methane forms an explosive mixture when mixed with air, so it can be used to run combustion engines (like the ones in cars). Twelve large engines run generators to make electricity.

Controlling conditions

The conditions inside each sludge digester have to be exactly right. An electronic computer controls these conditions. Sensors in and around the digester relay information to the computer about the temperature, sludge content and methane level. The computer then reacts accordingly, opening and shutting valves, to keep the microbes busy converting human waste into something useful.

Automatic alarms

The digesters also produce large quantities of carbon dioxide. This gas is dangerous because it collects in the lowest part of a building and can easily asphyxiate people who are working there. Therefore, the generator building is equipped with an automatic carbon dioxide alarm system.

The sensors are distributed around the lowest parts of the building where the gas is likely to build up. They are connected to a central electronic system. This activates the alarm if any one of the sensors detects a dangerous level of carbon dioxide.

Emergency communication

Julie spends a lot of time collecting samples from various places in the sewage works. It covers many acres of land, and she would be difficult to find in an emergency. So she carries a CB radio when she is out of the laboratory. Then she can be summoned back to the laboratory at a moment's notice.

Of course, this can work both ways. If Julie finds a problem when she is checking a sensor or analysing samples in the works, she can use her CB radio to summon help immediately.

Questions

1 Draw a block diagram for the electronic system which controls the digesters. Explain the function of each block.

2 Julie often takes electronic measuring devices into the sewage works. Describe and explain the important properties that such equipment should have for it to be useful in this way.

3 The effluent from the sewage works is automatically checked for suspended solids. If there are no suspended solids the water is completely transparent.

(a) Draw a block diagram of an electronic system which could measure how much light was absorbed by the effluent.
(b) Describe the function of each block.
(c) Explain how you would set about calibrating the system.

Assignment

Security alarms

Setting the scene

Electronic systems are very good replacements for security officers in shops and warehouses. They never doze off to sleep, take time off for meals or need pay rises.

You are going to assemble two security alarms. The first is a portable door alarm for use in a warehouse. The second can be used to protect goods in a shop.

The assignment

SAFETY:

- *carry out a risk assessment*
- *check this with your supervisor*
- *UV light*
- *hazardous etching solution*

You are to construct a door alarm and a theft alarm. For each device you must:

1 describe the purpose of the device
2 state the function of its component parts
3 assemble the device
4 evaluate and test the device.

Construction details for each device are given below.

Task 1: Construct a door alarm

The circuit diagram for this device is shown in Figure 3.3.32. The device fits into a small box. The lever on the microswitch must protrude from one end. The box can then be placed next to the door, so that the microswitch is pressed. An LED comes on to show that the system is active.

As soon as the door is opened, that switch is released, the LED goes off and the buzzer makes a noise.

1 Construct the device and test it.
2 Write a report describing the purpose of the device.
3 Draw block and circuit diagrams.
4 State the function of its parts.
5 Give a detailed evaluation of its performance.

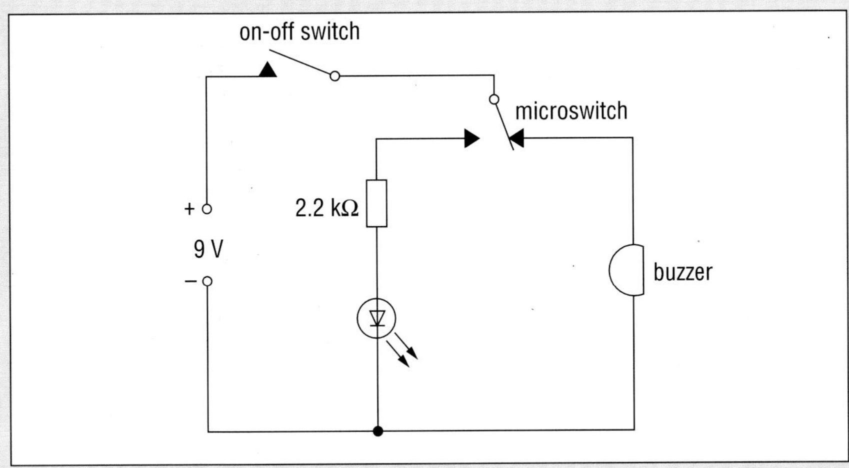

Figure 3.3.32 Circuit diagram for the door alarm.

Task 2: Construct a theft alarm

The circuit diagram for this device is given in Figure 3.3.33.

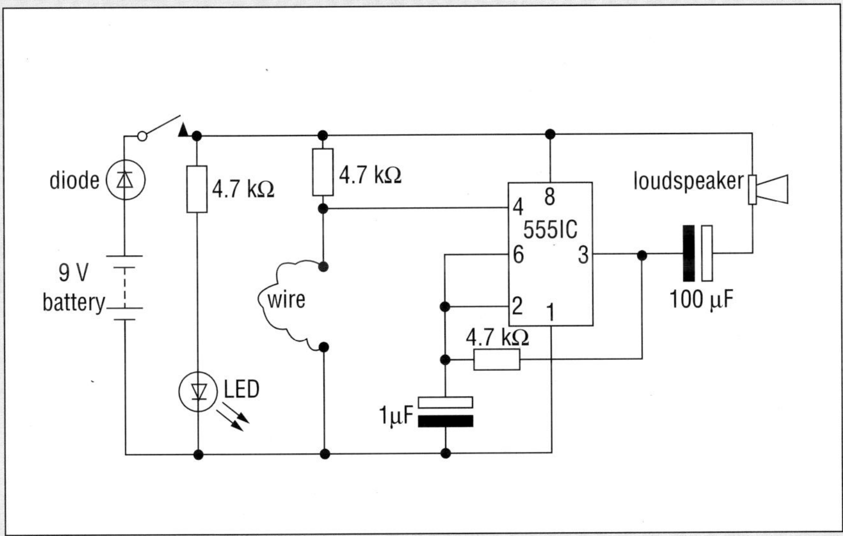

Figure 3.3.33 Circuit diagram for the theft alarm.

A long wire with plugs on its ends is threaded through the items to be safeguarded. The wire is plugged into the circuit. If the wire is cut or unplugged, the loudspeaker makes a noise.

1 Construct the device and test it. (See Figure 3.3.34 for a suitable layout.)
2 Write a report describing the purpose of the device.
3 Draw block and circuit diagrams.
4 State the function of its parts.
5 Give a detailed evaluation of its performance.

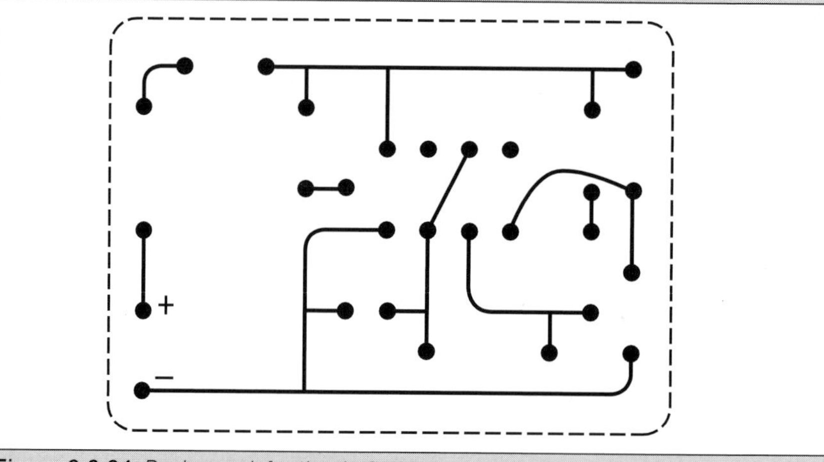

Figure 3.3.34 *P.c.b. mask for the theft alarm.*

Presenting your assignment

You should write a laboratory report of your investigation. You will be asked to discuss this with your supervisor. You should:

- Record your initial ideas and plans in an appendix to the report. The appendix should show how these were modified during the course of the investigation.
- In your conclusion, look back at what you did and state what changes or improvements you would make if the work was carried out again
- List all sources of information at the end of the report.

Grading

This assignment gives you ample opportunity to meet merit or distinction criteria. All four themes are covered: Planning, Information seeking and Information handling, Evaluation, Quality of Outcomes.

Opportunity to collect evidence
In completing this assignment you will have the opportunity to meet the following requirements for Intermediate GNVQ Science:

Science units
Unit 1:
Element 1.3, PCs 1, 2, 3, 4
Unit 3
Element 3.3, PCs 1, 2, 3, 4

Core skill units

Communication:
Elements 2.1, 2.2, 2.3, 2.4

Questions

1 Here is a list of electronic components:

timer capacitor amplifier relay motor LDR thermistor
logic gate resistor switch meter heater LED buzzer lamp

Which of them could:

(a) be integrated circuits?
(b) be input devices?
(c) be output devices?
(d) be used to control high voltages?
(e) combine two input signals?
(f) make light?
(g) measure temperature?
(h) make a sound?
(i) measure light levels?

2 State the five main purposes of electronic devices. Give one example of each purpose.

3 Name the four main parts of all electronic systems. Draw a block diagram to show how energy flows between them.

4 An electronic system controls the temperature of a reaction vessel in a chemical works. Suggest what input and output devices it will need.

4 Monitoring and controlling systems

Things are rarely still. The world around us is in a constant state of change. Sometimes this is helpful, on other occasions it is less so. The ability of the human body to repair itself is a natural change for the good. The rusting of cars and other metal objects is not. There are many examples of change which scientists monitor and control.

The human body has a remarkable capacity to do things which may require strength and skill. The more that scientists understand the workings of the body, the more we are able to improve our ability to do things, whether it be playing a piano, running 1500 m or recovering from injury.

Figure 4.0.1 The skills of this gymnast are largely natural. However, they can be improved through exercise and training.

Chemical reactions occur at rates which depend on the nature of the chemical change and the reaction conditions. A reaction which occurs too quickly can have devastating consequences, for example, an explosion. Some are too slow to allow a substance to be manufactured economically. It is important that scientists are able to control these reactions, increasing their rate or slowing them down, depending on circumstances and needs.

Figure 4.0.2 Several reactions occur in this complex chemical plant. All need to be monitored and controlled. Physical devices such as pumps and optical instruments are used. Their performance also needs to be monitored.

Physical devices may be, amongst others, mechanical (e.g. machines with gears, pulleys or levers) or optical (e.g. cameras and microscopes). Whatever their type and use, scientists need to monitor their performance and understand the factors which affect this performance. In this way, they can optimise and make best use of these devices.

The Elements

Element 4.1 Monitor the performance of tasks by the human body

Monitor the performance of tasks by the human body, page 186

You will need to show that you can:

- identify why performance needs to be monitored and the conditions which affect it
- monitor performance under different conditions
- explain why performance changes under different conditions
- describe the optimum conditions to carry out a task.

Element 4.2 Monitor and control chemical reactions

Monitor and control chemical reactions page 201

You will need to show that you can:

- explain why a reaction needs to be controlled
- describe the factors which affect its rate
- select a method and use it to monitor the change during a reaction
- describe why different conditions affect the rate
- determine the conditions necessary to bring about a specific rate.

Element 4.3 Monitor and control the performance of physical devices

Monitor and control the performance of physical devices page 219

You will need to show that you can:

- identify the performance needed from the device
- identify those factors which affect performance
- select a method to monitor the device's performance
- measure the change in performance as one of the factors is varied
- describe how the performance can be optimised.

Monitor the performance of tasks by the human body

You will need to show that you can:

- identify why performance needs to be monitored and the conditions which affect it
- monitor performance under different conditions
- explain why performance changes under different conditions
- describe the optimum conditions to carry out a task.

Why monitor the performance of tasks by the human body?

Why might a scientist monitor the performance of tasks by the human body? A number of reasons exist. For example, it might be to see how well someone is:

- **recovering from injury**
- **learning a new skill**
- **strengthening their muscles**
- **improving their posture.**

> **FOCUS**
> **A scientist might monitor the performance of tasks by the human body to see how well someone is:**
> - **recovering from injury**
> - **learning a new skill**
> - **strengthening their muscles**
> - **improving their posture.**

Recovering from injury

Physical injuries can affect your ability to perform tasks such as walking and lifting things. To check recovery, nurses and doctors monitor various functions of your body, (e.g. pulse, temperature, blood pressure), as well as others specific to the injury.

Suppose you unfortunately injure your neck, for example, while horse riding or playing rugby (see Figure 4.1.1). You should be taken straight to hospital. There, an X-ray will show if you have broken a bone or dislocated a joint. Let's be optimistic and assume that you haven't broken or dislocated anything, but that you are suffering from concussion. Concussion occurs when someone receives a violent blow to the head. The force causes the brain to shake violently and hit the sides of the skull. Too great a force causes the person to lose consciousness for anything upwards of a few seconds.

Figure 4.1.1 *Two common neck injuries. (a) Falling off a horse. (b) Falling awkwardly in rugby.*

(a)

(b)

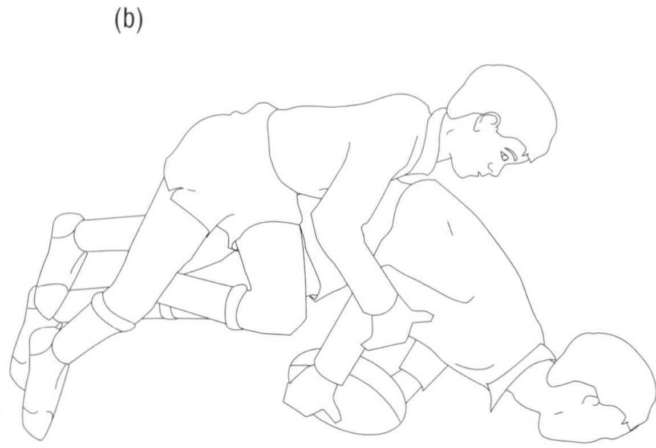

The *Glasgow Coma Scale* allows an assessment of the damage suffered once the person recovers consciousness (see Table 4.1.1). If repeated at intervals of 15–30 minutes use of this scale shows whether the person is becoming more responsive.

Table 4.1.1 Glasgow Coma Scale

The overall score is worked out by adding up the three subtotals. The best possible response is a score of 15.

Response	Score
Eye opening	
Spontaneous	4
When spoken to	3
Only when pricked with a pin	2
None	1
Best spoken responses	
Clear and appropriate sentences	5
Confused sentences	4
Inappropriate words	3
Incomprehensible	2
None	1
Best motor response	
Obeys commands	6
Localises (pinpoints) pain	5
Withdraws to pain	4
Flexes to pain	3
Extends to pain	2
None	1

Learning a new skill

Imagine that you are learning a new skill. It doesn't matter what it is. It might involve learning a new sport, playing a musical instrument, speaking a foreign language or learning to drive a car. You will probably be keen to monitor your performance to see if you are improving. You may rely on your own judgement or ask someone more experienced to give you their opinion.

Figure 4.1.2 *It takes time to learn a new skill. As we improve we monitor our performance or ask for feedback from someone else.*

Strengthening muscles

Each of us has over 600 muscles. Muscles are able to contract and relax. As a muscle contracts, it shortens in length. This property enables us to move the various parts of our body. For example, it allows us to bend our arms, move our eyes, to move food along our digestive tract, and to move our whole body from one place to another.

Two muscles are shown in Figure 4.1.3 – the biceps and the triceps. Both of these muscles are connected at their ends to bones via tendons. Contraction and relaxation enable the arm to be straightened or bent.

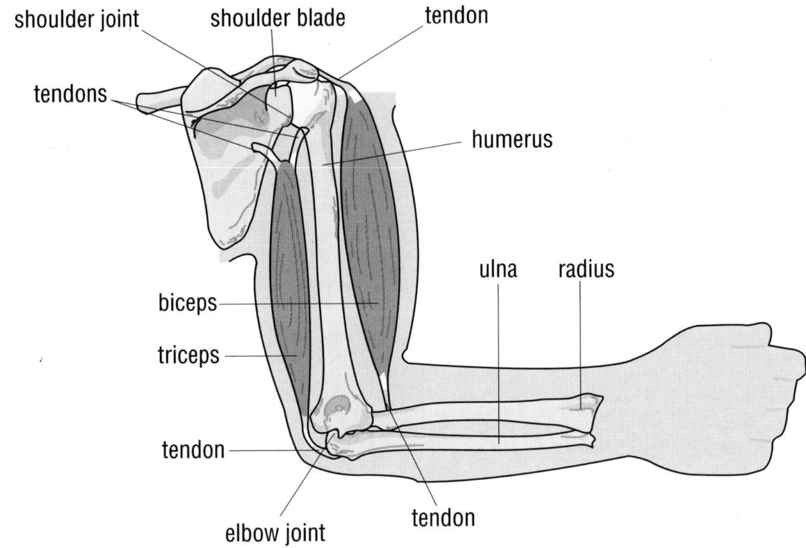

Figure 4.1.3 *Contraction of the biceps muscles produces the opposite effect to contraction of the triceps muscle. For this reason the two muscles are said to be antagonistic. How is bending of the arm achieved? What happens to the arm when the biceps relaxes and the triceps contracts?*

Strength, page 191

There might be all sorts of reasons why someone would want to strengthen their muscles. They might be hoping to improve at a new sport or other pastime, such as rock climbing. Or some of their muscles might have wasted away as a result of injury (see Figure 4.1.4). Once they recover from the injury, they may need to strengthen the relevant muscles carefully and gradually.

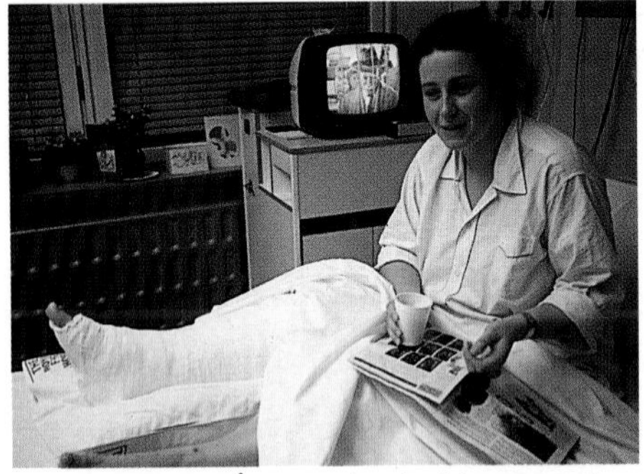

Figure 4.1.4 *The muscles in this person's broken leg will weaken while the leg is in plaster. Once the break has mended and the plaster is removed, the muscles will need, carefully, to be strengthened again.*

Improving posture

Do you ever get backache? There are many reasons why people do, but all too often back ache is due to poor posture (see Figure 4.1.5). At the turn of the century an Australian actor called F. Matthias Alexander found himself repeatedly losing his voice on stage. His doctors were unable to help him, and then he realised that his problem was due to his bad posture. He was standing in such a way that when he spoke his neck stiffened and his head was pulled downwards. The result was that strain was being put on his vocal chords.

After months off work, unable to speak well enough to earn his living, Alexander decided to try to change the way he stood. It worked. Once he had taught himself how to stand with a better posture he no longer lost his voice. You might think that was the end of the story. However, Alexander was so excited by his findings that he gave up his acting career and created an educational programme designed to eradicate bad posture.

Today the Alexander technique, as it is now called, is taught throughout the world. Many people, even those who have never had back ache, find it helps them to feel much healthier, because they do not get so tired and they move with a much better sense of balance.

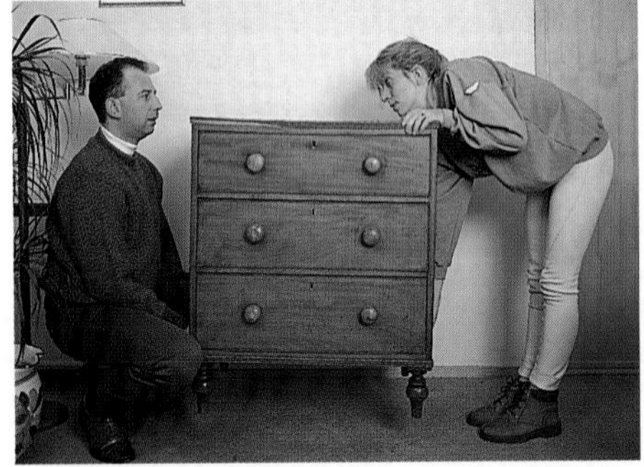

Figure 4.1.5 *One of these two people is much more likely to damage their back than the other. Which one?*

How do conditions affect the performance of tasks by the human body?

Let's concentrate on two fundamental human activities or tasks – **moving** and **lifting** – and ask how the performance of these tasks is affected by

various conditions. We will concentrate on three conditions that affect the performance of these two tasks:

- **load carried**
- **fitness of the body**
- **mental condition.**

We shall look at each of these in more detail and then examine the optimum (best) conditions for carrying out tasks such as moving or lifting.

FOCUS

The performance by the human body of tasks such as moving and lifting is affected by a number of conditions, including:

- **the load carried**
- **the fitness of the body**
- **the person's mental condition.**

Load carried

It is hardly surprising that, other things being equal, the greater the load (weight) carried, the poorer our performance of a task. This is true whether we are talking about moving (e.g. walking, running, swimming) or lifting (both objects and yourself). This is the reason why athletes, when competing, use equipment and clothing made from the lightest materials (see Figure 4.1.6). It is also the reason why, in a handicap race, the best horses are made to carry extra weights.

Fitness of the body

The fitter you are, the easier you will find it to carry out tasks such as moving or lifting. But what, precisely, is meant by fitness? No single answer can be given, but physical fitness has three main aspects to it:

- *stamina* – endurance, the ability to keep going without gasping for breath
- *strength* – muscle power
- *suppleness* – flexibility, having the maximum natural range of movement in your joints.

Activities differ in the effects they have on stamina, strength and suppleness (see Table 4.1.2). However, if you take up a new sport or form of exercise, be prepared to exercise for several weeks before you can expect to see any significant improvement in your physical fitness. The important thing is to do something you enjoy. For any lasting improvement in fitness, you will probably need to do the activity at least three times a week for 15 or more minutes on each occasion.

Figure 4.1.6 *The biathlon is an event in which the person skis cross-country and occasionally stops to shoot at a target. Not surprisingly, competitors minimise the weight of their skis and rifle.*

Mental condition

How well we perform at a physical task can depend on our mental condition. For this reason top-class athletes increasingly make use of sports psychologists. Sports psychologists do such things as:

- establish the psychological (mental) factors which contribute to success
- teach athletes the mental skills that allow them to perform to the peak of their potential
- help an athlete who is having psychological problems, such as a crisis of confidence.

There are many mental factors which affect how well we perform tasks. These can conveniently be divided into:

- internal factors, over which we have some control
- external factors, over which we have little direct control (see Figure 4.1.7).

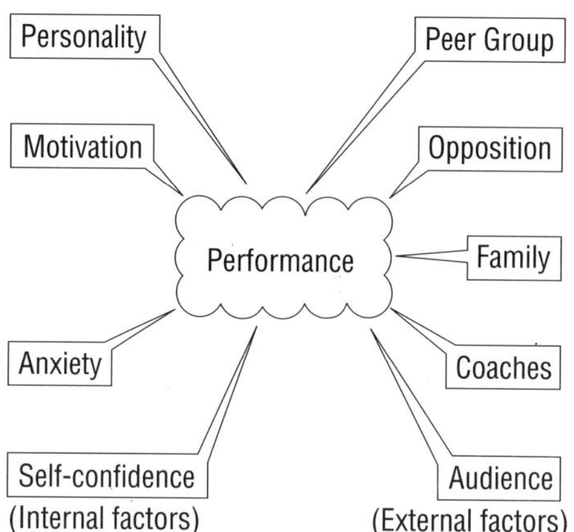

Figure 4.1.7 *Our performance at sports or other tasks is affected by our mental condition. Both internal and external factors play a part.*

What are the optimum conditions for carrying out a task?

It is extremely difficult to generalise as to the optimum (best) conditions for carrying out a task. However, suppose your task consists of a three hour walk across open ground (see Figure 4.1.8) There are two types of conditions to consider:

- conditions outside your control
- conditions within your control.

Here are some examples of the ways in which you can affect conditions within your control:

- *Clothing and footwear*. Make sure your clothing and footwear are comfortable, that you have used them before and that they are appropriate for the conditions and for any emergencies which may occur. You should have a map, a compass, a watch, waterproof clothing, emergency rations (including water), a whistle, a torch and spare warm clothing.

Table 4.1.2 The consequences of different activities for physical fitness

• = no real benefit •• = beneficial effect ••• = very beneficial effect •••• = excellent effect

Sport	Stamina score	Strength score	Suppleness score
Badminton	••	••	•••
Canoeing	•••	•••	••
Climbing stairs	•••	••	•
Cricket	•	•	••
Cycling (hard)	•••	•••	••
Dancing (ballroom)	•	•	•••
Dancing (disco)	•••	•	••••
Digging	•••	••••	••
Football	•••	•••	•••
Golf	•	•	••
Gymnastics	••	•••	••••
Hill walking	•••	••	•
Housework	•	•	••
Jogging	••••	••	••
Judo	••	••	••••
Rowing	••••	••••	••
Sailing	•	••	••
Squash	•••	••	•••
Swimming (hard)	••••	••••	••••
Tennis	••	•••	•••
Walking (briskly)	••	•	•
Weightlifting	•	••••	•
Yoga	•	•	••••

- *Fitness*. Obviously you can't increase your fitness overnight, but appropriate exercise carried out over a period of at least a few weeks can help to improve your stamina, strength and suppleness (see Table 4.1.2). In addition, make sure you aren't tired through lack of sleep before starting the task.
- *Company*. Walk with friends. For one thing, this will probably make the walk more enjoyable; for another it's safer than walking a long way on your own.
- *Weather and state of the ground*. Obviously these are not entirely within your control! However, keep in mind that if either of these are really bad, you can always postpone the walk or change the route.

Figure 4.1.8 Planning can help ensure that the optimum conditions for a task, such as a long walk, are in place.

How can the performance of tasks in different conditions be monitored?

The performance of a task can be monitored by measuring a person's:

- **speed**
- **strength**
- **stamina**
- **suppleness**
- **reaction time**
- **recovery rate.**

> FOCUS
>
> **The performance of tasks can be monitored by measuring a person's:**
> - **speed**
> - **strength**
> - **stamina**
> - **suppleness**
> - **reaction time**
> - **recovery rate.**

Speed

The speed with which someone can satisfactorily carry out a task is a measure of their performance at it. A professional secretary, for example, can type ten times faster, and more accurately, than someone who has spent only a few hours at a typewriter or word processor. Professional removal people are used to lifting heavy objects quickly and efficiently (see Figure 4.1.9). Scientists can monitor these activities, and others, to study the abilities of a wide range of people. Science affects everybody.

Strength

Few tasks can be achieved through strength alone. However, such activities as moving or carrying objects, not to mention most sports, require a certain amount of strength. A person's strength is a measure of how much force their muscles have. Some of the main muscles of a human are shown in Figure 4.1.10. Closer examination of a muscle shows that it is made up of large numbers of muscle fibres (see Figure 4.1.11).

Training to increase strength, such as weight training, has little effect on the number of muscle fibres. What it does do, though, is to increase:

- the number and size of the fibrils that make up each muscle fibre
- the amount of protein in the muscle
- the strength of tendons (which attach muscles to bones) and ligaments (which attach bones to bones at a joint)
- the blood supply to the muscles.

Note. *Weight training can lead to serious injury unless you are careful. It should never be undertaken without proper supervision.*

Figure 4.1.9 Professional removal people can shift large, heavy objects a lot more quickly than the rest of us can.

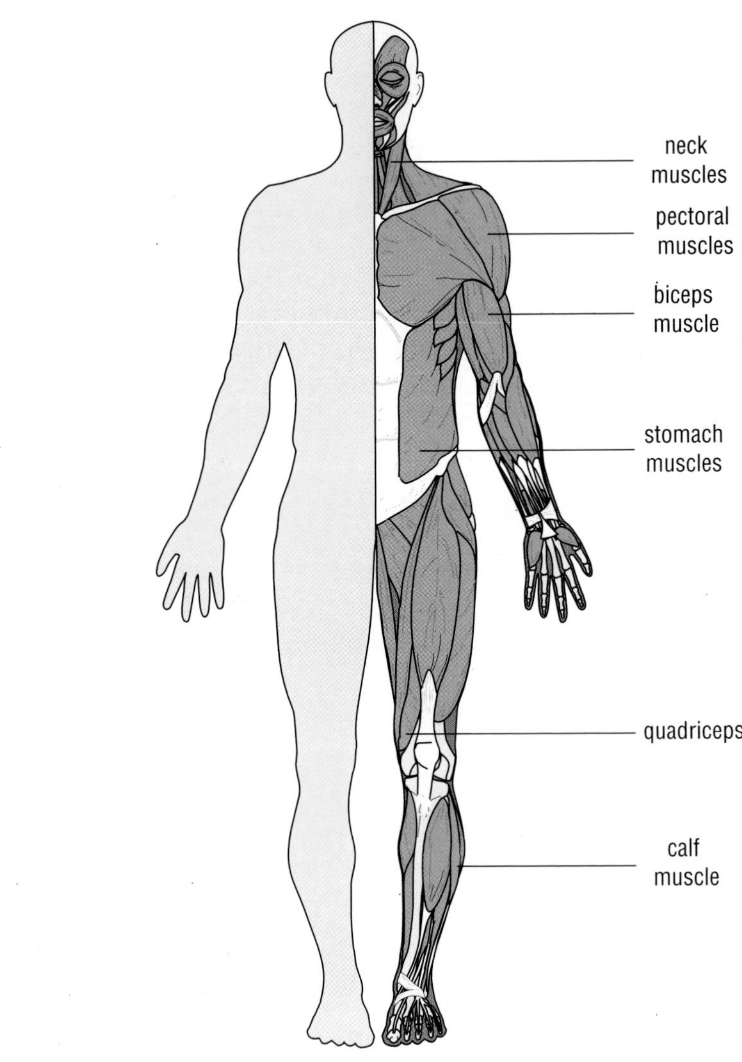

Figure 4.1.10 Some of the main muscles of a human body.

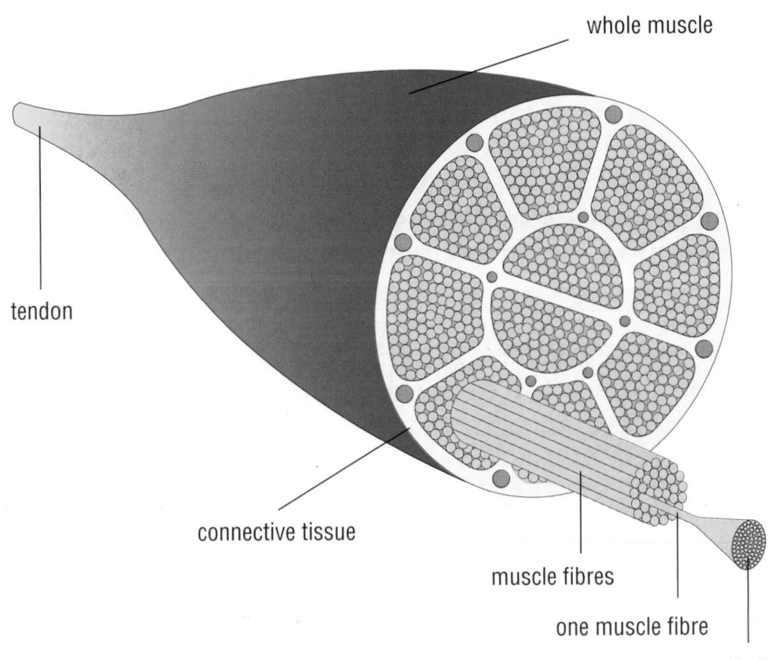

Figure 4.1.11 Muscles are made up of muscle fibres. A single muscle fibre contains a number of fibrils.

Procedure

Recording a person's strength

A number of measurements allow strength to be recorded:

- the maximum mass moved in a leg press (see Figure 4.1.12)
- the maximum mass lifted in a bench press (see Figure 4.1.13)
- the length of time a lateral hang lasts (see Figure 4.1.14)
- the maximum force exerted in a grip test (see Figure 4.1.15).

Record one or more of these four measures of strength before and after a period of training or rehabilitation. Compare the results to see whether strength has increased. If it has, by what percentage has the measure of strength increased?

Requirements

At least one of:

- ❐ Leg press
- ❐ Bench press
- ❐ Beam for pull-ups and watch with second hand
- ❐ Hand dynamometer

SAFETY: *A qualified person should be in attendance when such equipment is being used. You should warm up thoroughly before undertaking strenuous exercise.*

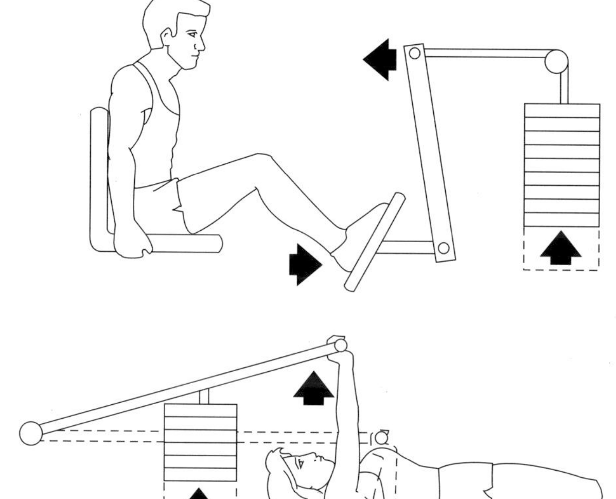

Figure 4.1.12 *Getting a measure of strength by doing a leg press. Sit with your back firmly against the seat with the angle at your knee joints being 90°. Hold the seat rails and straighten your legs. Record the maximum mass moved.*

Figure 4.1.13 *Getting a measure of strength by doing a bench press. Lie face up on a bench with your head nearest to the apparatus, and your feet placed flat against the ground. Keep your hips in contact with the bench and extend your arms fully. Record the maximum mass moved.*

Figure 4.1.14 *Getting a measure of strength by doing a lateral hang. Pull yourself up on a beam so that your eyes are above the top line of the beam. Without touching the beam, or kicking or struggling, record for how long you can hold this position.*

Figure 4.1.15 *Getting a measure of strength by using a dynamometer. Use both hands in turn. Place the dynamometer in your palm, dial up, with the needle adjusted, if necessary, so that it reads zero. Keep your arm well away from your body and squeeze as hard as possible. Record, for each hand, the best of three attempts.*

Stamina

A person's stamina is a measure of their staying-power or endurance.

Procedure

Recording a person's stamina

Requirements

- ❒ Running track
- ❒ Watch with second hand

Provided you are able to run, a good measure of stamina is provided by recording how long it takes to run a mile and a half (2400 m). Unless you are reasonably fit, you may not be able to run this far. If this is the case, run just half a mile and then multiply how long this takes by three to get an estimate of how long it would take you to run a mile and a half. (Obviously this will be an underestimate of how long it would take you to run a mile and a half.)

Don't attempt to run a mile and a half unless you have suitable running shoes. Table 4.1.3 indicates, for males and for females aged 17 to 29, what their stamina is as a function of how long it takes to run a mile and a half. Don't get too discouraged if you end up as poor or very poor. The table comes from the National Coaching Foundation, and they have quite high standards!

Table 4.1.3 Stamina as a function of how long it takes a 17-29 year-old to run a mile and a half (2400 m)

Stamina	Time for a woman	Time for a man
Superb	Under 9 min	Under 7 min 30 s
Excellent	9 min – 9 min 53 s	7 min 30 s – 8 min 14 s
Very good	9 min 54 s – 12 min 17 s	8 min 15 s – 10 min 14 s
Good	12 min 18 s – 14 min 23 s	10 min 15 s – 11 min 59 s
Fair	14 min 24 s – 17 min 23 s	12 min – 14 min 29 s
Poor	17 min 24 s – 19 min 47 s	14 min 30 s – 16 min 29 s
Very poor	Over 19 min 48 s	Over 16 min 30 s

Suppleness

Suppleness means the same thing as flexibility. It is affected by a number of things as well as by fitness. In particular, suppleness decreases with age and, after puberty, is generally less in men than in women (see Figure 4.1.16).

Figure 4.1.16 *Women are generally more supple than men. The younger you are, the more supple you tend to be. Competitive gymnasts and divers are particularly supple.*

Procedure

Recording a person's suppleness

The easiest way to measure your suppleness is to try to touch your toes as shown in Figure 4.1.16. Be careful. You should not strain, otherwise you risk injuring yourself:

- If you are unable to touch your toes, ask a friend to measure how far short you are.
- If you can touch your toes without difficulty, stand on a firm bench and ask a friend to see how far beneath your toes you can reach.

When you write your results down, record a distance short of your toes as a negative distance, and a distance below your toes as a positive distance.

Requirements

- ❒ Bench
- ❒ Ruler

Reaction time

Your reaction time is a measure of how long it takes for you to register a signal (such as a noise or a flash of light), process it in your brain and react by contracting certain muscles. Quick reaction times are important in many sports and, with practice, a person can improve their reaction time.

Procedure

Measuring a person's reaction time

Reaction times can be measured with considerable precision using a computer and a piece of software which records the time that elapses between the production of a noise, or the appearance of a visual signal on screen, and the subject hitting the space bar in response.

If you do not have access to this equipment, you can find your reaction time like this:

1. Ask another person to hold a ruler vertically.
2. Almost clasp the end nearer the floor with your thumb and index finger.
3. Your partner should then release the ruler without your knowing when.
4. Clasp the ruler as soon as you can.
5. Record the distance, d, the ruler has fallen in metres.
6. Use the following formula to convert d to time, t, in seconds:
   $t = \sqrt{d/4.9}$

Requirements

- ❒ Computer and software, or ruler

Recovery rate

One measure of fitness is that the fitter someone is, the quicker they recover after undertaking a task.

Procedure

Measuring a person's recovery rate

The easiest way to determine a person's recovery time is to measure their heart rate and see how long it takes to return to normal. Follow these instructions:

1. Ask the person to sit down quietly for 5 minutes.
2. Find their heart rate in beats per minute by counting their pulse for 30 seconds and multiplying by 2. The pulse can be felt either at the wrist or on the neck.
3. Wait 30 seconds and repeat step 2.

Requirements

- ❒ Watch with second hand

4 Ask the person to undertake a fixed task – e.g. 100 step ups. If you intend to compare the recovery rates of different people, make sure they undertake the same task, and take the same amount of time to complete it.
5 Ask the person to sit down and rest.
6 Thirty seconds after the end of the task, measure their heart rate by counting their pulse for 30 seconds and multiplying by 2.
7 Wait 30 seconds and then, again, measure their heart rate by counting their pulse for 30 seconds and multiplying by 2.
8 Repeat step 7 until their heart rate has returned to normal.
9 Plot a graph of heart rate against time.
10 Find out from your graph approximately how long it takes from the end of the exercise for the person's heart rate to return to normal (see Figure 4.1.17).

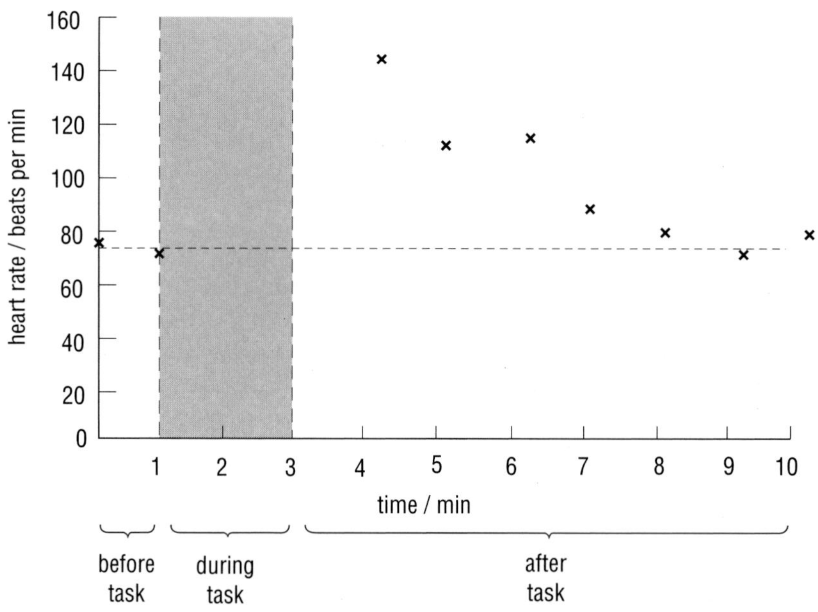

Figure 4.1.17 A hypothetical graph showing a person's heart rate before and after a period of exercise. Notice how the person's heart rate takes some time, in this case approximately five and a half minutes, to recover after the exercise has ended.

Why may our performance of tasks change?

Our **performance** at any task, whether physical or mental, depends on both internal and external factors. Amongst the reasons that may cause our performance of tasks to change are:

- **familiarity with task**
- **fatigue**
- **increased skill.**

> FOCUS
> **Our performance of tasks may change for a number of reasons including:**
> - **familiarity with task**
> - **fatigue**
> - **increased skill.**

Familiarity with task

The more familiar we are with a task, the better we perform. There are two main reasons for this, one mental, the other physical:

- we learn how to perform the task better
- we are physically more able to perform the task.

In an activity such as swimming, given a good coach, we improve. We become better at the stroke we are using (butterfly, crawl, back stroke or breast stroke), we learn how to breathe more effectively and how to turn more quickly at the end of a pool (see Figure 4.1.18). Learning involves change in the cerebral hemispheres in the brain (see Figure 4.1.19). This is the part of the brain responsible for memory.

Figure 4.1.18 One of the reasons we become better at performing tasks is that we learn how to do them better. This swimmer has learned how to turn underwater efficiently in the minimum time possible.

The other reason why coaching helps us to become better swimmers is that, as we train, we become fitter. Muscles used for swimming become stronger, joints become more supple and we are able to breathe in larger volumes of oxygen more rapidly. All of these are physical benefits of exercise.

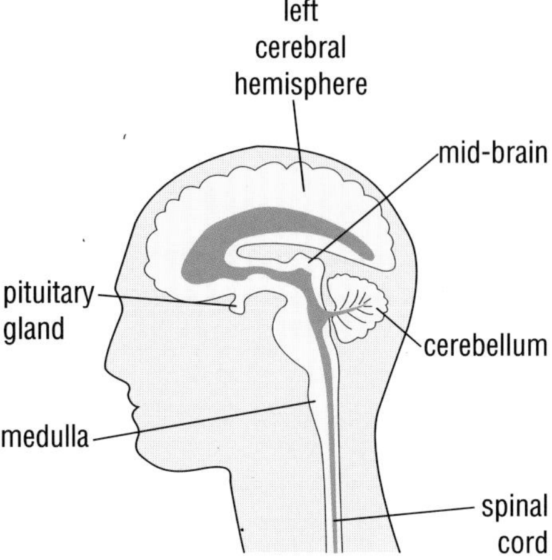

Figure 4.1.19 Learning involves subtle changes in the cerebral hemispheres of our brain.

Fatigue

If you carry out a task for a long time, fatigue sets in. You become tired. The main reason for fatigue is to do with our muscles. Muscles use up a lot of oxygen during aerobic respiration. In aerobic respiration, oxygen reacts with glucose to release energy. This energy can be used to make the muscles contract. However, when the muscles are working fast, and therefore short of oxygen, a waste product builds up. This waste product is called lactic acid. It causes our muscles to become 'wobbly' after we've exercised flat out for a while (see Figure 4.1.20).

Fatigue may also lead to a shortage of minerals, such as salt, reaching a muscle. The result is cramp, though there are other causes of cramp.

Figure 4.1.20 One reason for fatigue is a build up of lactic acid in muscles that have been working flat out.

Figure 4.1.21 If you devote most of your waking life to performing one task, such as playing tennis, supremely well, you may become totally bored with it and drop out early in your career. Think of a top sportsperson or musician you admire. Work out approximately how many hours they may have spent practising. Now work out approximately how long you have spent practising the same activity.

Increased skill

Familiarity with a task generally results in increased skill for reasons we have considered. However, it's worth pointing out that there is a limit to this. Too great a familiarity with a task can lead to boredom and a fall-off in performance. You may enjoy a particular sport, but would you enjoy doing it eight hours a day, six days a week, 48 weeks of the year for the next 20 years? One of the skills in being a coach or teacher is to motivate people so that they don't get bored while they put in all the hours needed to become really good at something (see Figure 4.1.21).

Familiarity with task, page 196

Case study

THINK BACK BEFORE YOU ACT

Just as there are commonsense rules to be followed in order to avoid back problems, so there are some points to be remembered by those who suffer chronic back pain to avoid adding stress to their spines. These suggestions also apply to those who have suffered acute back pain in the past and recovered, but in whom weaknesses may still exist and if they take care in the future they can reduce the risk of a repetition of debilitating back pain. To these points, sufferers and potential sufferers can add a regular daily pattern of exercises to strengthen the muscles of the abdomen, the back and the buttocks. However, since exercises should vary according to the nature of the spinal problem, which may be made worse if the wrong exercises are used, seek professional advice, from a doctor for example, before any exercise programme is undertaken. Exercises are not therefore included with this list of self-care suggestions.

GENERAL RECOMMENDATIONS

POSTURE

Always try to maintain an upright posture, with stomach in and the back kept straight. Imagine that you are being lifted up by the top of your head. This applies to standing, walking and sitting. Avoid hunching up the shoulders when angry or under stress.

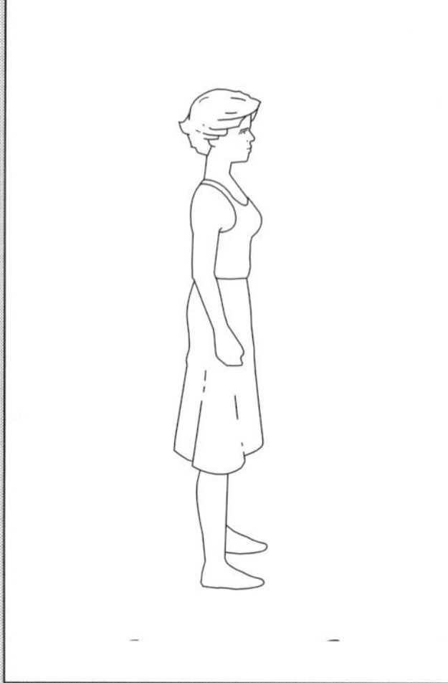

WEIGHT

Excess weight only adds to the stresses put upon the spine. Ask your doctor to advise you on a safe diet to reduce your body weight, if it is greater than the average for your height.

CHAIRS

Use straight-backed firm chairs, not heavily padded ones, and preferably shaped or with some support to the lumbar region of your back (just above the buttocks). If not, place a cushion there if sitting for a long period. Avoid slouching in deep easy chairs or settees, especially when concentrating a long time, such as with T.V.

BEDS

Use a firm mattress (this does not mean a hard bed. Firm mattresses allow some absorption of the hip and shoulder). If you find sleep difficult owing to the firmness, use a mattress that gives good support to the spine and, if it helps, lie horizontally in any position comfortable. Do not continue to use an old mattress which is worn out and gives insufficient support, as this will aggravate any stress for the long period when your spine needs the rest and time to "recharge" your discs. Beware of claims made by some "orthopaedic" bed manufacturers and once again ask your doctor's advice.

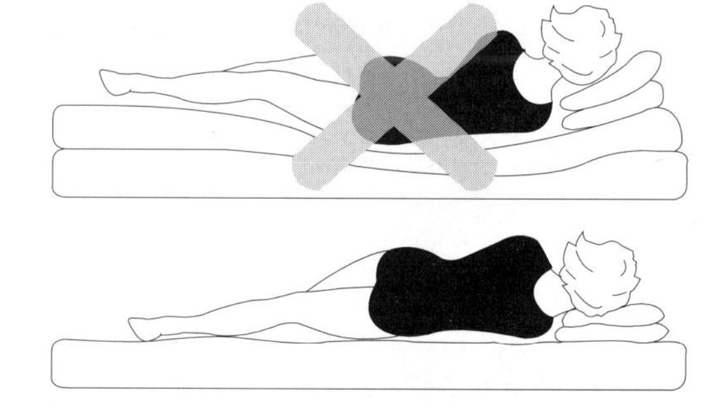

TAKE CARE WHEN LIFTING, BENDING, STRETCHING AND TWISTING YOUR BODY.

Perform all movements smoothly, avoiding jerks, to the body, and spine. Think about your fitness and try not to do too much.

Questions

1 What is meant by 'chronic back pain'?

2 Why do you think an upright posture can help prevent back pain?

3 What type of tasks put particular stress on the back?

4 Various recommendations are made to help protect the back from injury. How could you monitor the necessary changes in a person's posture and weight?

5 Why must a person be extremely wary about exercising to strengthen the muscles of the abdomen, the back and the buttocks?

6 What precautions should a person take when relaxing or resting?

Assignment

WHAT EFFECT DOES EXERCISE HAVE ON THE BODY?

Setting the scene

We are often told that exercise is good for us. But exactly what consequences does it have? In this assignment you can investigate both the short-term and the long-term consequences of exercise.

The assignment

You will need to work on this assignment in a group of at least two. Your task is to study the consequences of exercise in:

- the short-term
- the long-term.

Short-term consequences are those that happen during the exercise itself and as the person is recovering from the exercise. Exercise has short-term consequences for the following:

- body temperature
- pulse rate
- volume of blood pumped each time the heart beats
- breathing rate
- oxygen consumption
- build-up of an oxygen debt, to be paid off at the end of the exercise when extra oxygen is breathed in
- sweating and other ways of reducing overheating.

Long-term consequences of exercise are those that happen over a period of weeks as the body gets used to exercising. Exercise has long-term consequences for the following:

- resting heart rate
- volume of blood pumped each cardiac cycle
- vital capacity of the lungs
- number of (energy-producing) mitochondria in muscle fibres
- blood supply to muscles
- amount of the oxygen-holding molecule myoglobin found in muscle
- size of individual muscle fibres
- strength
- stamina
- suppleness
- feeling of well-being
- skin conditioning and tone
- tendon, ligament and bone strength.

SAFETY: *Get your plans checked by your supervisor before you start.*

You will need to:

1. find out which of these you can measure
2. work out how to use any specialised equipment that is available to you
3. arrange to have access to the equipment you need
4. decide how many experimental subjects (people) you will investigate and how to choose them

5 work out an exercise schedule which is appropriate for your subjects
6 resolve issues such as confidentiality and safety
7 have your plans checked by your teacher/lecturer before you start.

Presenting your assignment

You should:

- store your results appropriately (e.g. on a spreadsheet)
- present your assignment in a report, backed up by graphs and tables of your findings. The report should show what you did and what you found out, and should be capable of being understood by someone with no prior knowledge of your assignment.

Additional information

The following Procedures are available:

- recording a person's strength, page 193
- recording a person's stamina, page 194
- recording a person's suppleness, page 195
- recording a person's recovery rate, page 195.

Grading

This assignment gives you ample opportunity to meet merit or distinction criteria. All four themes are covered: Planning, Information Seeking and Information Handling, Evaluation, Quality of Outcomes.

Opportunity to collect evidence
In completing this assignment you will have the opportunity to meet the following requirements for Intermediate GNVQ Science:

Science units
Unit 1:
Element 1.2, PCs 1, 2, 3, 4, 5
Unit 4:
Element 4.1, PCs 1, 2, 3, 4

Core skill units

Application of number:
Elements 2.1, 2.2, 2.3

Communication:
Elements 2.1, 2.2, 2.3

Information technology:
Elements 2.1, 2.2, 2.3, 2.4, 2.5

Questions

1 Identify four reasons why a scientist might monitor the performance of tasks by the human body.

2 State one advantage of a good posture.

3 Give three conditions which can affect the performance of a task such as moving or lifting.

4 One aspect of physical fitness is suppleness. Give two others and explain what each means.

5 Name five features (apart from suppleness) of performance in carrying out a task.

6 Give three reasons why there may be a change in the performance of a task.

Monitor and control chemical reactions

You will need to show that you can:
- explain why a reaction needs to be controlled
- describe the factors which affect its rate
- select a method and use it to monitor the change during a reaction
- describe why different conditions affect the rate
- determine the conditions necessary to bring about a specific rate.

The need to control reaction rates

Chemical reactions can be made to go faster or slower. There are several reasons for controlling the rate of a reaction. These include the need to:
- control a production process
- control energy transfer
- ensure safety.

Scientists and engineers work together to ensure that reaction rates in industrial and other processes are controlled.

Rate of reaction

The rate of a chemical reaction is determined by measuring the changes in concentration of either reactants or products over a period of time.

$$\text{rate of reaction} = \frac{\text{change in concentration}}{\text{time taken for change}}$$

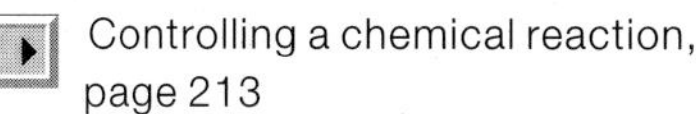
Monitoring change and measuring reaction rates , page 206

Controlling a chemical reaction, page 213

The concentration of reactants decreases in a reaction, while the concentration of products increases. Some reactions are extremely fast, for example the precipitation of an insoluble salt, while others are slow. In fact, some reactions are so slow that it is difficult to see that they are taking place at all by simply looking at them. For example, cars where the paintwork is scratched become rusty. This is a chemical reaction between oxygen and water vapour in the air and iron. You know rust when you see it, but you could watch a car all day and not notice a change.

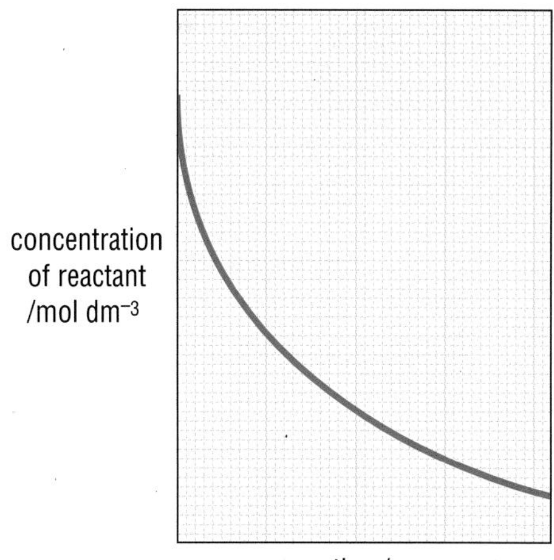

Figure 4.2.1 This graph shows how the concentration of a reactant changes with time during a chemical reaction. Can you draw a graph to show how the concentration of a product of the reaction changes with time?

Production processes

In most *production processes* the aim is to obtain high yields of pure product in the shortest time. Conditions are usually chosen to speed up the chemical reaction(s) involved. However, sometimes conditions which increase the rate give a low yield of product. A slower reaction rate must be accepted to achieve higher yields.

Two of the most important industrial processes are:
- the *Haber process* for the manufacture of ammonia. The reaction between nitrogen and hydrogen is used to make ammonia.

  nitrogen + hydrogen ⇌ ammonia

  $N_2(g) + 3H_2(g) \rightleftharpoons 2NH_3(g)$

- the *Contact process* for the manufacture of sulphuric acid. An important stage in the production is making sulphur trioxide from sulphur dioxide:

  sulphur dioxide + oxygen ⇌ sulphur trioxide

  $2SO_2(g) + O_2(g) \rightleftharpoons 2SO_3(g)$

Figure 4.2.2 Chemical reactions occur when concrete sets. The rate at which these reactions occur helps to determine the strength of the concrete. Why is it often suggested that concrete should be kept wet when laid on hot summer days?

Figure 4.2.3 There was a major disaster in 1974 at Flixborough. A massive explosion occurred in a chemical plant manufacturing nylon. Cyclohexane escaped and exploded in an uncontrollable reaction with oxygen in the air when it eventually ignited. 28 people died.

Neither of the reactions above go to completion. No matter how long they are left under particular conditions, the theoretical yields of products are never obtained. In these reactions, products are formed and then react with one another to reform starting materials. The reaction mixture contains both starting materials and products which are continually reacting to form one another. When forward and back reactions are occurring at the same rate, a *dynamic equilibrium* is said to be achieved. The sign $\rightleftharpoons$ is used to show an equilibrium reaction.

In both reactions, lower temperatures lead to higher yields. However, the rate of a chemical reaction decreases with decreasing temperature. A compromise is needed and a balance between high yield and the time it takes to achieve it must be struck.

Energy transfer

All chemical reactions involve the *transfer of energy*, often in the form of heat energy.

Exothermic reactions give out heat energy. Heat produced increases the rate, producing more heat more quickly, increasing the rate even more, and so on. The danger of a runaway reaction getting out of control is easy to see.

Endothermic reactions absorb heat energy from the surroundings. This means that the surroundings get cooler and the rate of reaction decreases. The reaction mixture may need to be heated to maintain an acceptable rate.

The temperature of an exothermic reaction can be maintained by cooling while the temperature of an endothermic reaction can be maintained by heating.

Safety

The control of reaction rates is essential to ensure the *safety* of processes, whether they are being carried out in the laboratory or on an industrial scale. A reaction which occurs too quickly may get out of control. This might lead to an explosion with the resulting damaging effects.

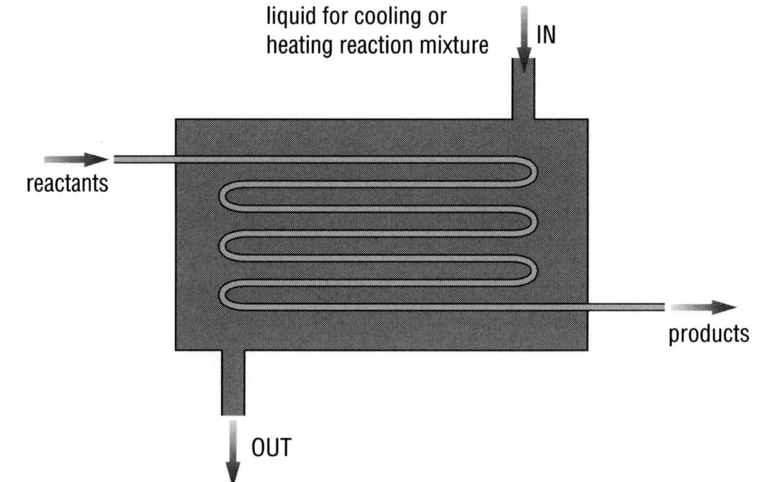

Figure 4.2.4 In this reactor, either a hot or a cold liquid or gas can be passed around the tube containing the reaction mixture. Cold liquids or gases are used to stop the temperature of an exothermic reaction from reaching an unacceptable, possibly dangerous, level. Why do you think the reaction tube is coiled?

Conditions affecting reaction rates

The rate of a chemical reaction is affected by:

- the concentration of reactants
- temperature.

Figure 4.2.5 Freezers and refrigerators are used to store food which would otherwise decay. Why do foods keep longer in a freezer than in a refrigerator?

Explaining rates of reaction, page 211

It may also be affected by:

- the surface area of a solid
- the presence of a catalyst.

Concentration of reactants

Rate of reaction increases with increasing **concentration of reactants.** It decreases with decreasing concentration of reactants.
For example, magnesium reacts with hydrochloric acid:

magnesium + hydrochloric acid → magnesium chloride + hydrogen

$Mg(s) + 2HCl(aq) \rightarrow MgCl_2(aq) + H_2(g)$

The rate of this reaction can be judged by how quickly the mixture effervesces (fizzes), giving off hydrogen. Effervescence is more vigorous with more concentrated samples of acid. You can show this in a simple experiment. Add separate lengths of magnesium ribbon to samples of hydrochloric acid of differing concentration. To make it a fair test, other factors which might affect the rate must be the same in each experiment, for example temperature, and whether or not the ribbon is cut into smaller lengths.

> **FOCUS**
> **Effect of concentration of reactants on rate:**
> - **increase in concentration causes an increase in rate**
> - **decrease in concentration causes a decrease in rate.**

Figure 4.2.6 Many animals hibernate when food is in short supply. This is their built-in safety mechanism to avoid starvation. Their body temperature drops, which, in turn, causes the chemical reactions occurring in the body to slow down. They survive on stored energy until warm weather triggers their return to normal living. Why do you think that many people feel lethargic in hot weather?

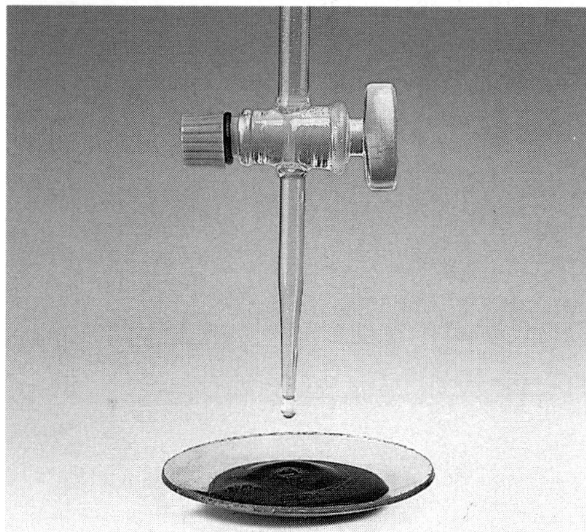

Figure 4.2.7 Manganese(IV) oxide catalyses the decomposition of hydrogen peroxide into water and oxygen. The rate of effervescence shows the rate of reaction. The more concentrated the hydrogen peroxide being dropped on to the catalyst, the more vigorous is the reaction.

Reactions slow down as reactants become used up. This is simply because their concentrations are decreasing and, as we have said, rate depends on concentration.

> **FOCUS**
> **Effect of temperature on rate:**
> - **increase in temperature causes an increase in rate**
> - **decrease in temperature causes a decrease in rate.**

The rate of gaseous reactions increases with increasing pressure. This is because higher pressures bring the reactants closer together. Therefore, the concentration increases, which increases the reaction rate.

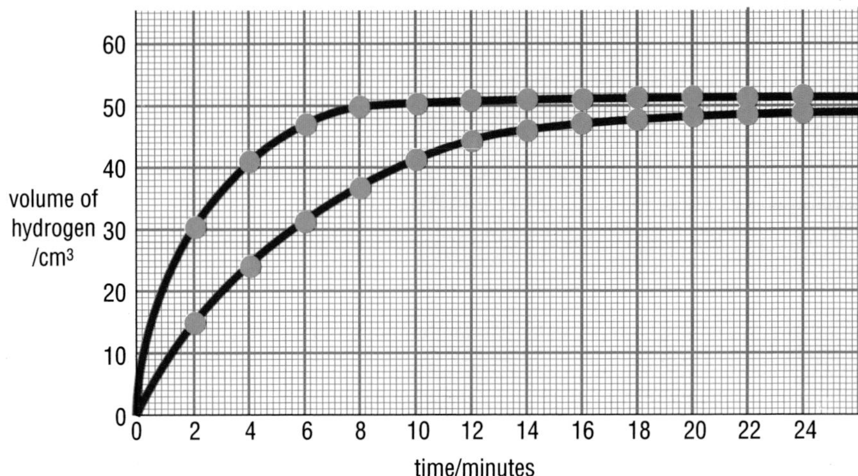

Figure 4.2.8 Zinc reacts more rapidly with 2 mol dm^{-3} sulphuric acid than with 1 mol dm^{-3} sulphuric acid. These graphs show the results of two experiments. Can you sketch the graph that would be obtained if 0.5 mol dm^{-3} sulphuric acid were used?

Temperature

An increase in **temperature** increases the rate of a chemical reaction. For example, a 10 °C rise in temperature can double the rate of reaction at room temperature. Similarly, decreasing the temperature will cause a reaction to slow down.

High temperatures are often necessary in industrial processes. However, the supply of energy to heat reaction mixtures is expensive. Sometimes speed has to be sacrificed for cost-effectiveness.

> **FOCUS**
> **Effect of surface area of a solid reactant on rate:**
> - **increase in surface area causes an increase in rate**
> - **decrease in surface area causes a decrease in rate.**

Surface area

The more finely divided a solid is, the more rapidly it reacts with a liquid or a gas. The **surface area** is the amount of surface that is exposed. A powdered solid has a higher surface area than the same mass of the solid in the form of lumps or granules.

Figure 4.2.9 Ethanol is manufactured by the reaction of ethene with steam: $C_2H_4(g) + H_2O(g) \rightarrow C_2H_5OH(g)$. However, the reaction is very slow. The rate is increased to an acceptable level by using a catalyst and a temperature of 300°C. Why do you think that higher temperatures are not used?

Catalysts

Catalysts are substances which increase the rate of a chemical reaction. Importantly, they are not used up in the reaction. Catalysts can be recovered chemically unchanged at the end of the reaction.

Catalysts are vital to many industrial processes, making them economically viable.

> **FOCUS**
> **The presence of a suitable catalyst increases the rate of a reaction.**

Figure 4.2.10 There are two ways to cook potatoes faster: using a higher temperature (frying rather than boiling them), or cutting them into smaller pieces.

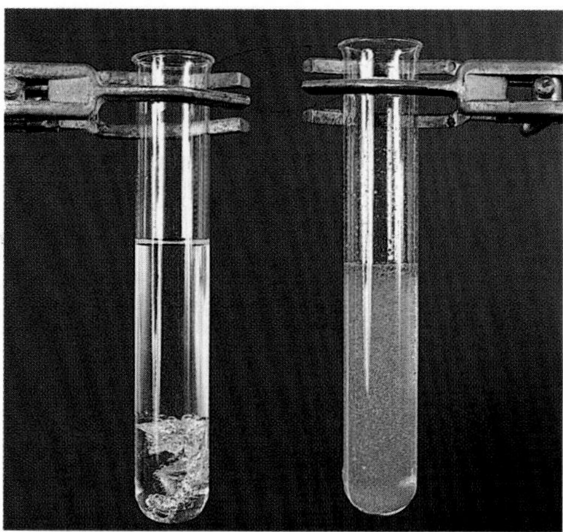

Figure 4.2.11 Powdered magnesium reacts more rapidly with dilute sulphuric acid than does magnesium ribbon. Why is this?

Catalysts are particularly useful in industry, when without them acceptable rates can only be achieved by high temperatures or pressures. Both of these make big energy demands and so are expensive. Suitable catalysts allow lower temperatures and pressures to be used.

Catalysts are of two types:

- *homogeneous* – a catalyst which is in the same state as the reactants (e.g. a soluble catalyst for a reaction which occurs in aqueous solution)
- *heterogeneous* – a catalyst which is in a different state from the reactants (e.g. a solid which catalyses a gaseous or liquid reaction).

The rates of chemical reactions which occur in our bodies, and in the cells of other animals and plants, are also controlled by catalysts. These biological catalysts are called *enzymes*.

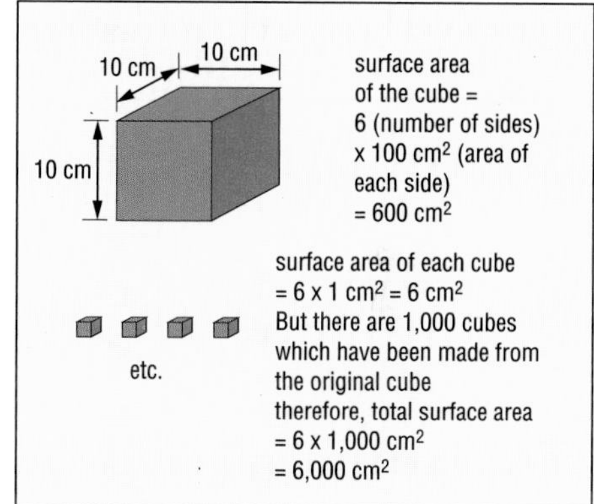

Figure 4.2.12 Breaking a solid into smaller pieces increases its surface area. By cutting the 10 cm x 10 cm x 10 cm cube into 1000 smaller cubes (each 1 cm x 1 cm x 1 cm), the surface is increased from 600 cm^2 to 6000 cm^2. The smaller the pieces, the more of the solid that can come into contact with other chemicals.

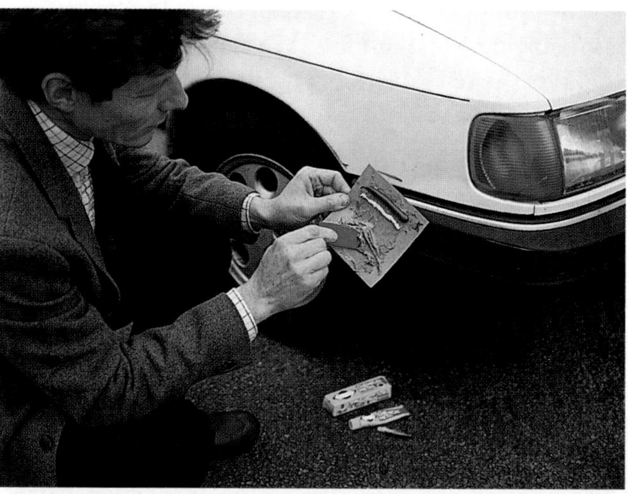

Figure 4.2.13 Small dents and holes in car bodies can be repaired with 'plastic metal'. But it isn't plastic at all. One tube contains styrene and an inorganic bulking agent, the other contains a catalyst. When combined, the catalyst speeds up the polymerisation of styrene to give polystyrene. The bulking agent gives the material added strength.

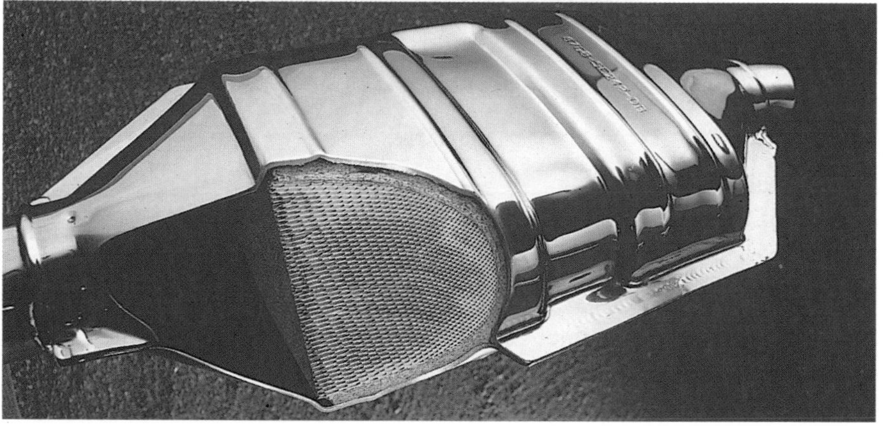

Figure 4.2.14 Catalysts are used to reduce the emission of poisonous gases from car exhausts. The catalysts used (mixtures of platinum and rhodium) are very expensive. In a catalytic converter, the catalyst is produced as a very thin layer on the surface of an inert substance. A honeycomb structure is used. Can you suggest why?

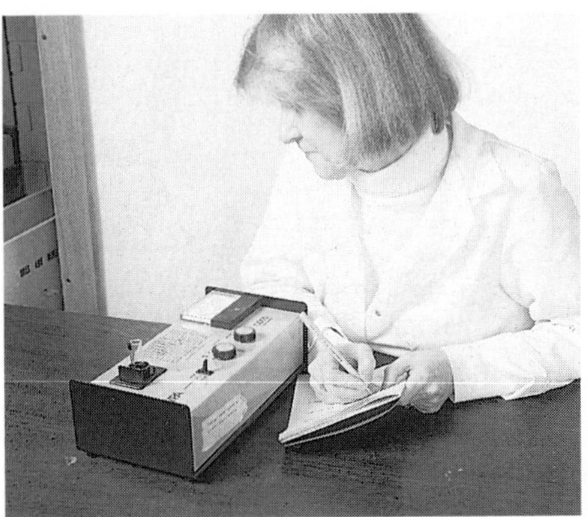

Figure 4.2.15 A colorimeter being used to measure colour changes during a chemical reaction.

Monitoring change and measuring reaction rates

Formation of product or consumption of reactant

The concentration of a component in a sample from a reaction mixture can be determined by *quantitative analysis*. For example, the concentration of an acid in a reaction mixture can be determined by taking a sample from the mixture and carrying out an acid-base titration. When the sample is taken, the reaction in the sample must be stopped (the reaction is said to be *quenched*).

Suppose the mixture contains an acid. The sample is withdrawn with a pipette using a safety filler and added to a measured volume of alkali of known concentration. The acid is neutralised by some of the alkali (to give a salt). The unreacted alkali is titrated against an acid of known concentration. This technique is called a *back titration*.

Rate of effervescence

When gas is given off in a reaction, the reaction mixture *effervesces*, in other words it fizzes. The rate of reaction can be determined by measuring the volume of the gas that is produced. There are two techniques for measuring volume:

- displacing of water from a graduated measuring container, e.g. a measuring cylinder or a burette
- collecting the gas in a large graduated gas syringe.

Since the evolution of a gas means that the reaction mixture loses mass, the rate of reaction can also be determined by measuring the change in mass of the reaction mixture. This method is only suitable for reactions where the gas given off is insoluble in the reaction mixture. The gas given off must also have a reasonably large molar mass. We can show this with two calculations, for example: the reaction of 6.5 g zinc with 50 cm^3 of dilute sulphuric acid. Hydrogen is given off:

$$Zn(s) + H_2SO_4(aq) \rightarrow ZnSO_4(aq) + H_2(g)$$

A_r [Zn] = 65, A_r [H] = 1
Therefore:

mass of 1 mol Zn = 65 g
mass of 1 mol H_2 = 2 × 1 = 2 g

The mole, the scientist's counting unit, page 13

One mole of zinc (65 g) gives one mole of hydrogen molecules (2 g). Therefore, 6.5 g zinc gives 0.2 g hydrogen. Although electronic balances can weigh to the nearest 0.001 g, this is a small loss in mass to measure.

Compare this with the reaction of 5 g calcium carbonate with 50 cm^3 of dilute hydrochloric acid. Carbon dioxide is given off:

$$CaCO_3(s) + 2HCl(aq) \rightarrow CaCl_2(aq) + CO_2(g) + H_2O(l)$$

A_r [Ca] = 40 (approx), A_r [C] = 12, A_r [O] = 16
Therefore:

mass of 1 mol $CaCO_3$ = 40 + 12 + (3 × 16) = 100 g
mass of 1 mol CO_2 = 12 + (2 × 16) = 44 g

Using graphs, page 45

One mole of calcium carbonate (100 g) gives one mole of carbon dioxide (44 g). Therefore, 5 g calcium carbonate gives 2.2 g carbon dioxide. This is a more significant mass loss than for the reaction between zinc and sulphuric acid described above.

Procedure

SAFETY: Hazards depend on the substances being used. Either carry out a risk assessment or ask your supervisor for help.

Eye protection must be worn

HIGHLY FLAMMABLE magnesium calcium hydrogen

IRRITANT dilute hydrochloric acid

Measuring the volume of gas given off during a reaction

1 Displacement of water

1 Place a weighed quantity of one reactant in a conical flask which has a side arm (the type used for suction filtration – a Büchner flask).
2 Measure the required volume of liquid into a measuring cylinder.
3 Assemble the apparatus as shown in Figure 4.2.16. Remove the bung from the flask, pour in the liquid and immediately replace the bung before any gas escapes. Start a stop-watch.
4 At regular time intervals, read the volume of water displaced from the inverted burette. You will need to check with your supervisor about how often to take readings.
5 Plot a graph of volume of gas given off (on the vertical axis) against time (on the horizontal axis) (Figure 4.2.17).

Requirements

❒ Weighed quantity of reactant

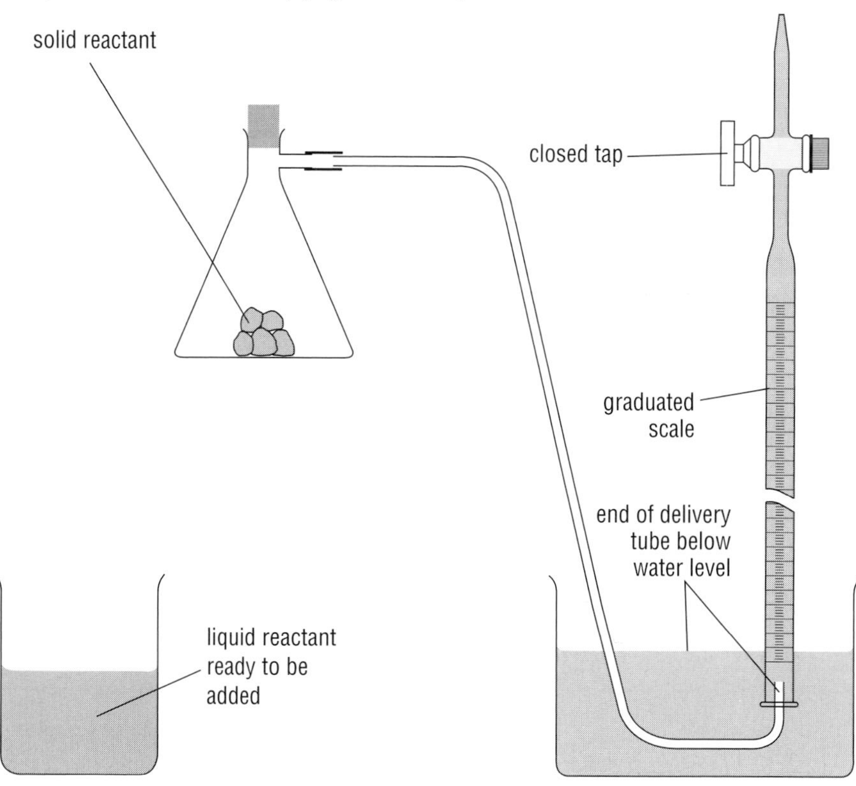

Figure 4.2.16 *The volume of water displaced equals the volume of gas given off in the reaction.*

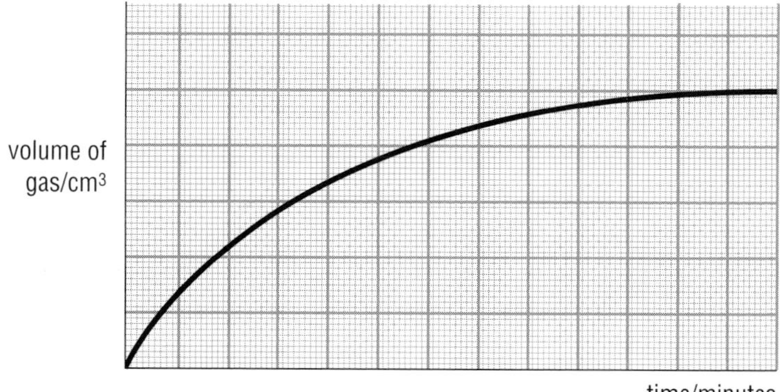

Figure 4.2.17 *A graph of the volume of gas given off against time. The axes are labelled, including the appropriate units.*

Eye protection must be worn

HIGHLY FLAMMABLE magnesium calcium hydrogen

IRRITANT dilute hydrochloric acid

2 Using a gas syringe

1 Place a weighed quantity of one reactant in a conical flask which has a side arm.
2 Measure the required volume of liquid into a measuring cylinder.
3 Assemble the apparatus as shown in Figure 4.2.18. Remove the bung from the flask, pour in the liquid and immediately replace the bung before any gas escapes. Start a stop-watch.
4 At regular time intervals, read the volume of gas given off from the syringe. You will need to check with your supervisor about how often to take readings.
5 Plot a graph of volume of gas given off (on the vertical axis) against time (on the horizontal axis) (Figure 4.2.17).

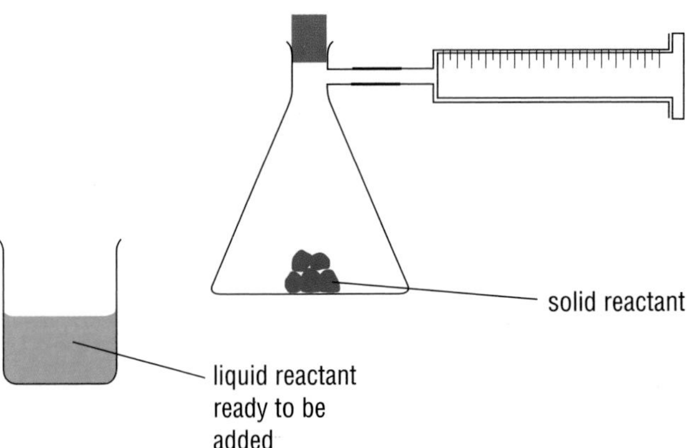

Figure 4.2.18 *As gas is given off it moves the plunger of the gas syringe. The volume of gas can be measured directly from the graduated syringe.*

Note.This method is useful for reactions in which hydrogen is given off. To obtain a maximum of about 50 cm^3 of gas, 0.002 mol of reactant is required. A large excess of the other reactant (e.g. acid or water) is used. For example,

- 0.05 g magnesium and 50 cm^3 dilute hydrochloric acid give approximately 50 cm^3 hydrogen
- 0.13 g zinc and 50 cm^3 dilute hydrochloric acid give approximately 50 cm^3 hydrogen
  (The concentration of the acid can be varied to investigate how it affects the rate of reaction.)
- 0.08 g calcium and 50 cm^3 distilled water give approximately 50 cm^3 hydrogen

Procedure

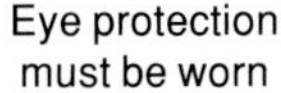

Eye protection must be worn

HARMFUL copper(II) carbonate

IRRITANT hydrochloric acid anhydrous sodium carbonate sodium carbonate-10-water

SAFETY: Hazards depend on the substances being used. Either carry out a risk assessment or ask your supervisor for help.

Measuring the loss in mass of a reaction mixture

1 Place the required volume of liquid in a conical flask and put this on a direct reading balance.
2 Add the solid and put a cotton wool plug in the neck of the flask to prevent any spray from the reaction mixture escaping (Figure 4.2.19).
3 At regular time intervals, record the mass of the reaction mixture. You will need to check with your supervisor about how often to take readings.
4 Plot a graph of mass of gas given off (on the vertical axis) against time (on the horizontal axis).

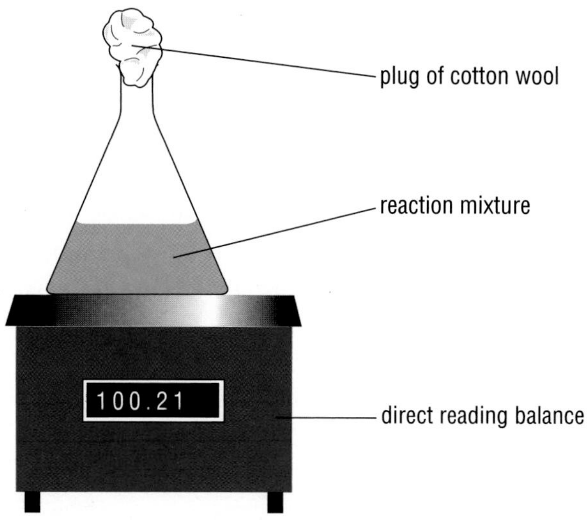

Figure 4.2.19 The loss in mass of the reaction mixture is due to the gas which is being given off. The cotton wool plug prevents any spray escaping. Why is this important?

Note. This method is particularly good for reactions in which carbon dioxide is given off. The following quantities of solids react with an excess of dilute hydrochloric acid (about 100 cm^3) and give a mass loss of about 2.2 g:

4.2 g magnesium carbonate
4.2 g sodium hydrogen carbonate
5 g calcium carbonate
5.3 g anhydrous sodium carbonate
6.2 g copper(II) carbonate
6.3 g zinc carbonate
14.3 g sodium carbonate-10-water (washing soda crystals)

pH

pH is a measure of acidity. The pH scale is shown in Figure 4.2.20. The pH of a solution can be estimated using Universal Indicator solution. The colour produced when a few drops of this indicator are added to a solution gives a rough guide to the pH. Alternatively, a drop of the solution can be put on a piece of Universal Indicator paper.
An accurate pH value for a solution can be measured using a pH meter.

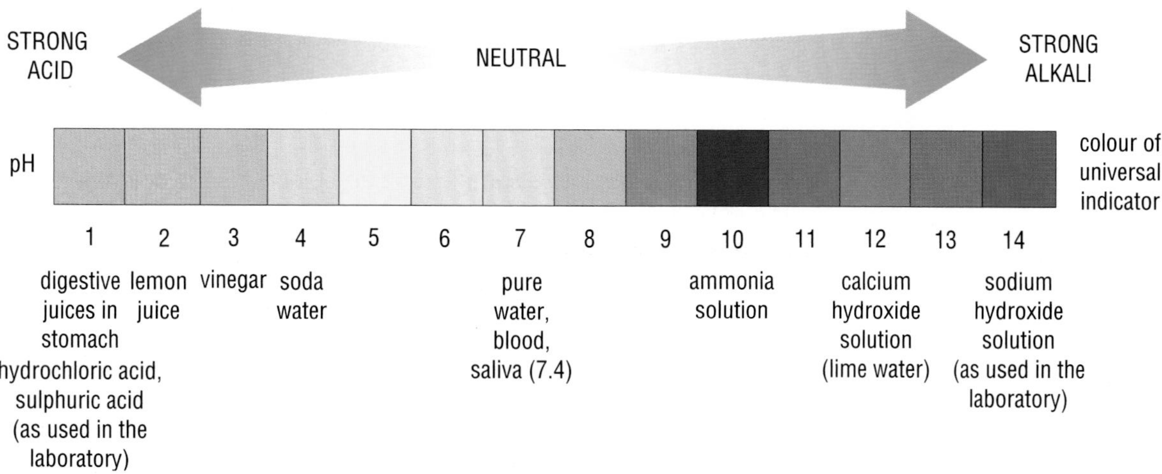

Figure 4.2.20 The pH scale.

Procedure

Measuring pH

1. Connect the pH electrode to a pH meter.
2. Place the pH electrode in a solution of known pH (called a buffer solution) and calibrate the instrument.
3. Remove the pH electrode, rinse it with distilled water and place it in the solution to be tested. Read the pH from the meter.
4. After each measurement wash the pH electrode with distilled water and store it with the bulb wet.

Note. You will need to read through the instructions for the particular pH meter you use since the precise procedure varies from one to another.

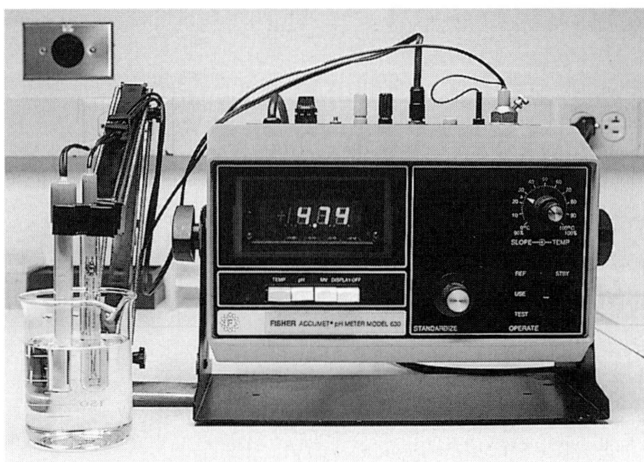

Figure 4.2.21 *A pH electrode and meter. The electrochemical cell is in the form of a glass probe. It is usually stored in a buffer solution. Before use the pH meter should be calibrated by putting the probe into a buffer solution of known pH.*

Colour changes

The concentration of a coloured reactant or product can be monitored with a colorimeter. A colorimeter measures the amount of coloured light that does not pass through a solution. This is called *absorbance*.

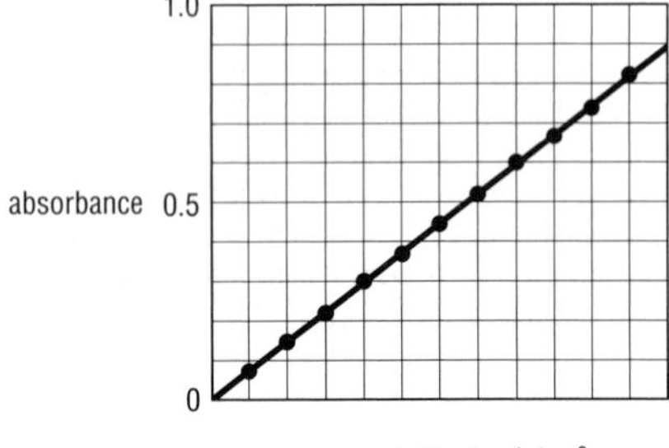

Figure 4.2.22 *A calibration curve of absorbance against concentration. To obtain it, a number of solutions of known concentration are made. The absorbance of each solution is measured. Using the curve, the concentration of a solution can be calculated from its absorbance.*

Procedure

Using a colorimeter

1. Switch on the colorimeter about 10 minutes before use.
2. Choose an appropriate coloured filter. This should be a complementary colour to that of the substance under investigation. For example, a blue filter is used for red solutions.
3. Zero the colorimeter using the solvent (water in the case of an aqueous solution).
4. Pour the solution into a sample tube and place it in the colorimeter. Take the absorbance reading.
5. If the colour changes during the course of a reaction, take absorbance readings at appropriate time intervals.

Note. You will need to read through the instructions for the particular colorimeter you use since the precise procedure varies from one to another.

Temperature

A thermometer is the simplest way to measure temperature. It is important to choose one which meets the needs of the job. Different types are available, varying in the temperature range they can measure and their precision.

An electronic temperature probe can also be used. With the probe placed in the sample and connected to a recording instrument, the temperature can be read directly from the display.

Changes in temperature during a reaction can be obtained by taking temperature readings at various times. A graph of temperature (on the vertical axis) against time (on the horizontal axis) is a convenient way of recording this information.

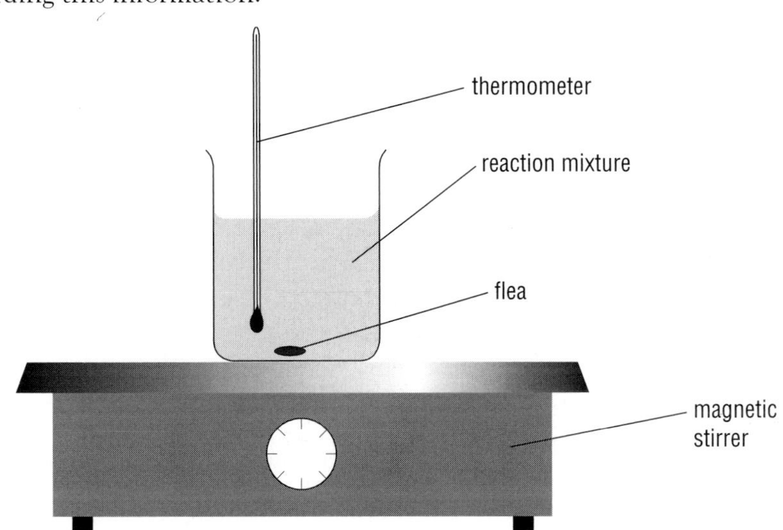

Figure 4.2.23 The bulb of the thermometer must be in the reaction mixture. Stirring makes sure that there are no 'hot or cold spots'.

Explaining rates of reaction

Gases consist of atoms or molecules moving about in a chaotic way. Similarly, in solution, ions or molecules move about randomly.

For a reaction to occur, particles (atoms, ions or molecules) of reactant must **collide** with one another. The more often particles collide, the faster the reaction. Not all collisions lead to reaction. Those which do are called **effective collisions**. Particles must have sufficient energy to undergo an effective collision. This means they must have sufficient energy for the chemical bonds to break. It is called the **activation energy**. This model of how chemicals react is called *collision theory*. Put simply, the lower the activation energy, the faster the reaction.

FOCUS

A chemical reaction occurs when particles undergo effective collisions. They must collide with sufficient energy to overcome the activation energy for the reaction.

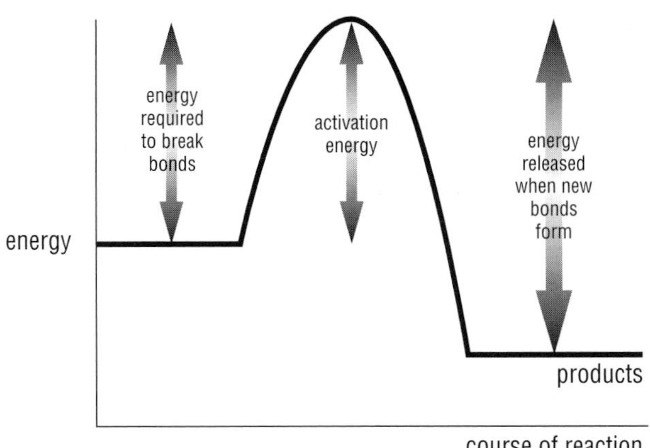

Figure 4.2.24 An energy level diagram. It shows that the energy of a mixture changes if a chemical reaction occurs. The energy barrier must be overcome if a reaction is to take place.

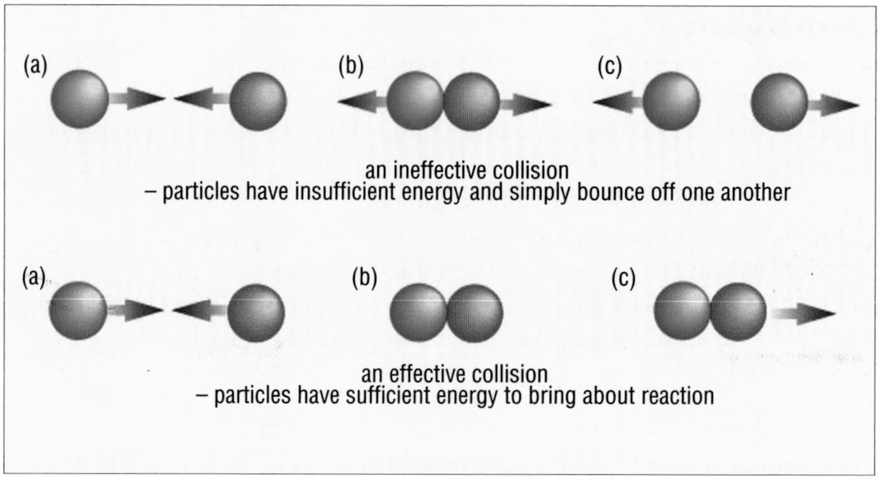

(a) (b) (c)

an ineffective collision
– particles have insufficient energy and simply bounce off one another

(a) (b) (c)

an effective collision
– particles have sufficient energy to bring about reaction

Figure 4.2.25 *Collisions must occur between particles for a reaction to occur. Furthermore, the colliding particles must have enough energy to bring about a reaction (they must undergo an effective collision).*

This model helps us to understand how conditions affect the rate of a reaction.

Concentration

Concentration is the number of particles in a given volume. The more particles in the reaction mixture (the higher the concentration), the greater the number of collisions and, therefore, the faster the reaction. Both the total number of collisions and the number of effective collisions increases. The proportion of effective collisions is not changed.

Temperature

Particles move more quickly at high temperatures than at low temperatures. Because of this, they have greater energy. This has two effects. At higher temperatures:

- particles collide with one another more frequently (because they are moving more rapidly)
- the number of effective collisions is higher (because a greater proportion of particles have sufficient energy to overcome the activation energy).

Together, these effects mean that increasing the temperature of a reaction mixture increases the rate quite markedly. The total number of collisions increases and the proportion that are effective is higher.

Surface area

Increasing the surface area of a solid exposes more of it to other substances with which it might react. This allows more effective collisions to occur. The outcome is a faster rate of reaction.

Figure 4.2.26 *Acid rain is a problem of the late twentieth century. It is causing the destruction of stonework that is made from limestone or marble (two natural forms of calcium carbonate). Why does stonework with much fine detail deteriorate most rapidly?*

SURFACE AREA
surface area of
calcium carbonate **low**

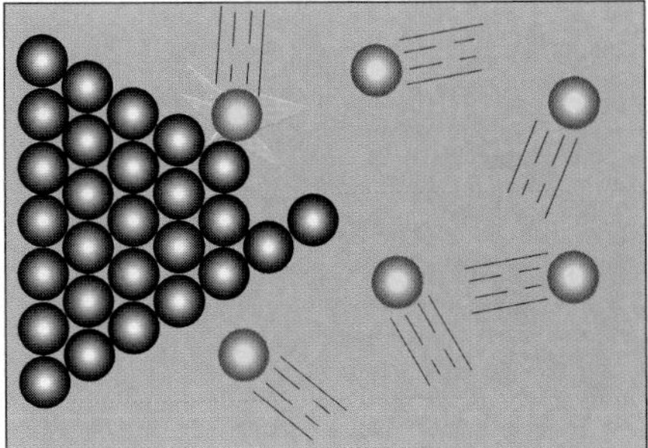

surface area
higher – more calcium carbonate
exposed to collisions

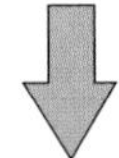

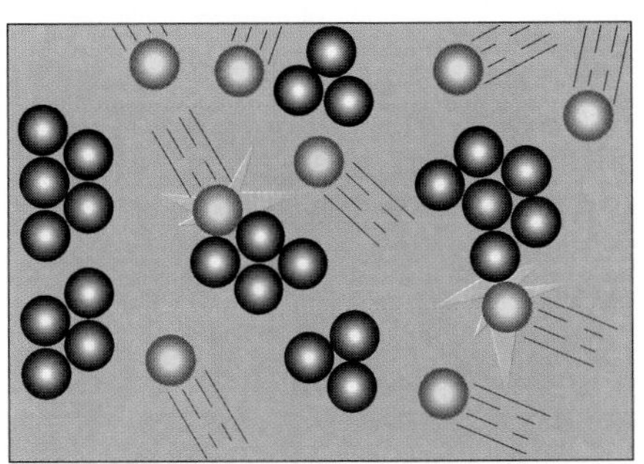

CONCENTRATION
concentration of
hydrochloric acid **low**

concentration
higher – more chance
of particles colliding

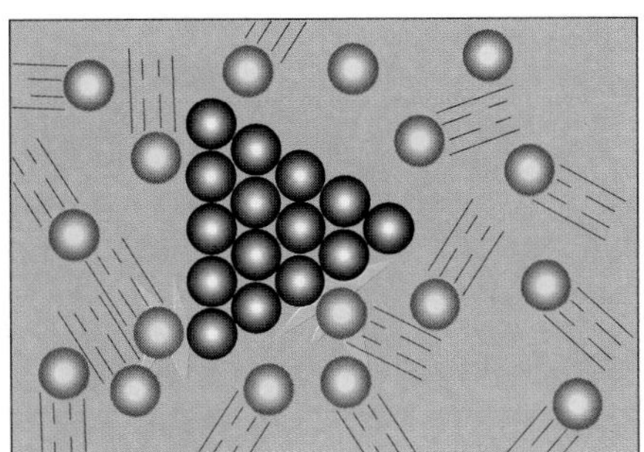

TEMPERATURE
temperature **low**

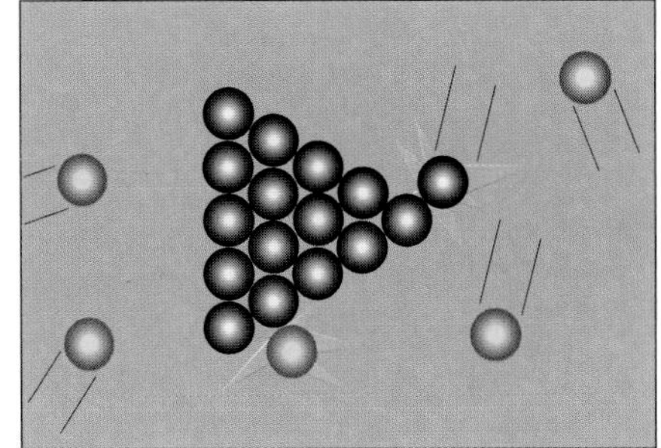

temperature
higher – particles
collide with more energy

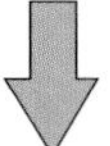

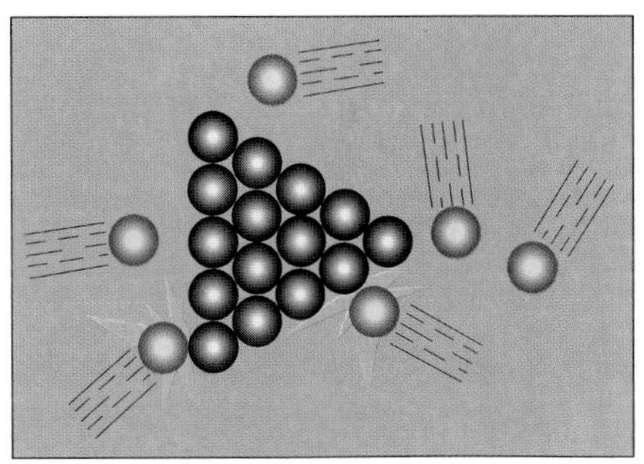

Figure 4.2.27 *The effect of conditions on the rate of reaction between calcium carbonate and hydrochloric acid can be explained by the collision theory.*

Controlling a reaction

Once you have decided the rate of reaction you want, you will need to select the appropriate conditions. This summary will remind you:

- conditions which increase the rate of reaction:
  - increasing concentration of reactants
  - increasing temperature
  - increasing surface area (if a solid is involved)
  - using a suitable catalyst
- conditions which decrease the rate of reaction:
  - decreasing concentration of reactants
  - decreasing temperature
  - decreasing surface area (if a solid is involved).

Case study

SULPHURIC ACID: SPEED IS ECONOMY

Sulphuric acid is made exclusively by the Contact process. More is manufactured each year than any other chemical. It is used to make fertilisers, paints, pigments, detergents, fibres and plastics, as well as a number of speciality chemicals (chemicals manufactured in small quantities for specialist uses).

This important chemical must be manufactured cheaply. The best way to ensure this is to do it quickly. Remember the old adage, 'time is money'. So how is this achieved?

The starting point is sulphur. Two major sources are underground deposits of sulphur and sulphur that is recovered from the oil and gas industry.

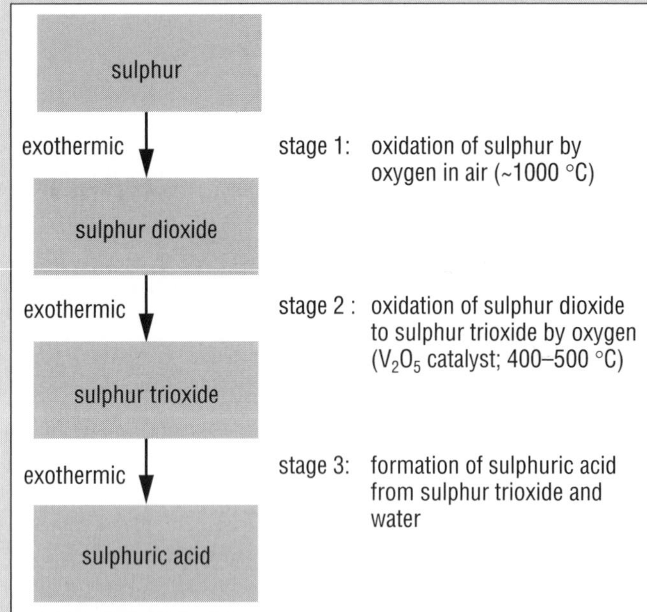

Illustration 1 *A summary of the Contact process.*

There are three stages in the process:

Stage 1 Molten sulphur is sprayed into a current of air at about 1000 °C. Sulphur dioxide is formed. The reaction is extremely fast.

sulphur + oxygen → sulphur dioxide

$$S(l) + O_2(g) \rightarrow SO_2(g)$$

Sulphur dioxide can be obtained directly by heating naturally-occurring sulphide ores in air.

Stage 2 The sulphur dioxide is converted into sulphur trioxide by reaction with oxygen. This reaction does not go to completion and is said to be in equilibrium. Furthermore, the reaction is slow.

sulphur dioxide + oxygen ⇌ sulphur trioxide

$$2SO_2(g) + O_2(g) \rightleftharpoons 2SO_3(g)$$

The sulphur dioxide is cooled before being passed into the reactor. Although high temperatures promote fast reaction there are three reasons for avoiding them in this case:

- the extent of the reaction, that is the amount of sulphur dioxide converted into sulphur trioxide, is less at higher temperatures
- at very high temperatures the sulphur trioxide breaks down to sulphur dioxide again
- high temperatures require large amounts of energy, and energy is expensive.

A compromise is needed. A temperature of 400–450 °C is used. However, the rate is increased by the use of a suitable catalyst. Platinum was used but it has been replaced by the cheaper vanadium(V) oxide, V_2O_5.

Higher pressures would increase the reaction rate but are not used.

Stage 3 The final reaction is also extremely fast. In fact it is too fast. The sulphur trioxide needs to be dissolved in water to form sulphuric acid.

sulphur trioxide + water → sulphuric acid

$$SO_3(g) + H_2O(l) \rightarrow H_2SO_4(aq)$$

Because the reaction is so fast, a fine mist of sulphuric acid droplets is formed. This is unacceptable both commercially and environmentally. Instead, the sulphur trioxide is dissolved in 98% sulphuric acid. The resulting solution is about 99.5% sulphuric acid (it is called 'oleum'). It is diluted to the required concentration. The reaction is highly exothermic. The acid is cooled by passing it through glass or high-silicon iron pipes which are sprayed with cold water.

Illustration 2 *A sulphuric acid plant.*

Questions

1 Explain why it is important to control the last two stages of the process.

2 How do you think the sulphur dioxide is cooled before conversion to sulphur trioxide?

3 All three stages are exothermic. How can the heat energy released be harnessed and used?

4 Which of the three stages has the lowest activation energy? Explain your answer.

5 What factors affect the rate of conversion of sulphur dioxide into sulphur trioxide? Explain why the reaction conditions chosen are used.

6 ICI have developed a process for converting sulphur dioxide into sulphur trioxide at high pressure (5-7 times atmospheric pressure). Explain why this would make for a faster reaction.

7 How do you think the rate of reaction between sulphur dioxide and oxygen could be measured?

8 Explain why high temperatures promote a faster reaction between sulphur dioxide and oxygen.

Assignment

THE ANALYSIS OF HYDROGEN PEROXIDE

Setting the scene

Over half a million tonnes of hydrogen peroxide are manufactured each year. It is a chemical of major industrial importance. Its uses include:

- acting as a bleach in the textile and paper industries
- making bleaching agents, such as sodium perborate, which are used in detergents
- the manufacture of many organic chemicals, including polymers
- combatting environmental pollution such as domestic and industrial effluent treatment (it destroys the chemicals responsible for the unpleasant smells).

Hydrogen peroxide can still be bought in some shops, such as Boots. However, its use in the home as a mild disinfectant or to bleach hair is declining. It is usually for sale as a '20 volume' solution. This means that when 1 volume of the solution decomposes it gives 20 times that volume of oxygen:

$$2H_2O_2(aq) \rightarrow 2H_2O(l) + O_2(g)$$

For example, 10 cm^3 of 20 volume hydrogen peroxide would decompose to give 200 cm^3 oxygen. The decomposition is catalysed by a number of chemicals.

The assignment

You should work on this assignment by yourself. You should produce a plan and discuss it with your supervisor before starting any practical work.

Your assignment is to devise an analytical procedure to check the strength of a sample of 20 volume hydrogen peroxide. The procedure should involve the decomposition of hydrogen peroxide and measurement of the volume of oxygen produced. You will need to ensure that oxygen is given off at a safe and acceptable rate for the analysis.

IRRITANT hydrogen peroxide

OXIDISING oxygen

HAZARDOUS some catalysts

1. You will need a suitable catalyst for the decomposition of hydrogen peroxide. Find out which substances catalyse the decomposition. Classify them as either homogeneous catalysts or heterogeneous catalysts.
2. Carry out a series of simple experiments to investigate how the decomposition of hydrogen peroxide is affected by any of the catalysts which are available to you.
3. Select a suitable catalyst and investigate the rate of decomposition of hydrogen peroxide in its presence. Determine which conditions would be best for the decomposition reaction in order that the oxygen is given off at an acceptable rate which allows the volume to be measured easily and safely.

Presenting your assignment

You should:

- write a report of your investigations; this should be word-processed and include text, tables of numerical data and graphs

- write a laboratory worksheet for the analysis of 20 volume hydrogen peroxide.

Opportunity to collect evidence
In completing this assignment you will have the opportunity to meet the following requirements for GNVQ Intermediate Science:

Science units
Unit 1:
Element 1.3 PCs 1, 2, 3, 4
Unit 4:
Element 4.2 PCs 1, 2, 3, 4, 5, 6

Core skill units

Application of number:
Element 2.2

Communication:
Element 2.2

Information technology:
Elements 2.1, 2.2, 2.3

Additional information

The following *procedures* are available:

- measuring the gas given off during a reaction, page 207
- measuring the loss in weight of a reaction mixture, page 209

Grading

This assignment gives you the opportunity to meet merit or distinction criteria. All four themes are covered: Planning, Information Seeking and Information Handling, Evaluation, Quality of Outcomes.
Read through the grading criteria carefully and make sure you know what must be done to gain evidence that you are worthy of a merit or distinction.

You will need help with some of the science in this assignment, so don't be afraid to ask.

Assignment

AN INVESTIGATION OF THE MANUFACTURE OF ZINC SULPHATE

Setting the scene

Zinc sulphate is a salt which is soluble in water. It crystallises from solution as zinc sulphate-5-water, $ZnSO_4.5H_2O$.

It has antiseptic properties and is used in mouthwashes. Most of the preparations intended to reduce excessive sweating contain zinc sulphate, although aluminium chloride is the most active ingredient.

Zinc sulphate can be made from zinc oxide and sulphuric acid. It can also be prepared by the reaction between zinc and sulphuric acid:

$$Zn(s) + H_2SO_4(aq) \rightarrow ZnSO_4(aq) + H_2(g)$$

EXPLOSIVE hydrogen gas — HARMFUL dilute sulphuric acid

The assignment

You should work on this assignment by yourself. Read through what is required and then produce a plan to tackle the assignment. *Discuss it with your supervisor before starting any practical work.*
Imagine you are working for an industrial company which specialises in making zinc compounds. You have been given responsibility for investigating the reaction between zinc and sulphuric acid as a possible route for the manufacture of zinc sulphate. The criteria for a successful method are:

- a rapid reaction
- a safe reaction (hydrogen gas is explosive if mixed with air and, therefore, must be vented safely away)
- the temperature should not exceed 60 °C
- low material costs
- pure product.

1 You are provided with:
zinc powder
zinc granules
dilute sulphuric acid (about 1 mol dm^{-3})
usual laboratory apparatus
Carry out a series of experiments to find out how the following factors affect the rate of reaction between zinc and sulphuric acid:
(a) particle size of the zinc
(b) temperature
(c) concentration of sulphuric acid
(d) addition of copper(II) sulphate solution as a catalyst.
Produce a chart to summarise the dependence of reaction rate on these reaction conditions.

2 Looking at the criteria above, choose an appropriate set of reaction conditions to make zinc sulphate from zinc and sulphuric acid in a laboratory preparation.
Design and carry out an experiment to measure the rate of the reaction under these conditions. Determine how long the reaction takes to go to completion.
Write an account of the experiment.

3 Looking at your results to question 1 above, describe how the changing conditions affect the rate of reaction. You should use the collision theory of chemical reactions to help you explain these effects.
Use a series of labelled diagrams to show how the rate of reaction depends on:
- particle size of the zinc
- temperature
- concentration of sulphuric acid
- the addition of a suitable catalyst.

5 Prepare a sample of zinc sulphate from 10 g zinc. Dilute sulphuric acid and the usual apparatus and chemicals are available in the laboratory.
(a) Determine the yield of zinc sulphate.
(b) Calculate the theoretical yield of zinc sulphate that can be obtained from 10 g zinc.
(c) Calculate the percentage yield of zinc sulphate.
(d) Your yield is likely to be less than 100%. What is the main reason for this?
(e) Use a chemical supplier's catalogue to calculate the cost of zinc and sulphuric acid used in the preparation.
(f) Think about how long it took you to carry out the preparation. Assume that labour is about £5 an hour and other costs (e.g. energy and wear on equipment) are about ten times the cost of the starting materials. Estimate the cost of making your sample of zinc sulphate.

6 Draw a diagram of a chemical plant which could be used to manufacture zinc sulphate from zinc and sulphuric acid. Label the diagram clearly to indicate the reaction conditions to be used.

Opportunity to collect evidence
In completing this task you will have the opportunity to meet the following requirements for GNVQ Intermediate Science:

Science units
Unit 1:
Element 1.3 PCs 1, 2, 3, 4
Unit 3:
Element 3.2 PCs 2, 3, 4, 5
Unit 4:
Element 4.2 PCs 1, 2, 3, 4, 5, 6

Core skill units

Application of number:
Elements 2.2, 2.3

Communication:
Element 2.1, 2.2, 2.3

Presenting your assignment

Write a report of your investigation and present it together with your sample of zinc sulphate. Include the chart and the diagram of chemical plant described above.

Additional information

The following procedures are available:

- measuring the volume of gas given off during a reaction, page 207
- measuring the loss in weight of a reaction mixture, page 209
- preparation of salts by an acid-base reaction, page 150. (**Note.** Although this is not an acid-base reaction, the experimental technique is the same.)

Grading

This assignment gives you the opportunity to meet merit or distinction criteria. The following themes are covered: Planning, Information Seeking and Information Handling, Evaluation, Quality of Outcomes. Read through the grading criteria carefully and make sure you know what must be done to gain evidence that you are worthy of a merit or distinction.

Questions

1 Give three reasons why is is important to be able to control the rate of a chemical reaction.

2 How do the following affect the rate of reaction which occurs in solution:
(a) concentration of reactants
(b) temperature?

3 How do the following affect the rate of reaction between a solution and a solid:
(a) concentration of reactants
(b) surface area of the solid
(c) temperature?

4 Why are catalysts important?

5 Explain how
(a) the number of collisions between reactants, and
(b) the energy of particles of reactants affect the rate of a reaction.

Monitor and control the performance of a physical device

You will need to show that you can:

- identify the performance needed from the device
- identify those factors which affect performance
- select a method to monitor the device's performance
- measure the change in performance as one of the factors is varied
- describe how the performance can be optimised.

The performance of mechanical devices

A familiar machine is shown in Figure 4.3.1. Like all machines, it changes the size and direction of a force. The large downwards force of your foot on the pedal is transformed into a smaller horizontal force on the bicycle.

In fact, a bicycle is made from a number of smaller machines. The pedals are connected to the back wheel by pulleys. There are gear wheels inside the hub of the back wheel. The brakes use levers. This section will help you to find out what these machines do, how their performance can be measured and how that performance can be optimised.

Figure 4.3.1 *A bicycle is a machine made from a number of other machines.*

Performance

The performance of a machine tells you what it does and how well it does it. Three quantities are particularly useful in specifying the performance of any machine. They are: mechanical advantage, velocity ratio and efficiency.

FOCUS

A machine produces a force which has a different size and direction to the force fed into it. The performance of a machine can be specified further by its:

- **speed**
- **sensitivity**
- **power**
- **efficiency.**

Measuring performance, page 223

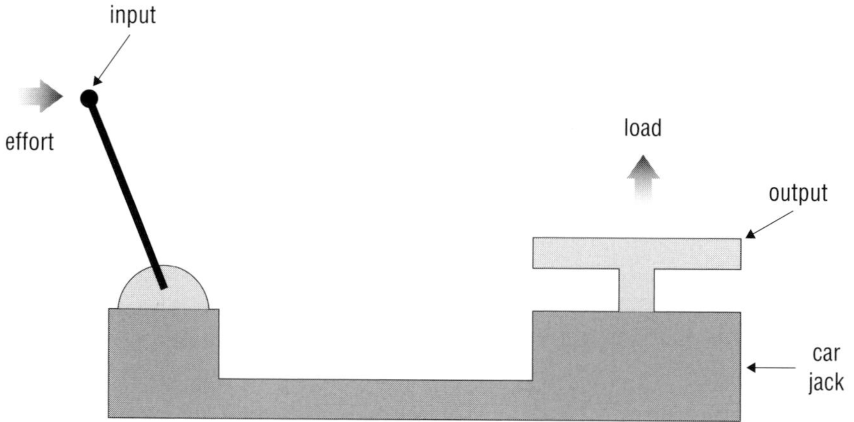

Figure 4.3.2 *The direction of forces acting on a car jack.*

Size and direction of forces

An example of a machine is shown in Figure 4.3.2. It is a jack, designed to lift heavy items. When the *input* is pushed to the right, the *output* moves up. A small horizontal force applied at the input results in a much larger vertical force appearing at the output.

Sensitivity

The force applied at the input is called the *effort*. The force which pushes against the output is of the machine called the *load*. The *mechanical advantage* or MA of the machine tells you how big the load is compared with the effort.

$$\text{MA} = \frac{\text{load}}{\text{effort}} = \frac{\text{force provided at the output}}{\text{force applied at the input}}$$

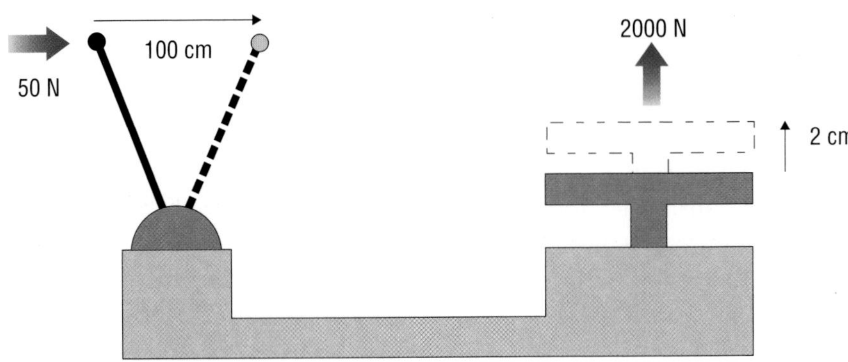

Figure 4.3.3 Data for calculating the MA and VR of a car jack.

A sensitive machine has a large value for its MA.

Here is an example of the MA in action. The details are given in Figure 4.3.3. A force of 50 N at the input of the jack is enough to lift a 2 000 N weight. How much force would you expect to need to lift a 3 200 N weight?

Calculate the MA first.

load = 2 000 N
effort = 50 N

$$\text{MA} = \frac{\text{load}}{\text{effort}} = \frac{2000}{50} = 40$$

You would expect the load to always be 40 times larger than the effort. Therefore, a load of 3 200 N should need an effort of 3 200/40 = 80 N.

Speed

Being able to convert a small force into a large one is very useful, but there is a price to be paid. The small force has to move a much larger distance than the large one does. So the output and input will move at different speeds.

The *velocity ratio* or VR of a machine tells you about this aspect of its performance.

$$\text{VR} = \frac{\text{distance moved by effort}}{\text{distance moved by load}}$$

Look at Figure 4.3.3. When the effort moves 100 cm to the right, the load only moves up 2 cm.

effort distance = 100 cm
load distance = 2 cm

$$\text{VR} = \frac{\text{effort distance}}{\text{load distance}} = \frac{100}{2} = 50$$

So for every 50 cm the input moves to the right, the output moves up by only 1 cm. The input moves fifty times faster than the output.

Efficiency

The VR of a machine is always fixed directly by the size and arrangement of its components. So you can always predict exactly what the VR is going to be by making measurements of the component parts of a machine.

For example, the jack has a VR of 50 because of the length of the input lever and the pitch of the screw thread.

The MA is fixed by the VR and how much energy is wasted in the machine.

$$\text{Efficiency} = \frac{\text{MA}}{\text{VR}} \times 100$$

A machine which wastes no energy at all has an *efficiency* of 100%. So its MA has the same value as its VR. All machines waste some energy, so their MA is always going to be less than their VR. For example, consider the jack.

MA = 40
VR = 50

$$\text{Efficiency} = \frac{\text{MA}}{\text{VR}} \times 100 = \frac{40}{50} \times 100 = 80\%$$

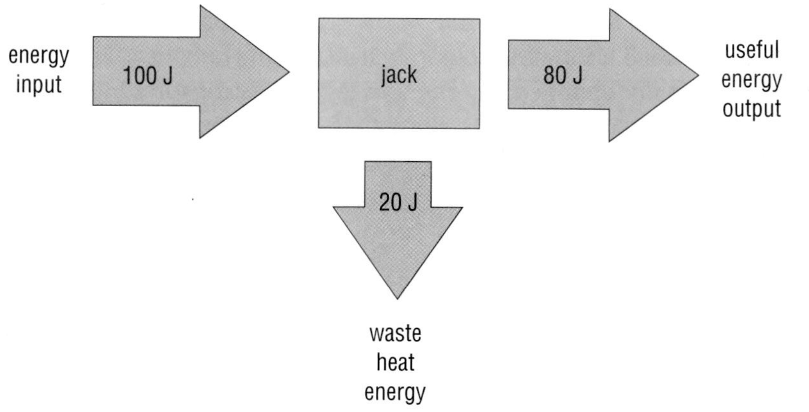

Figure 4.3.4 Energy flows through the car jack.

Figure 4.3.4 illustrates what this means. For every 100 joules (J) of energy fed into the machine at its input, only 80 J appears at the output. The other 20 J is wasted inside the machine, mostly converted to heat energy.

Power

The *power* of a machine tells you how quickly it can deliver useful energy at its output.

$$\text{power (watts)} = \frac{\text{energy output (joules)}}{\text{time (seconds)}}$$

Figure 4.3.5 Using a hoist to lift a heavy weight.

Here is an example of the calculation of power. A machine delivers 6 000 J in 30 s. What is its power?

energy = 6 000 J
time = 30 s

$$\text{power} = \frac{\text{energy}}{\text{time}} = \frac{6000}{30} = 200\ \text{W}$$

If the machine can feed out 3 000 J of useful energy per minute, can you show that its power is 50 W?

Types of machine

There are three different types of machine in common use: levers, gears and pulleys. Each of them is described below.

Levers

A **lever** is the simplest machine of all – just a solid bar with a pivot somewhere along its length. There are some examples in Figure 4.3.6. In each case, the VR is fixed by the distance of the effort and the load from the pivot.

$$\text{VR} = \frac{\text{distance from effort to pivot}}{\text{distance from load to pivot}}$$

Gears

A simple gear train is shown in Figure 4.3.7. Each time that the input shaft does nine complete revolutions, the output shaft goes round just once. The direction of rotation has not changed, but the torque (or twisting force) on the output shaft is up to nine times larger than the torque put on the input shaft.

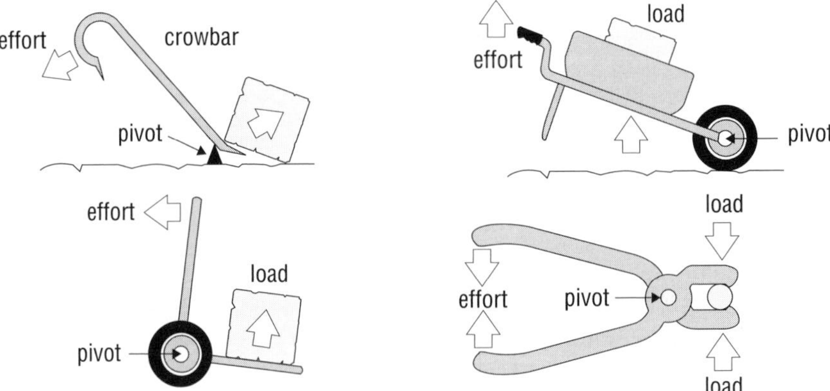

Figure 4.3.6 Some machines which use levers.

The VR of a pair of gear wheels is given by this rule:

$$\text{VR} = \frac{\text{diameter of output gear}}{\text{diameter of input gear}} = \frac{\text{teeth on output gear}}{\text{teeth on input gear}}$$

The two shafts rotate in opposite directions.

Pulleys

Pulleys can be used to make machines move in two different ways.

Belts

Pulley wheels can transfer rotation from one shaft to another with a belt (Figure 4.3.8). Unlike gears, the two shafts rotate in the same direction. Like gears, the VR is determined by the relative sizes of the pulley wheels.

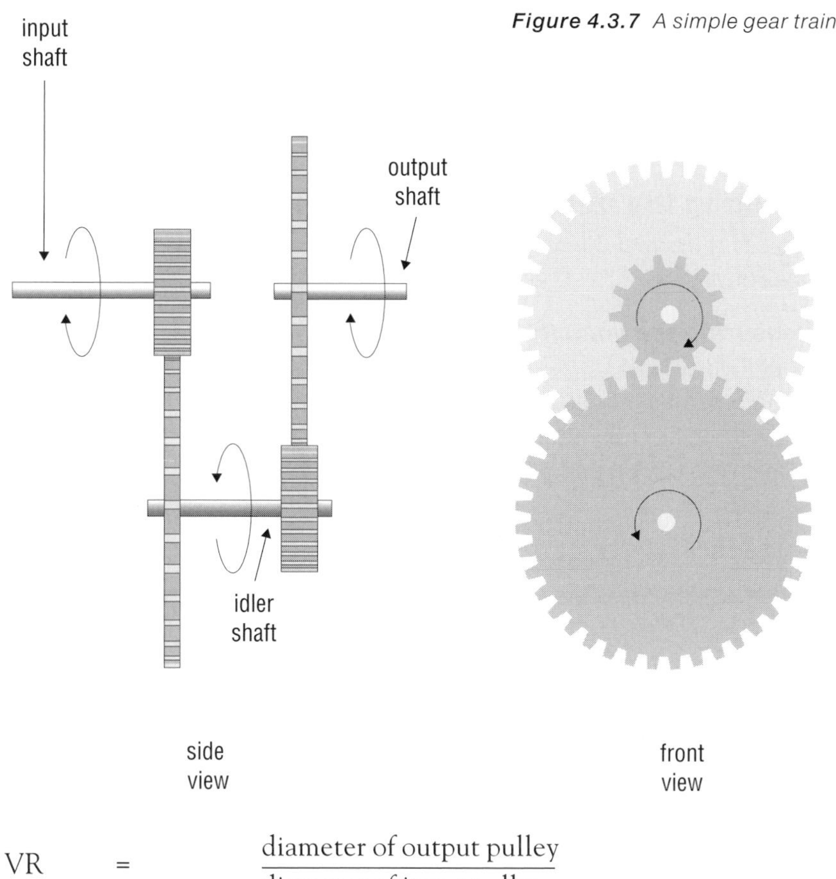

Figure 4.3.7 A simple gear train.

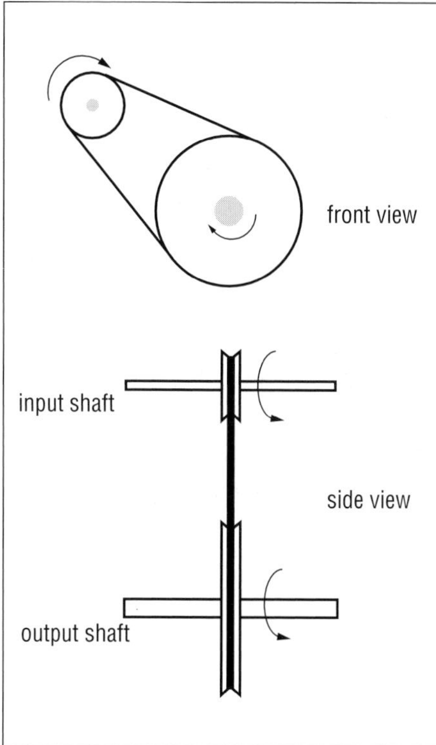

Figure 4.3.8 Belts and pulleys.

$$\text{VR} = \frac{\text{diameter of output pulley}}{\text{diameter of input pulley}}$$

Cords

Figure 4.3.9 shows how some pulleys and a length of cord can be used to make a hoist.

The VR of the system is equal to the number of lengths of cord which hold up the bottom set of pulley wheels (the size of the wheels is not important). In the case of Figure 4.3.9, this is 3. So for every 1 cm the load moves up, the effort has to move 3 cm down.

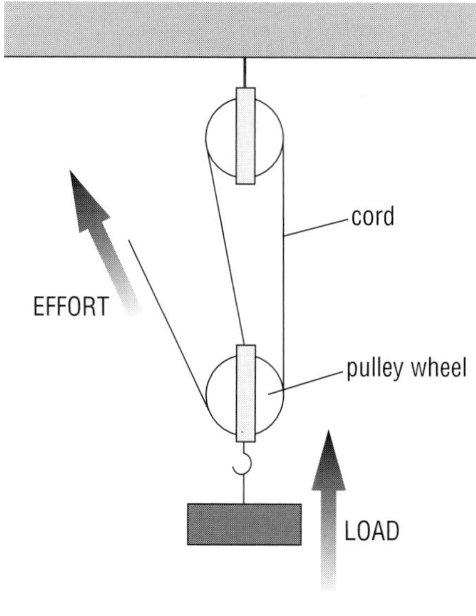

Figure 4.3.9 A hoist made from pulleys and cord.

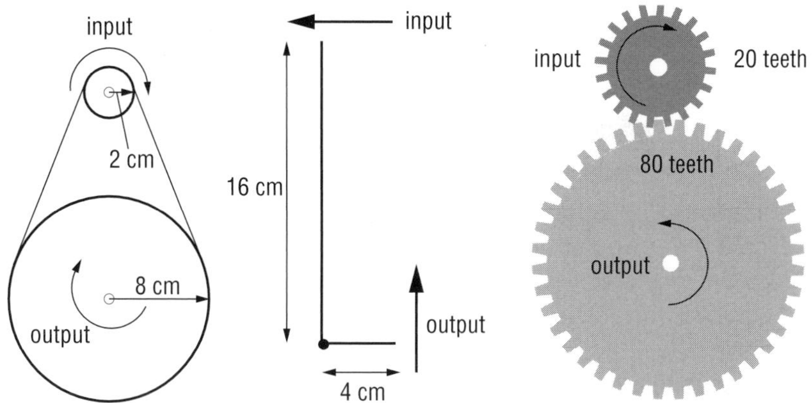

Figure 4.3.10 Different machines with the same VR.

Measuring performance

The performance of any machine is found by making separate measurements of its MA and VR. These can then be used to calculate the efficiency. The techniques employed depend on whether the forces to be measured are linear or rotary.

Efficiency, page 221

Linear forces

Levers and hoists are examples of linear machines. They transform forces rather than torques.

Procedure

Measuring the performance of a linear machine

WARNING

SAFETY: If the load is large there is the risk of dropping the weight on toes – or trapped fingers.

Requirements

- ❒ Two single sheave pulleys
- ❒ Card
- ❒ Two rulers clamped upright
- ❒ Forcemeter O-ION
- ❒ 1 kg mass (ION weight)

1 Measuring the velocity ratio (VR)

Look at Figure 4.3.11.

1. Use one ruler to measure how far the effort moves.
2. Use the other ruler to measure how far the load moves in the same time.
3. Calculate the VR using the formula:

$$VR = \frac{\text{distance moved by effort}}{\text{distance moved by load}}$$

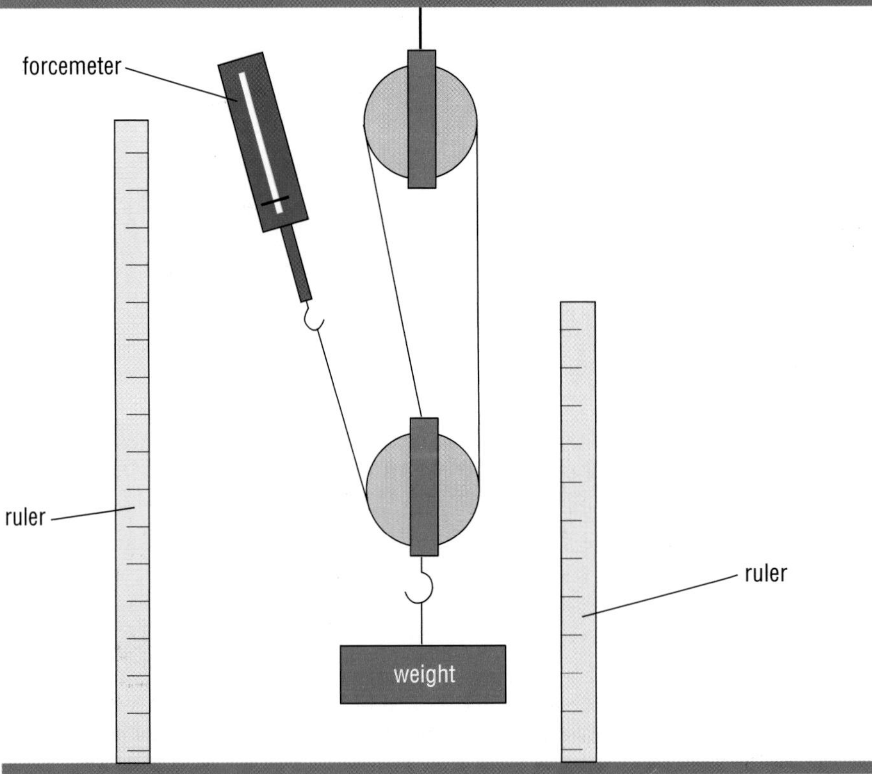

Figure 4.3.11 Measuring the performance of a hoist.

2 Measuring the mechanical advantage (MA)

1. Find the weight of a lump of metal with the help of a forcemeter.
2. Use the machine to lift this lump and use the forcemeter to measure the effort required (Figure 4.3.11). You now know the effort needed to lift a known load.
3. Calculate the MA using the formula

$$MA = \frac{\text{load}}{\text{effort}} = \frac{\text{force provided at the output}}{\text{force applied at the input}}$$

Rotary forces

Torques are not as straightforward to measure as other forces. On the other hand, measuring VR is very easy for rotary machines.

Procedure

Measuring the performance of a rotary machine

SAFETY: If the load is large there is the risk of dropping the weight on toes – or trapped fingers.

Requirements
- ❐ Rotary machine
- ❐ Cord
- ❐ Forcemeter (O-ION)
- ❐ Weight (ION)

1 Measuring the velocity ratio (VR)

1. Make two small marks, one on the input shaft and one on the output shaft.
2. Find the shaft which rotates most slowly. Turn it round through exactly one turn. Count how many times the other shaft goes round.
3. Calculate the VR using the formula:

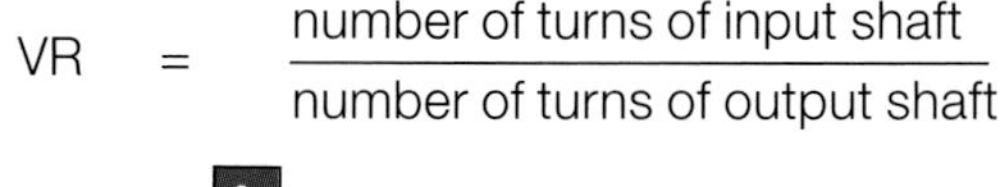

$$VR = \frac{\text{number of turns of input shaft}}{\text{number of turns of output shaft}}$$

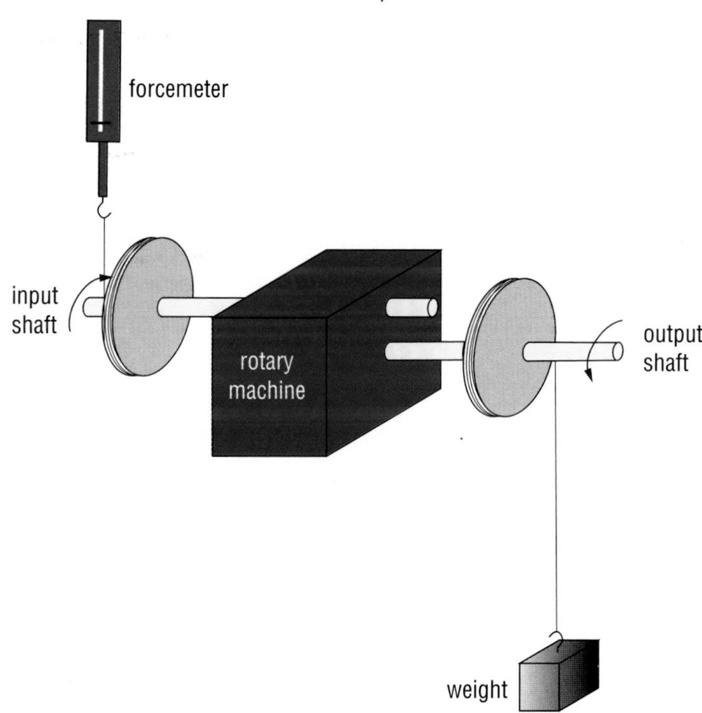

Figure 4.3.12 *Measuring the MA of a rotary machine.*

(2) Measuring the mechanical advantage (MA)

1. Fit both shafts with wheels of the same diameter (Figure 4.3.12).
2. Fix cords to the wheels and wrap them around the rims a few times.
3. Suspend a known weight from the output cord.
4. Use a forcemeter to measure the force needed to move the input cord.
5. Calculate the MA using the formula

$$MA = \frac{\text{load}}{\text{effort}} = \frac{\text{force provided at the output}}{\text{force applied at the input}}$$

Optimising performance

No machine can ever be more than 100% efficient. So whatever you do to a machine, you will never be able to make its MA greater than its VR. However, if the MA is much less than the VR, energy is being needlessly wasted. It is often worth trying to make the **efficiency** as near to 100% as you can.

FOCUS

The optimum machine has an efficiency of almost 100%. This can be achieved by reducing friction to a minimum and ensuring that the effort does not have to move the weight of the machine itself.

Levers

There are two reasons why a lever may not have an efficiency of 100%. First, there may be friction at the pivot. Second, the effort may have to lift the lever itself as well as the load.

Friction

Friction is the force which acts between surfaces when they move against each other. It is very good at generating heat energy. (Try rubbing your hands together!) Friction at a pivot can be minimised by:

- using a lubricant (oil or grease)
- by arranging that surfaces roll against each other rather than sliding.

Lever weight

The weight of a lever acts through its centre of gravity. The nearer this is to the pivot, the less effect it will have on the MA of the lever. You can assess the importance of the weight of the lever by measuring the effort when there is no load.

Hoists

The main source of friction is where the pulley wheels rotate on their shafts. Lubricating it with a small amount of oil at regular intervals will help.

The efficiency can be close to 100% if the load is big enough. If the load is too small, the weight of the bottom pulleys becomes significant.

Gear trains

Figure 4.3.13 If the gear teeth have the correct shape they can mesh without sliding over each other.

Gear trains have two sources of friction. The first acts at the shaft supports. The second acts between the gear teeth as they mesh and unmesh with each other.

The first can be minimised by using roller bearings and lots of grease. The second can be eliminated by choosing the correct profile for the gear teeth (Figure 4.3.13). The gear teeth roll over each other, without slipping.

Gears often suffer from backlash. If you only give the input shaft a slight twist, the output shaft may not move at all.

Belts and pulleys

The pulley wheels have the same friction problems as gear trains.

If the load gets too great, the belt may slip on the pulleys. Furthermore, the elastic properties of the belt mean that the input and output shafts may not always be bound to follow each other firmly.

The performance of optical devices

Figure 4.3.14 Some optical devices.

Optical devices are things like cameras, microscopes, telescopes and magnifying glasses (Figure 4.3.14). They use lenses and mirrors to form images.

Scientists routinely use optical devices to study objects which are too small or too far away to be seen easily with the naked eye. They need to know how to set up optical devices so that they give the most useful image.

Lens systems are very advanced technology. For simplicity, the discussion below will be restricted to devices which use a single converging lens to form the image.

Performance

An **optical device** takes in light from an object and uses that light to form an image. For optimum **performance** the image needs to be in the right place, have the right size and be sharp.

FOCUS

The performance of an optical device can be assessed by studying the position, size and sharpness of the image.

Factors which affect performance, page 228

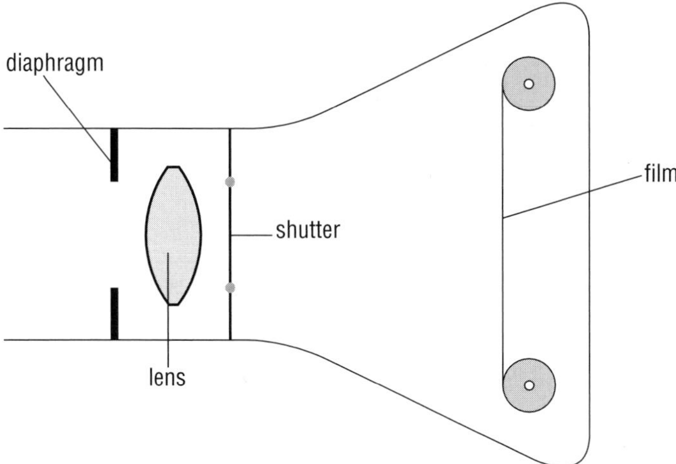

Figure 4.3.15 Basic features of a typical lens camera.

Lens camera

The essential components of a lens camera are shown in Figure 4.3.15. The lens collects light from the *object* and makes it fall on the film. The film is a sheet of polymer coated with light-sensitive chemicals which can store the image. The shutter normally stops light from reaching the film; it is opened for a short time while the photograph is being taken. The diaphragm controls the amount of light which can pass through the lens.

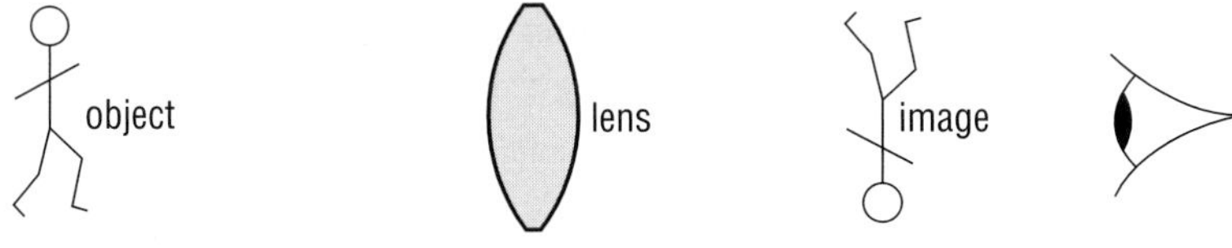

Figure 4.3.16 The image is upside down and behind the lens.

Image position

The object gives out light or reflects light from somewhere else. Any of the light which hits the lens is used to make an *image* inside the camera (Figure 4.3.16). If you look at the image, it will appear as an upside-down copy of the object suspended in space.

For a photograph to be successful, the image must be focused on the film. So the image position must be the same as the film position. The focus adjustment on a camera allows you to adjust the distance between the film and the lens.

Image size

The size of the image on the film is much smaller than the size of the object. The film is only a few mm across, so images must be smaller than this to be successfully recorded on it.

Sharpness

The sharpness of an image gets worse as you move away from the centre of the field of view. For example, take a look at Figure 4.3.17. The image formed by the camera is good in the centre, but is bad at the edges. No amount of adjusting the focus will get around this. It is a defect in the lens itself.

Figure 4.3.17 Only the centre of the image is in perfect focus.

Investigation

Looking at images produced by a magnifying glass

SAFETY: Never look directly at the Sun through a lens or other optical device.

1. Obtain a magnifying glass. Stand at one end of a room, away from a window.
2. Face the wall and use the magnifying glass to form an image of the window on the wall.
3. Study the image formed by the lens.
4. Repeat with a variety of lenses.
5. Write a short report describing the performance of the lenses.

FOCUS

The factors which affect the performance of an optical device are the power of the lens, how far away the object is and the aperture of the lens.

Measuring performance, page 231

Factors which affect performance

If you want to improve the quality of an image, you must have some understanding of the physics behind its creation. If you know how a lens creates an image, an understanding of the factors which affect it will come easily.

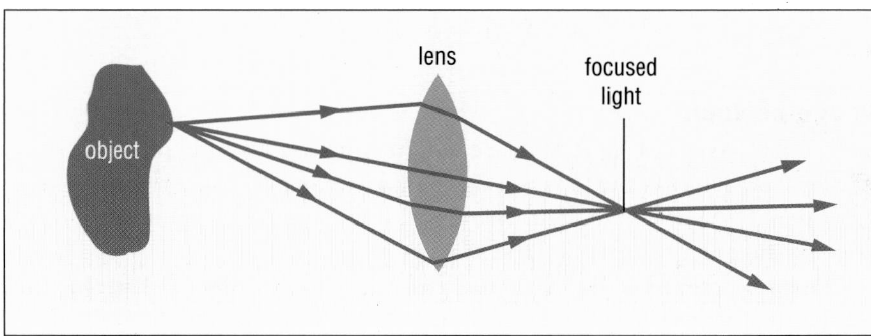

Figure 4.3.18 All of the rays from a point on the object which hit an ideal lens are focused on a single point on the other side.

Image formation

Look at Figure 4.3.18. It shows how light from part of the object is focused by an ideal lens. The path taken by the light is represented by *rays*, straight lines with arrows on them. Any light from a point on the object which hits the lens is focused somewhere the other side of the lens. All of the rays pass through a single point.

Figure 4.3.19 shows what happens to light from two points on the object. All the light rays from these points which pass through the lens go through one of two points on the other side of the lens. For each point on the object, there is a unique point behind the lens where its light will be focused.

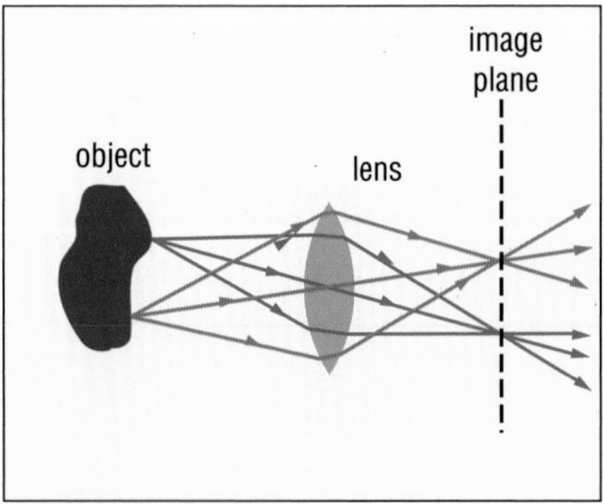

Figure 4.3.19 Image formation.

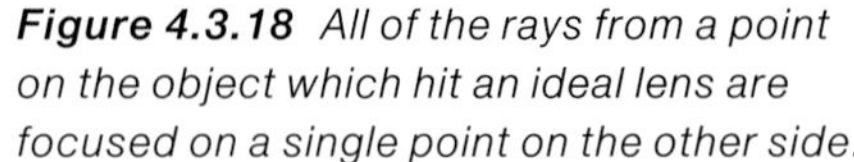

Image position

The position of the image behind the lens is fixed by two things - the power of the lens and how far away it is from the object.

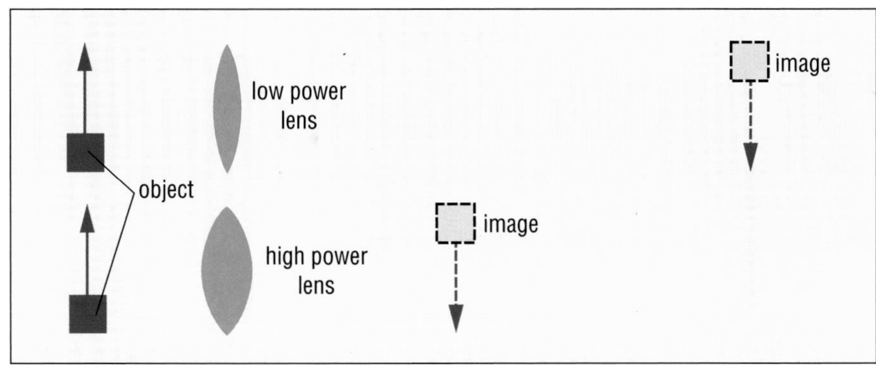

Figure 4.3.20 As the power of the lens is increased, the image gets closer to the lens.

Lens power

Figure 4.3.20 shows what happens to the position of the image as the power is changed. A high power lens is fatter and more curved than a low power one.

Lenses in optical devices are made from glass or polymer, so altering their power is not an option. (You would have to alter their shape!) The only way of getting the image in the right position is by moving the lens towards or away from the object.

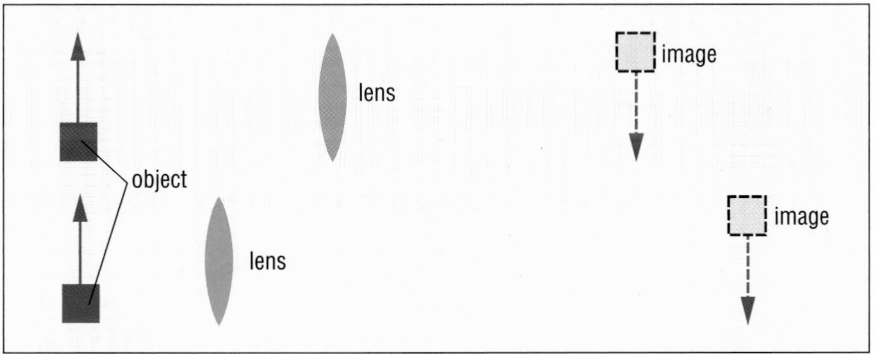

Figure 4.3.21 The image moves away from the lens as the lens moves towards the object.

Object position

As you move the lens towards the object, the image gets further away from the lens (Figure 4.3.21). Once the object is less than one focal length away from the lens, there will be no image at all.

If the object is a long way from the lens, the image will be one focal length the other side of the lens. The focal length can be calculated from the power with this rule:

$$\text{focal length (in cm)} = \frac{100}{\text{power (in dioptres)}}$$

Can you show that a 7 dioptre lens has a focal length of 14 cm?

FOCUS

Ray tracing can be used to find the position and size of the image created by a lens of known focal length.

Requirements

- ❒ Graph paper
- ❒ Ruler
- ❒ Sharp pencil

Image size

Ray tracing can be used to find the position and size of the image formed by a lens.

Procedure

Making a ray tracing

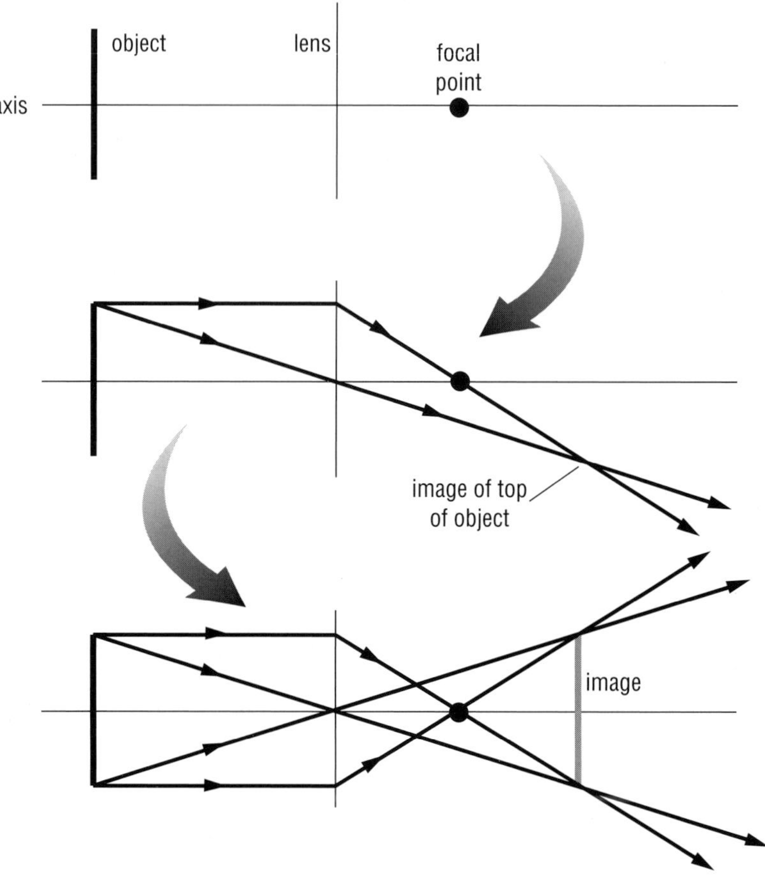

Figure 4.3.22 *Tracing rays to find the size and position of an image.*

1. Start off with a scale drawing of the object and lens. Draw in the axis, a line at right angles to the surface of the lens which goes through its centre.
2. Mark the focal point on the axis (this is one focal length from the centre of the lens).
3. Draw the object centred on the axis.
4. Draw two rays of light from the top of the object, one through the centre of the lens without changing direction, the other parallel to the axis. The lens changes the direction of this ray so that it goes through the focal point.
5. The image of the top of the object is where the two rays cross.
6. Do exactly the same for two rays from the bottom of the object. Where they cross is the bottom of the image.
7. You can now measure the size of the image directly from your drawing.

Example:
A lens has a focal length of 5 cm. A 4 cm high object is placed 10 cm in front of it. Make a scale drawing to show that the image will also be 10 cm away from the lens.

Magnification

The magnification of an optical device tells you how much bigger the image is than the object. So if the magnification is 2, the image appears to be twice as large as the object.

Magnification can be calculated once you know the distances of the object and image from the lens (Figure 4.3.23).

$$\text{magnification} = \frac{\text{image distance}}{\text{object distance}} = \frac{\text{image height}}{\text{object height}}$$

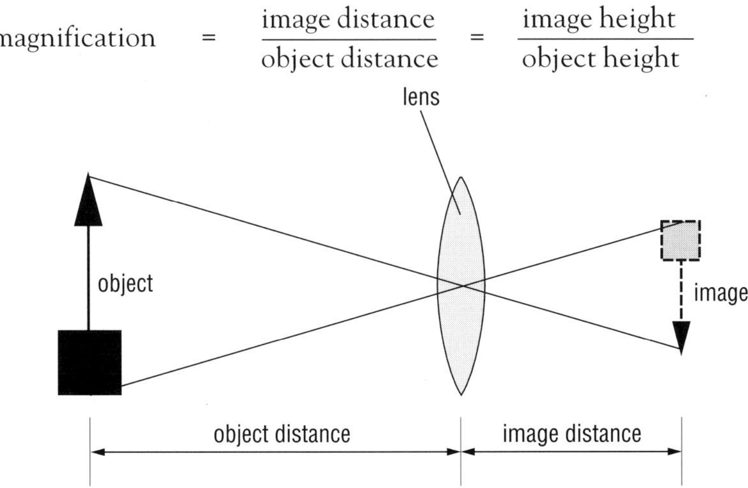

Figure 4.3.23 *The magnification is easily predicted because rays go straight through the centre of a lens.*

A tree 10 m in front of a camera is 4 m high. If the image of the tree is 2.5 cm behind the lens, can you show that the image height will be 1 cm?

Image sharpness

An ideal lens should give an image which is a perfect copy of the object. No real lens can do this. It cannot give an image which is in perfect focus over the whole field of view. A real lens introduces aberration. There are several causes.

Colour aberration

The focal length of a lens (which fixes the image position) depends on the colour of the light. So the different coloured lights coming from an object are focused in slightly different places. If the system is in focus for red light, it will be slightly out of focus for blue light.

Spherical aberration

The focal length of a lens depends on which part of the lens you use. The further you are away from the axis, the smaller the focal length becomes. Light from the object which passes through different parts of the lens will end up focused in different places.

Aperture

All forms of aberration get worse as the diameter of the lens increases. The aperture of the lens is the area of the lens which contributes light to the image. So as the aperture is reduced, the image gets sharper.

FOCUS

The performance of an optical system can be assessed by taking measurements of the height of its image and making observations about its sharpness. This can be done by placing a screen at the image position.

Measuring performance

In order to measure the **position**, **size** and **sharpness** of an image, you need a suitable screen.

A flat sheet of waxed paper held securely in a frame is ideal. Alternatively, you could use a smooth sheet of frosted glass.

▶ Optimising performance, page 231

Procedure

Requirements
- ❒ +7D lens
- ❒ Tracing paper scan
- ❒ Light bulb and power source

Comparing the quality of images

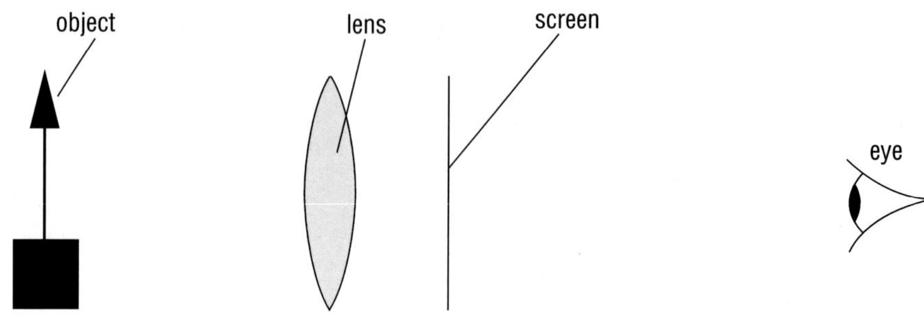

Figure 4.3.24 *How to view an image with a screen.*

1 Stand with one eye in line with the lens and the object.
2 Place the screen between the lens and your eye.
3 Move it back and forth until you obtain a focused image on the screen.
4 The position of the image is simply the position of your screen.
5 The image can be recorded by making pencil marks on the screen. You can then use these marks and a ruler to measure the size of the image.
6 Look for the results of aberration.

FOCUS

The performance of an optical device is optimised by making the image fill the field of view and by using only the centre of the lens.

Optimising performance

An optical device is properly adjusted if the image is in the right place, fills the **field of view** and is in focus all the way across.

Optimum position

In the case of a camera, the best place for the image is the sensitive surface of the film. For a video camera, the image must lie on the electronic sensor (called a CCD).

If the image is to be viewed by a person, the best place for it is about 25 cm in front of their eyes. This leaves their eyes relaxed and unlikely to get tired.

Optimum size

The size of an image is important. Ideally, it should almost fill the field of view.

For a camera, this means that the image size should be slightly smaller than the size of the film. If the image is much smaller than this, the photograph will have to be enlarged, leading to a loss of quality. Of course, if the image is larger than the film, part of it will not be recorded (Figure 4.3.25).

Figure 4.3.25 *An ideal image fills the field of view.*

Reducing aberration

Colour aberration can be reduced by replacing a single lens with a pair made out of different types of glass (Figure 4.3.26). These achromatic doublets are widely used in high quality optical systems.

Optimum sharpness

There is always a trade-off between the brightness of an image and its sharpness.

The brightness is fixed by the amount of light that can pass through the lens to the image. The bigger the aperture, the more light can pass through, so the brighter the image becomes. Unfortunately, as the aperture is increased, the image becomes more blurred at its edges.

In practice, stops are placed in front of a lens so that only its **centre** is used. The stop lets enough light through to form an image which can be seen easily.

Cameras can compensate for a dim image by having a long exposure time for the film. If the aperture is reduced, the shutter is opened for longer to allow the same amount of light to reach the film. Of course, this is only possible if the object being photographed does not move during the exposure time!

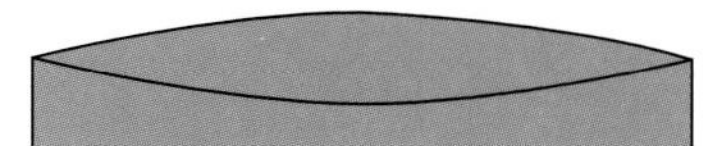

Figure 4.3.26 *An achromatic doublet for reducing chromatic aberration.*

Case study

MUSCLES, BONES AND MACHINES

For most people the answer to the question 'Which parts of your body help you to move?' is 'My muscles'. In fact, muscles on their own are almost useless. You can't move without bones as well.

We use many machines as extensions to our arms and legs. In particular, hydraulic machines do a lot of work, digging, lifting and moving. These machines use the same principles of leverage that we do. They have their equivalents of muscle and bone and have them arranged them in similar ways to achieve their purpose.

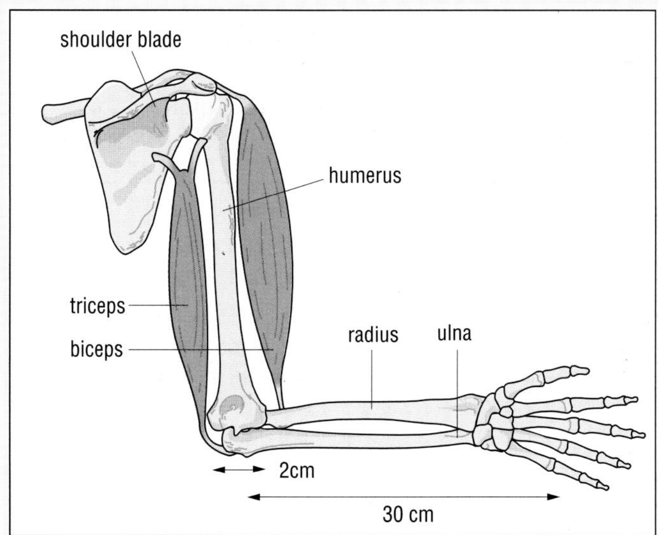

Illustration 1 *Muscles used to move a human forearm.*

Human arms

Illustration 1 shows how the muscles which move your hand around are connected to your arm bones. Only two muscles, the biceps and triceps, have been shown (to keep things simple). Each muscle is a bundle of long thin fibres connected to bone at either end by tendons.

Short stroke muscles

Muscle fibres contract when stimulated by electrical signals from the nerves which lead to them from the brain. The force they can exert is quite large, but each fibre can only contract by about 10%. A muscle has a short stroke.

If you wanted to use a muscle directly to lift a weight from the floor to a table, it would have to be about 10 m high! This is clearly not practical. Evolution has produced a better solution.

Bones increase the stroke

Consider the biceps muscle. When it contracts, it exerts an upwards force on the radius. One end of that bone is held in place by the joint at the end of the humerus, but is free to swing around. So there is a pivot at one end of the radius and the other end has a hand on it.

Illustration 2 shows the forces which act on the radius when the hand is trying to raise something.

When the biceps contract, the hand will move much further than the muscle does. The price paid for this is that the force from the muscle must be much greater than the force on the hand.

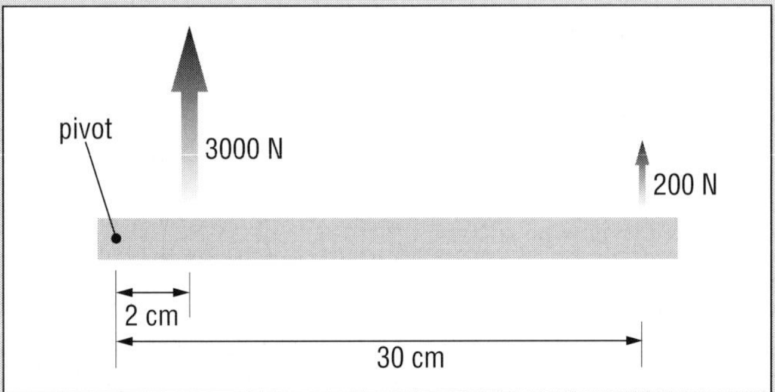

Illustration 2 *A lever force diagram for a human forearm.*

Muscle force

The muscle tugs on the radius about 2 cm from the pivot. The load on the hand is about 30 cm from the pivot. So the VR of the system is 30/2 = 15. If the efficiency is 100% (and, of course, it never will be), the MA will also be 15. If your hand is able to lift a weight of 200 N (about half a child), the biceps must be able to exert a force of at least 15 × 200 = 3 000 N!

Making muscles stronger

Each fibre in a muscle can exert a given force. If you want to make a muscle stronger, you just need more fibres. Strong muscles are fat ones: weak muscles are thin.

The triceps muscle in Illustration 1 is thin. It doesn't need to be very strong as its job is to lower the hand. When the biceps muscle relaxes, the weight of the arm and hand is often enough to lower it down. The biceps and triceps are an example of an antagonistic pair. They both act on the same bone, but provide forces in different directions.

Efficiency

The efficiency of all levers is limited by two factors: the weight of the lever itself and the friction at the pivot. The joints between our bones are lubricated by the synovial fluid trapped between them. Pads of smooth cartilage at the ends of the bones also help to reduce friction.

Our bones are hollow. This reduces the weight of the levers attached to our muscles without significantly reducing their strength.

Hydraulic machines

Illustration 3 shows a typical hydraulic machine (a digger). It uses a series of pistons acting on levers, almost the same way that muscles use bones.

Illustration 3 *A hydraulic digger.*

Push and pull

Each cylinder contains a piston which behaves like an antagonistic pair of muscles. Oil at high pressure can be fed into either end of the cylinder. Provided that the oil at the other end is free to leave the cylinder, the piston can be forced along the cylinder.

The stroke of the piston is fairly short, about the length of the cylinder. This is similar to muscle. Another similarity is that a fat cylinder exerts a larger force than a thin one.

Optimal arrangements by evolution

The design of both human arms and hydraulic diggers is probably close to optimal. Neither is perfect, but they are the best compromise. Both have evolved by trial and error; the only difference is the timescale. Human beings have taken several million years to become what they are, whereas hydraulic diggers are barely a hundred years old!

Questions

1 Find out about the arrangement of muscles which move your foot relative to your leg. Discuss the factors which affect their performance.

2 A solenoid is a device which uses electricity to create linear motion. When electricity passes through it, a slug of iron is tugged in. The slug is released when the electricity is turned off. A force of 5 N with a stroke of 1 cm is typical.

Show how you could use a lever to increase the force to 50 N. Discuss the factors which affect the performance of the system.

Case study

SLIDE PROJECTORS

Scientists frequently give talks to explain their work to other scientists. Many of these talks take place at conferences, and they are a very useful way of exchanging facts and ideas. The slide projector is an indispensable tool at these events. Getting one to work properly is an art!

Purpose

A slide projector has to produce an image of a slide on a screen. The image needs to be large so that people sitting some way off can see it clearly. It also needs to be fairly bright. Finally, it must be in sharp focus right the way across.

Projection

Illustration 1 shows the essential parts of a slide projector. The projection lens takes light from each part of the slide and throws it onto the screen to form the image.

Illustration 1 *A slide projector.*

For the image to be in focus, the slide has to be in the right place. Unfortunately, many slide projectors do not hold the slides very securely; there is a lot of room for the slide to move back and forth. So it is not unusual for the image to gradually drift out of focus while the speaker talks on and on and on ...

High quality projectors measure the position of the slide and continually adjust the position of the lens to keep the image sharply in focus on the screen.

Image quality

As you can see from Illustration 1, the projection lens is actually a number of different lenses placed together. A single lens will always give spherical and chromatic aberration. A combination of lenses with the right profile and made from the right materials can act like a single lens with very little aberration. These lens systems are often designed by computer with the help of ray tracing. The computer alters the shape of the lenses until it finds a combination which gives satisfactory images.

Image brightness

If you use a slide projector to throw an image on a nearby screen, that image will be small, bright and easily visible. Throw the image on a screen much further away and the image will be larger, but alas, it will also be dimmer. The power of the lamp in the projector usually sets the limit on how large you can make the image before it becomes too dull.

The light source

The correct design of light source is crucial. Illustration 2 shows the optical arrangement for illuminating the slide. Light from the hot filament of a high power lamp is focused through the slide onto the centre of the projection lens. A curved mirror behind the lamp reflects light which would not normally hit the condenser lens, doubling the light which passes through the slide.

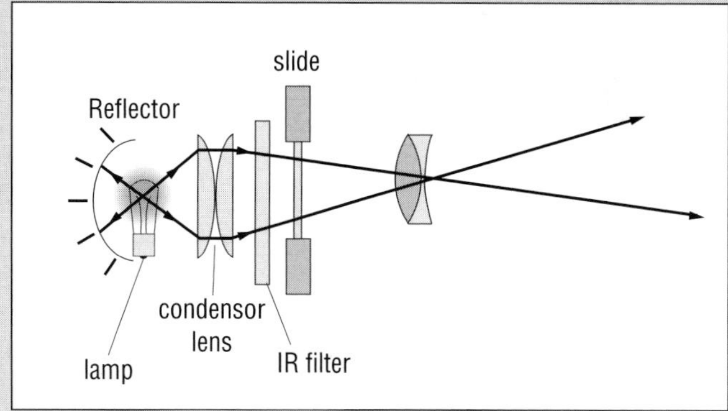

Illustration 2 *Optical details of a slide projector.*

Because most of the light passes through the centre of the projection lens, aberration is reduced to a minimum. The main function of the condenser lenses is to illuminate the slide evenly, so that each part of it receives the same amount of light. This is not easily done as all of the light does not come from a single point in the lamp. It comes from a distributed mass of white hot metal. Much trial-and-error is involved in the design of a good condenser lens!

Waste heat

A high power lamp generates a lot of waste heat. For every joule of light energy which passes through the slide, twenty joules of heat energy have to be disposed of. Slide projectors have to be fitted with fans to provide forced convection of this heat energy. Almost invariably these fans are noisy, so the projector has to be set up in a separate room from the audience, shining through a glass window onto the screen.

Infrared screens

As well as producing light, the lamp produces a lot of infrared (IR). When this is absorbed by the slide, it heats up. So if a slide is left too long in the projector there is a risk that it will overheat and melt. A good projector will have an IR filter between the lamp and the slide to avoid this problem. However, many is the time that a scientist has seen his favourite slide crumple and melt simply because he has chosen to talk about it for too long!

Questions

1 State the required performance for a slide projector.

2 Identify the factors which affect the performance of a slide projector.

3 Describe how you would set about measuring the following quantities for a slide projector image:

(a) the position of the image
(b) the size of the image
(c) how the sharpness and brightness of the image varies across the field of view.

4 State how the performance of a slide projector can be optimised.

Assignment

LIFTING HEAVY OBJECTS

Setting the scene

Hoists (Figure 4.3.5 on page 222) are used to help people to lift very heavy objects in laboratories, factories and garages. It is often much safer to use a hoist than to try and lift a heavy object directly!

The assignment

An example of a hoist is shown in Figure 4.3.9 on page 223. You pull upwards on the input cord to raise the weight suspended from the bottom pulleys.

1 State the performance required of a hoist.
2 Decide which factors will affect the performance of the device.
3 Construct the hoist shown in Figure 4.3.9. Measure its performance.
4 Make a series of measurements to find out what happens to the performance of the hoist when you change just one factor. For example, you could change the weight being lifted, or you could alter the number of pulley wheels instead.
5 Explain how you could arrange the hoist so that it has optimum performance.

SAFETY: *Make sure that the hoist is suspended firmly, and that the suspension point can carry the load you are using. If it collapses suddenly it could harm you. There should be a box of cushioning (such as waste paper) to catch the weight if the cord is released or snaps.*

Presenting your assignment

Write a laboratory report of your investigation. You will be asked to discuss this with your supervisor. Make sure that you:

- record your initial ideas and plans in an appendix to the report (the appendix should show how these were modified during the course of the investigation)
- evaluate what you did and state what changes or improvements you would make if the work was carried out again
- list all sources of information at the end of the report.

Additional information

The following procedures are available:

- measuring the performance of a linear machine, page 224
- measuring the performance of a rotary machine, page 225.

Grading

This assignment gives you the opportunity to meet merit or distinction criteria. The following themes are covered: Planning, Information Seeking and Information Handling, Evaluation, Quality of Outcomes.

Opportunity to collect evidence
In completing this assignment you will have the opportunity to meet the following requirements for GNVQ Intermediate Science:

Science units
Unit 1:
Element 1.3 PCs 1, 2, 3, 4
Unit 4:
Element 4.3 PCs 1, 2, 3, 4, 5

Core skill units

Application of number:
Element 2.2

Communication:
Elements 2.1, 2.2

Assignment

OVERHEAD PROJECTORS

Setting the scene

Overhead projectors (OHPs) are often used in education and business to project images onto screens.

The optical arrangement of a typical OHP is shown in Figure 4.3.27.

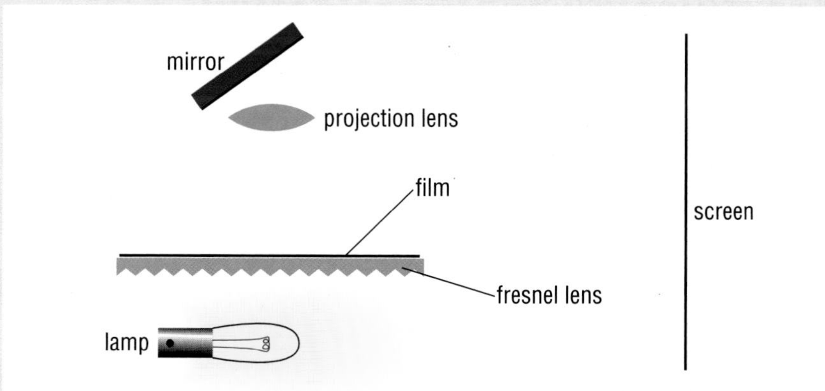

Figure 4.3.27 An OHP.

The image to be projected is drawn on transparent plastic film with felt-tip pens. Light from a high-power lamp is directed through the transparency by a Fresnel lens. A single projection lens takes that light and uses it to form an image on a screen via a mirror.

SAFETY: *Do not open the projector when it is switched on.*

The assignment

1 Use an OHP to form an image on a screen. Think about the performance of an ideal OHP.
2 Decide on the factors which affect the performance of the system.
3 Make measurements of the size, position and sharpness of the image formed by an OHP. You might also consider using a light meter to find out how the brightness of the image varies across the field of view.
4 Investigate how the performance of the OHP changes as you alter one of the factors.
5 Decide how the OHP needs to be set up for optimal performance.

Presenting your assignment

Write a report of your investigation. You will be asked to present your findings to the rest of your group. Your written report should include:

- a record of your initial ideas and plans in an appendix to the report (the appendix should show how these were modified during the course of the investigation
- a conclusion in which you look back at what you did, stating what changes or improvements you would make if the work was carried out again
- a list of all sources of information that you used.

Additional information

The following investigation and procedures are available:

- looking at images produced by a magnifying glass, page 228
- making a ray tracing, page 230
- comparing the quality of images, page 231

Grading

This assignment gives you the opportunity to meet merit or distinction criteria. The following themes are covered: Planning, Information Seeking and Information Handling, Evaluation, Quality of Outcomes.

Opportunity to collect evidence
In completing this assignment you will have the opportunity to meet the following requirements for GNVQ Intermediate Science:

Science units
Unit 1:
Element 1.3 PCs 1, 2, 3, 4
Unit 4:
Element 4.3 PCs 1, 2, 3, 4, 5

Core skill units

Application of number:
Elements 2.2

Communication:
Elements 2.1, 2.2

Assignment

HOW DIRTY IS THE WATER?

Setting the scene

River water is often murky because it contains small particles of earth. Pure water is transparent, it lets light pass through it. Any small particles in the water absorb the light, preventing some of it from getting through.

The amount of light getting through a sample of water can therefore be used to measure the amount of soil material suspended in it. This is a quick and convenient method of making this type of measurement. It is certainly much quicker than filtering the water, drying the filter paper and weighing it!

The assignment

You are going to set up and calibrate the apparatus shown in Figure 4.3.28. The lens forms an image of the lamp filament on the surface of the LDR (light-dependent resistor). On its way to the LDR, the light passes through a flat-bottomed cylinder which contains the water being tested.

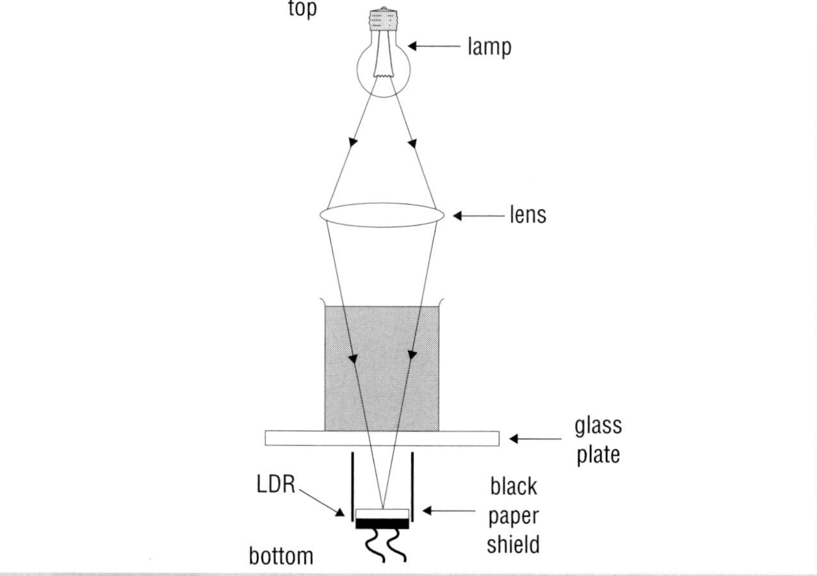

Figure 4.3.28 *The arrangement of the apparatus for the murkmeter. The lamp, lens, glass plate and LDR need clamping onto the same stand. the black paper shield fits snugly around the LDR so that it is only illuminated by light from the lamp.*

1 Set up the apparatus as shown in Figure 4.3.28.
  Fill the cylinder with distilled water.
2 Decide on the factors which affect the optical performance of the system.
3 Make measurements of the size, position and sharpness of the image on the surface of the LDR.
4 Investigate how the performance of the system changes as you alter one of the factors.
5 Decide how the system needs to be set up for optimal performance.
6 Make the LDR part of the electrical circuit shown in Figure 4.3.29.

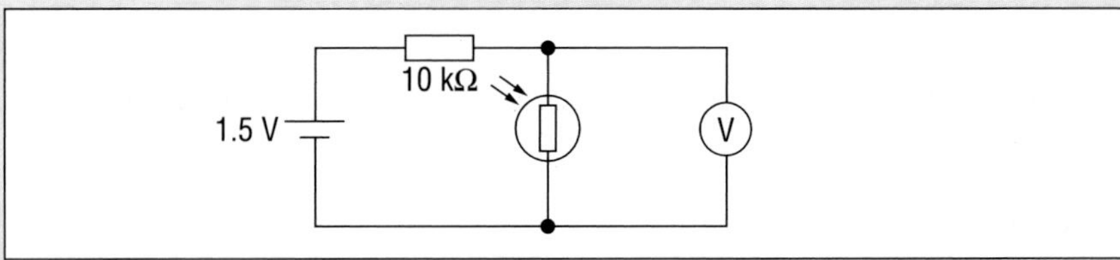

Figure 4.3.29 *Circuit diagram for the murkmeter.*

SAFETY: *Cover up cuts with waterproof plasters before you begin.*

7 Note the reading on the voltmeter when the cylinder is filled with distilled water.

8 Create a standard suspension of earth in water as follows:
  (a) suspend as much earth as you can in 1 dm^3 of water. Store it in a plastic bottle so that you can shake it up thoroughly before pouring it out.
  (b) weigh a dry filter paper
  (c) pour 500 cm^3 of the dirty water through the filter paper
  (d) dry the filter paper in an oven
  (e) re-weigh the filter paper. You should now be able to state the mass of earth suspended in 1 dm^3 of the dirty water. This is full strength murk.

9 Calibrate the system as follows:
  (a) measure the voltmeter reading when the cylinder is filled with full strength murk.
  (b) make some half strength murk by mixing equal volumes of full strength murk and distilled water
  (c) fill the cylinder with half strength murk
  (d) make some quarter strength murk by mixing equal quantities of half strength murk and distilled water
  (e) fill the cylinder with quarter strength murk ...
  (f) continue until your diluted murk gives the same reading as distilled water.

10 Use your data to draw a graph which shows how the voltmeter reading depends on the murkiness of the water in mg dm^{-3}.

11 Evaluate the performance of the whole system as a useful means of measuring the murkiness of a water sample.

Presenting your results

Write a report of your investigation. You will be asked to discuss this with your supervisor. Your written report should include:

- a record of your initial ideas and plans in an appendix to the report (the appendix should show how these were modified during the course of the investigation)
- a conclusion in which you look back at what you did, stating what changes or improvements you would make if the work was carried out again
- a list of all sources of information that you used.

Grading

This assignment gives you the opportunity to meet merit or distinction criteria. The following themes are covered: Planning, Information Seeking and Information Handling, Evaluation, Quality of Outcomes.

Opportunity to collect evidence

In completing this assignment you will have the opportunity to meet the following requirements for GNVQ Intermediate Science:

Science units

Unit 1:
Element 1.3 PCs 1, 2, 3, 4
Unit 3:
Element 3.3 PCs 1, 2, 3, 4
Unit 4:
Element 4.3 PCs 1, 2, 3, 4, 5

Core skill units

Application of Number:
Elements 2.2, 2.3

Communication:
Elements 2.1, 2.2, 2.3, 2.4

Questions

1 State five characteristics that can be used to measure the performance of a mechanical device.

2 Here are some simple machines: crowbar, scissors, wheelbarrow.
(a) State their purpose. Use a diagram to show where the forces act.
(b) Identify the factors which affect their performance.
(c) Describe how to optimise the performance of each device.

3 Draw a gear train which has the output and input shafts in line and going in the same direction. Select diameters for the gear wheels which will give an overall VR of 100.

4 Belts and pulleys can do the same job as trains of gears. Why are gears always used in cars to connect the engine to the wheels?

5 Why do motorbikes use a sprocket and chain system between the gearbox and the back wheel? How do you optimise their performance?

6 State three characteristics that can be used to measure the performance of an optical device.

7 Here are some optical devices: slide projector, magnifying glass, microscope, video camera, telescope. State the required performance of each device.

8 State which features of an image can be used to assess its quality.

9 State the factors which affect the performance of an optical device which uses a lens.

10 Explain how ray tracing can be used to find the size and position of an image formed by a lens.

Bibliography/ useful addresses

1 Further reading

Author	Title	Publisher	Year of publication
Adams, C., Bamford, K. and Early, M.	*Principles of Horticulture, 2nd ed*	Butterworth Heinemann	
Association for Science Education	*SATIS (Science and Technology in Society* Project) 14–16 Units, Books 1–12 and Index	ASE	1986–91
	SATIS Update		1991
	SATIS 14–19 Atlas		1992
	SATIS 16–19 Units, Files 1–4		1990–92
	SATIS 16–19 Readers		
	Science Nomenclature, Symbols and Systematics		1995
Association of the British Pharmaceutical Industry	*Medicines, Health and You poster series*	ABPI	1991 and 1993
Austwick, K. and Harper, E. (eds)	*Working Science*	CUP	1991
Baggley, S. Cammiss, C., Gow J and Noone P.	*Understanding and Applying Science, Books 4 and 5*	John Murray	
Beashel, P. and Taylor, J.	*Sport Examined, 2nd edn*	Nelson	1992
	Biological Science Review	Philip Allen	
Boatfield, G.	*Farm Crops, 2nd edn*	Farming Press	1983
Brimicombe, M.	*Introducing Electronic Systems*	Nelson	1987
Budavari, S. et al.	*The Merck Index: An Encyclopaedia of Chemicals, Drugs and Biologicals, 11th edition*	Merck and Co Inc	1989
Chemical Industry Education Centre	*Exciting Science and Engineering* series	CIEC	1995
Coleman, V.	*How to Conquer Backache*	Hamlyn	1993
Collins, H. and Pinch, T.	*The Golem: What Everyone Should Know About Science*	Cambridge University Press	1993
Dobson, K.	*The Physical World*	Nelson	1995
Dunn, S.	*Electronic Projects Made Easy*	Collins Educational	
Egger, G., Champion N. and Hurst, G.	*The Fitness Instructor's Exercise Manual*	David and Charles	1988
England, N.	*Physics Matters*	Hodder & Stoughton,	1989
Fox, E.	*Sports Physiology, 2nd ed.*	William C. Brown Publishers	1988
Hibberd, B. (ed.)	*Forestry Practice 11th ed.*	HMSO	1991
Hubbard, L.	*The Essential Chemical Industry*	Chemical Industry Education Centre	1994
Holman, J.	*The Material World*	Nelson	1995
Jackson, R.	*Chemistry in Use*	Pitman	1984
Lachmann, S. and Jenner, J.	*Soft Tissue Injuries in Sport, 2nd ed.*	Blackwell Scientific Publications	1994
Lewington, A.	*Plants for People*	National History Museum	1990
Minett, P., Wayne, D. and Rubenstein D.	*Human Form and Function*	Collins Educational	1989
McLoughlin, M.	*Electronics for You*	Hutchinson	1989
National Dairy Council	*Dairy Microbiology*	National Dairy Council	1981

Pyke, M.	*Butter Side Up! or the Delights of Science*	Pan Books	1978
Roberts, M.	*Biology for Life, 2nd ed,*	Nelson	1986
Royal Society of Chemistry	*Chemistry and the Environment*	Royal Society of Chemistry	1994
Royal Society of Chemistry	*Interfacing Chemistry Experiments*	Royal Society of Chemistry	1993
Royal Society of Chemistry	*The Periodic Table Competition*	Royal Society of Chemistry	1994
Technology Ed Research Unit	*Science Activities For ClarisWorks*	Collins Educational	
Tomkins, S., Reiss M. and Morris, C.	*Biology at Work*	Cambridge University Press	1992
Williams, G.	*Techniques and Fieldwork in Ecology*	Collins	1987

2 Health and Safety Executive publications:

Control of Substances Hazardous to Health and Control of Carcinogenic Substances; Control of Substances Hazardous to Health Regulations, 1988: Approved Code of Practice 4th edn, 1993

GS23 Electrical Safety in Schools, 1990

HS(R)25 Memo of Guidance on the Electricity at Work Regulations 1989 (1990)

IND(G) 160 Maintaining Portable Electrical Equipment in Offices and Other Low Risk Environments, 1994

L21 Management of Health and Safety at Work Regulations 1992: Approved Code of Practice, 1992

L25 Personal Protective Equipment at Work Regulations 1992: Guidance on Regulations, 1992

PM32 The Safe Use of Portable Electrical Equipment

3 Safety

CLEAPPS Laboratory Handbook, CLEAPPS School Science Service, 1989 and later supplements

COSSH: Guidance for Schools, HMSO, 1989

Hazardous Chemicals – A Manual for Schools and Colleges, SSSERC/Oliver and Boyd, 1979

Hazcards, CLEAPPS School Science Service, 1989. New edition in preparation 1995

Microbiology, an HMI Guide for Schools and Further Education, HMSO, 1985

Association for Science Education,Safeguards in the School Laboratory, 9th edn, ASE, 1988. New edition in preparation 1994

Association for Science Education, *Topics in Safety*, 2nd edition, ASE, 1988

Nichols D, (ed.) *Safety in Biological Fieldwork: guidance notes for codes of practice*, Institute of Biology, 1990

Safety in Outdoor Education, HMSO, 1989

Tawney, D. *'Assessment of Risks and School Science'*, *School Science Review*, 1992, 74(267), 7–14

4 CD-ROMS and Videos

Chemistry in Action	Granada TV	1987
The Chemistry Set	New Media	1994
The Periodic Table	ATTICA Cybernetics	1993

5 Useful organisations and their addresses

Action on Smoking and Health (ASH)
109 Gloucester Place
LONDON W1H 3PH

Age Concern
Astral House
1268 London Road
LONDON SW16 4ER

Alcohol Concern
305 Gray's Inn Road
LONDON WC1X 8QS

Arthritis and Rheumatism Council
Copeman House
St Mary's Court
St Mary's Gate
CHESTERFIELD S41 7TD

Association for Science Education (ASE)
College Lane
HATFIELD AL10 9AA

Association of the British Pharmaceutical Industry
12 Whitehall
LONDON SW1A 2DY

Asthma Research Council
St Thomas's Hospital
Lambeth Palace Road
LONDON SE1

AVP
School Hill Centre
Chepstow
GWENT
NP6 5ZZ (videos and computer software)

BP Educational Service
PO Box 934
POOLE BH17 7BR

British Agrochemicals Association
4 Lincoln Court
Lincoln Road
PETERBOROUGH PE1 2RP

British Ecological Society
26 Blades Court
Deodar Road
Putney
LONDON SW15 2NU

British Gas Education
PO Box 70
Wetherby
WEST YORKSHIRE LS23 7EA

British Gas, Education Liaison Officer
Room 707A
326 High Holborn
LONDON WC1V 7PT (for information)

British Heart Foundation
14 Fitzhardinge Street
LONDON W1H 4DH

British Steel Education Service
PO Box 10
WETHERBY LS23 7EL

BT Education Service
British Telecommunications plc
81 Newgate St
LONDON EC1A 7AJ

Chemical Industry Education Centre,
Dept of Chemistry
University of York
Heslington
YORK Y01 5DD

Community Relations Executive
PO Box 129
160 Euston Road
LONDON NW1 2BP

Coronary Prevention Group
Plantation House
31–35 Fenchurch Street
LONDON EC3M 3NN

Council for Complementary and Alternative Medicine
Suite 1, 19A Cavendish Square
LONDON W1M 9AD

Countryside Restoration Trust
Bird's Farm Cottage
BARTON, CB3 7AG

Education Officer
The Science Museum
LONDON SW7 2DD

English Nature
Northminster House
PETERBOROUGH PE1 1UA

Health and Safety Executive
PO Box 1999
Sudbury
SUFFOLK CO10 6FS

Health Education Authority
Hamilton House
Mabledon Place
LONDON WC1H 9JP

HMSO Publications Centre
PO Box 276
LONDON SW8 5DT

Homerton College
Hills Road
CAMBRIDGE CB2 2PH

Institute of Biology
20–22 Queensbury Place
LONDON SW7 2DZ

Institution of Electrical Engineers (Schools, Education and Liaison), Michael Faraday House
Six Hills Way
STEVENAGE SG1 2AY

Institute of Food Science and Technology
5 Cambridge Court
210 Shepherd's Bush Rd
LONDON W6 7NL

Institute of Physics/IOP Publishing
Techno House
Redcliffe Way
BRISTOL BS1 6NX

Institute for the Study of Drug Dependence
Waterbridge House
32–36 Loman Street
LONDON SE1 OEE

Medical Research Council
20 Park Crescent
LONDON W1N 4AL

National Centre of Biotechnology Education
Department of Microbiology
University of Reading
Whiteknights
READING RG6 2AJ

National Dairy Council
5–7 John Princes St
LONDON W1M 0AP

Plantlife
The National History Museum
Cromwell Road
LONDON SW7 5BD

Royal Society for Nature Conservation
The Wildlife Trust
The Green
Witham Park
Waterside South
LINCOLN LN5 7JR

Royal Society for the Promotion of Health
RSH House
38A St George's Drive
LONDON SW1V 4BH

Royal Society of Chemistry
Turpins Transactions Ltd
Blackhorse Rd
Letchworth
HERTS SG6 1HN

RTZ Educational Resources for Schools
6 St James's Square
LONDON SW1Y 4LD

Science and Plants for Schools (SAPS)
Shell Education Service
Shell UK Ltd
Shell-Mex House
Strand
LONDON WC2R ODX

The Chartered Society of Physiotherapy
422 Fulton House
Jessop Avenue
Cheltenham
GLOUCESTERSHIRE GL50 3SH

The Institute of Biology
20–22 Queensbury Place
LONDON SW7 2DZ

The Institute of Food Science and Technology
5 Cambridge Court
210 Shepherd's Bush Road
LONDON W6 7NL

The National Coaching Foundation
4 College Close
Beckett Park
LEEDS LS6 3QH

The Royal Society for the Protection of Birds (RSPB)
The Lodge
SANDY SG19 2DL

The Standing Conference on Schools' Science and Technology
76 Portland Place
LONDON W1N 4AA

The Wellcome Foundation Ltd
Community Relations Executive
PO Box 129
160 Euston Road
LONDON NW1 2BP

Understanding Electricity Education Service
30 Millbank
LONDON SW1P 4RD

Unilever Educational Liaison
PO Box 68
Unilever House
LONDON EX4P 4BQ

Wessex Publications
Elwell House
Stocklinch
Ilminster
SOMERSET TA19 9JF

The Woodland Trust
Autumn Park
GRANTHAM NG31 6LL

World Wide Fund for Nature (WWF) UK
Panda House
Weyside Park
GODALMING GU7 1XR

Answers to end of element questions

Unit 1

1 (i) ab I; (ii) e S; (iii) b S; (iv) b d I; (v) a S; (vi) bd I

2 (a) see page 5, figure 0.5
(b) The standards marks are used to indicate that certain minimum standards of reliability and safety have been met. CE marks indicate metric measurements have been used and that a product complies with essential requirements of the European Union's New Approach Directives (NAD). The CE mark is intended to be easily recognisable throughout the EU and to give users confidence in a product.

3 Any suitable examples may be given, such as the following: diagnosis, e.g. detection of glucose in the urine may indicate diabetes; treatment, e.g. surgery to remove a tumour; therapy, e.g. a physiotherapy course of exercises to improve the strength of a limb that has become weakened because it has been immobilised for a long time; monitoring, e.g. taking blood samples and testing them to check that an antibiotic is working to cure a bacterial disease.

4 Costs will be involved in employing the research scientists, buying the new machinery and paying for and training the new operatives. These costs will set the level of investment that will be necessary. Continuing costs will involve wages and buying raw materials. The price of the product will need to be set at a high enough level to cover these costs, pay for the investment and make a profit for future investment for expansion or development. It will need to be set at a low enough level to compete with rival products in the marketplace.

5 There are many possible examples that you could use to illustrate how these apply. Some examples are given below:
(a) testing appliances regularly/operation of equipment: e.g. checking that the wiring to a plug for a portable electrical appliance (such as an electrical kettle) is safe
(b) controlling substances hazardous to health/handling of materials: using a fume cupboard when preparing a toxic chemical gas such as hydrogen sulphide
(c) preventing exposure to hazardous substances: (i) disposal of wastes, e.g. using an autoclave (pressure cooker) to sterilise dishes in which microbes have been grown; (ii) quality control, e.g. testing eggs for Salmonella

(d) defining danger areas/supervision of others: e.g. laboratory manager imposes rules forbidding eating in laboratories
(e) defining procedures for emergencies/communication of information: e.g. fire regulations for the evacuation and assembly of laboratory workers are posted in a prominent position in a laboratory and regular fire drills are held
(f) using personal protective equipment/use of safety equipment: e.g. use of eye protection (such as goggles) when heating liquid in test tube using a Bunsen burner.

6 Examples include:
(a) using a fume cupboard when toxic gases are produced (or using smaller quantities and/or different chemicals.
(b) checking the cases of mains electrical equipment and the insulation of electric cables for flaws
(c) using personal protective clothing such as goggles for eye protection in case apparatus shatters or boiling liquids spurt
(d) taping lids on dishes in which bacteria are grown. Sterilising these in an autoclave (pressure cooker) before disposing of them.

7 (a) Foods eaten by a woman in one week

	Number of good sources	°
3 nutrients	3	120
2 nutrients	3	120
1 nutrient	1	40

(b) 9 foods therefore $\frac{360}{9}$ = 40 degrees for each.

3 nutrients: $3 \times 40 = 120$ degrees, 2 nutrients: $3 \times 40 = 120$ degrees, 1 nutrient = 1×40 degrees, no nutrients = 2×40 degrees = 80 degrees. ($120 + 120 + 40 + 80 = 360$)

8 Mean = $\frac{17.50}{10} = 1.75$ m

Median is central value of those placed in order:
1.50 1.67 1.67 1.67 1.74 1.78 1.79 1.83 1.89 1.96
Even number of values, therefore mean of central two values:

$$\frac{1.74 + 1.78}{2} = \frac{3.52}{2} = 1.76 \text{ m}$$

Mode = most common value = 1.67 m

9 (a) $R = \frac{V}{I}$ therefore (i) $V = IR$ and (ii) $I = \frac{V}{R}$

Substituting: (iii) $V = 1.70 \times 1.88 = 3.196$ volts, which is 3.20 volts to 3 significant figures (iv) $I = \frac{9.4}{2.5} = 3.76$ amps, 3.8 amps to 2 significant figures

(b) (i) Acceleration is the amount by which the velocity changes every unit time. An acceleration of 1 km per second per second means increasing speed by 1 km per second every second. If it started at rest, after 10 s it would be travelling at 10 km s^{-1} or $10 \times 60 \times 60 = 3600$ km h^{-1}

(ii) 1800 km h^{-1}, $\frac{1800}{60} = 30$ km min^{-1} $= \frac{30}{60} = 0.5$ km s^{-1}.

If $v = u + at$, when $u = 0$, $v = at$, therefore acceleration , $a = \frac{v}{t}$

$= \frac{0.5}{10} = 0.05$ km s^{-2}

10 (a) (i) Most of the results lie close to a straight line passing through the origin indicating reliable measurements, but the point for current measured at 6.0 volts is further away from the line and appears to be incorrect: it should be re-measured.

(ii) m stands for the gradient, rearranging the formula, $m = \frac{y}{x}$.

(iii) Graph is of form $y = mx$, as $V = RI$. (iv) The resistance, $R = \frac{V}{I}$, can therefore be found from the gradient of the graph.

Drawing the best straight line helps to eliminate slight inconsistencies in the results due to experimental errors.

$\frac{8.3}{10} = 0.83$ ohms.

(b) (i) $v = u + at$ can be rearranged in the form $y = mx + c$ as $v = at + u$.

(ii) Smooth acceleration from 10 to 40 seconds as the graph is a straight line, but then the rate of acceleration appears to slow down as the 50 second point is below the line.

(iii) The intercept on the y axis will be the initial velocity, $u = 13$ km h^{-1}.

(iv) The gradient of the graph will be the acceleration, $a = 3.2$ km per hour per second.

11 a xi, b vii, c viii or xii, d ii, e xvii, f xv, g xvi, h vi, i iv, j viii or xii, k xiii, l iii, m i, n xviii, o v, p x, q xiv or xv, r ix

12 (a) (i) Valid. Organic molecules are made from carbon dioxide by using the energy of light in the earth process of photosynthesis.

(ii) Invalid, the organic molecules could have been in the soil already or another process not found on earth could have been used to make them.

(b) Control experiments were also carried out. Another soil sample that had been heated was also tested to show that sterile soil did not give the same results. Another sample was not exposed to $^{14}CO_2$ to show that the radioactivity was not already present in the soil.

(c) (i) Valid. Organic food molecules are oxidised in respiration to produce carbon dioxide which is excreted.

(ii) Valid. Heating to 160 °C for 3 hours will kill most earth organisms.

(iii) Valid. If the results were the same as those obtained for the raw soil samples, it would not be necessary to assume an explanation that depended on living organisms.

(iv) Invalid. The graph rises then falls, but the rate at which radiation is being released could be falling rather than stopping completely to give the same results. The results do not tell us how quickly the radiation is being lost.

(v) Valid. The amount of radiation continues to rise for the whole of the time.

(vi) Valid. The amount of radioactivity is higher for longer in the raw samples of the three soils tested.

(vii) Invalid. The tests suggest that this is a possible, but by no means the only explanation! We do not know what other differences there are on Mars when compared to Earth. The same tests carried out on Earth soil would be strong indicators of the presence of life, because we have yet to find other possible explanations after many years of carrying out such tests.

(d) Possible sources of error include faults in the equipment due to damage in the violent stages of take-off and landing, e.g. radiation counts too high. Possible contamination of the Martian soil by earth organisms carried on the spacecraft. Unrepresentative samples of Martian soil may have been collected.

13 (a) iv (b) iii (c) i (d) ii (e) v or i

14 Measuring cylinder e.g. to find an approximate volume to make up a reaction mixture where the precise volume is not important
Volumetric flask e.g. to make up 1 dm^3 of a 2.00 mol dm^{-3} solution of a solid
Burette e.g. to find the strength of an unknown acid solution by titrating it with an alkali of known strength
Pipette e.g. to make up an accurate dilution series of an enzyme solution to test the effect of varying concentration on its rate of reaction

15 (a) Examples include using cyclohexane as a solvent instead of tetrachloromethane (toxic), heating an inflammable solvent using a water bath instead of a naked flame, reducing the amounts of chemicals that are used in a reaction.

(b) The clinical thermometer is shorter, as it needs a much narrower range. This makes it less easy to break. It also allows the diameter of the capillary tube to be much narrower and the mercury to expand over a greater distance, so that it can be much more sensitive to small changes in temperature. The mercury cools quickly when the thermometer is removed from the body, so the kink in the tube is necessary to stop it from contracting back into the bulb. The maximum reading is retained until it can be read, but the thermometer must be shaken before re-use.

Element 2.1

1 Obtaining energy (respiration), obtaining nutrients, growth, reproduction, responding to the environment, excretion and movement.

2 (a) Green plants obtain their energy from sunlight. They use this energy to make carbohydrates, such as glucose and starch, from carbon dioxide and water. (b) Animals obtain their energy from feeding on other organisms. (c) Some micro-organisms obtain their energy from sunlight and use it in photosynthesis; others obtain their energy by breaking down organic molecules made by other organisms.

3 (a) Green plants obtain their nutrients in the form of carbon dioxide from the atmosphere and ions such as nitrate and phosphate from the soil.
(b) Herbivores obtain their nutrients from the plants they feed on.
(c) Carnivores obtain their nutrients from the animals they feed on.

4 Growth is the increase in size of an organism as it gets older.

5 Sexual reproduction involves the production of gametes, often by two separate individuals. The gametes fuse, resulting in fertilisation. Asexual reproduction does not involve the production of gametes. It can be done by one individual on its own.

6 Growth, reproduction, movement, death.

7 (a) Most plants grow faster the higher the light intensity up to the point where light no longer limits photosynthesis. (b) The need of plants for water differs from species to species. In general, however, if the moisture level is too low (too dry), they grow more slowly. If the soil is too wet it may become waterlogged and plants then grow more slowly then die (owing to shortage of oxygen to the roots).

8 To avoid predation; in response to temperature; to go to areas where there is a greater availability of food.

9 (a) Micro-organisms have an optimum temperature which differs from species to species. At temperatures below this they grow more slowly. At temperatures above it they are usually killed.
(b) Many species of micro-organisms have very precise nutrient requirements. In the absence of specific nutrients, they will fail to grow.

Element 2.2

1 (a) Tough, elastic, good conductor of electricity and heat, high density.
(b) Strong, hard, can be transparent, good electrical and heat insulator.
(c) Good electrical insulator, tough, low density.
(d) Strong, tough, hard, stiff.

2 (a) Transparency, strength, thermal insulation.
(b) Strength, hardness, stiffness.
(c) Toughness, lightness, flexibility.
(d) Strength, toughness, hardness.

(e) Thermal insulation, cheapness, strength.
(f) Electrical insulation, hardness, strength.
(g) Impermeability to water, flexibility, strength.

3 (a) Ceramics, polymers.
(b) Metals, ceramics, composites.
(c) Metals, ceramics.
(d) Metals.
(e) Metals.

4 (a) Metal.
(b) Ceramic.
(c) Polymer.
(d) Composite.

5 A crystalline structure has its atoms or molecules arranged in an orderly pattern. An amorphous structure has a random arrangement of its atoms or molecules.

6 Metals, ceramics and composites have strong bonding between their atoms. The molecules in polymers are weakly bound to each other.

7 (a) atoms
(b) nucleus, electrons
(c) molecules
(d) boiling
(e) electrons
(f) covalent
(g) ionic
(h) electron
(i) giant
(j) polymer
(k) composite

Element 2.3

1 (a) a single sample.
(b) several representative samples.

2 See page 104.

3 See page 105.

4 See page 105.

5 (a) $HCl(aq) + NaOH(aq) \rightarrow NaCl(aq) + H_2O(l)$
(b) $HNO_3(aq) + NaOH(aq) \rightarrow NaNO_3(aq) + H_2O(l)$
(c) $2HCl(aq) + Ca(OH)_2(aq) \rightarrow CaCl_2(aq) + 2H_2O(l)$
(d) $H_2SO_4(aq) + 2NaOH(aq) \rightarrow Na_2SO_4(aq) + 2H_2O(l)$
(e) $H_2SO_4(aq) + 2NH_3(aq) \rightarrow (NH_4)_2SO_4(aq)$

6 (a) 0.125 mol dm^{-3}
(b) 0.1768 mol dm^{-3}
(c) 0.114 mol dm^{-3}

7 (a) 0.75 mol dm^{-3}
(b) 0.134 mol dm^{-3}
(c) 0.248 mol dm^{-3}

Element 3.1

1 Natural plant products are obtained directly from plants and require little or no processing. Derived plant products require some degree of processing before they can be used. See Table 3.1.1 (page 121) and Table 3.1.2 (page 122) for examples.

2 (a) A sand is a soil with large inorganic particles.
(b) A loam is a soil made of particles with a range of sizes.
(c) A clay is a soil with very small inorganic particles.
(d) A compost is a growing medium for a plant which, as it breaks down in the soil, releases nutrients which become available to the plant.

3 (a) Some plants require a pH close to 7 (neutral); others require the pH to be less than 7 (acidic); others require it to be more than 7 (alkaline).
(b) Plants need water, but most plants can be killed by waterlogging.
(c) Plants need a lot of mineral nutrients to grow – in particular, a shortage of nitrate, phosphate or potassium ions will lead to less growth.

4 Plants generally grow better the greater the average temperature. However, extremes of temperature (i.e. too great a temperature range) can kill them.

5 Plants generally grow better the more hours of sunlight there are and the more rainfall there is. However, waterlogging is bad for most plants.

6 Two of the following together with a brief explanation: soil sterilisation; pesticides (herbicides, insecticides and fungicides); biological control; breeding (traditional plant breeding and genetic engineering).

7 If the unsterilised soil contains pests or diseases.

8 Advantages: kill pests, quick to apply. Disadvantages: rarely selective, often expensive, usually can't be applied shortly before harvest.

9 (a) Harvesting, grading, conversion to product, packaging.
(b) A natural plant product doesn't require the graded material to be converted to a product.

10 If your output value is less than your input costs you lose money.

11 Profit equals the output value minus the input costs; economic efficiency is given by the equation:

$$\text{economic efficiency} = \frac{(\text{output value} - \text{input costs})}{\text{input costs}} \times 100\%$$

12 (a) Profit = £15 000
(b) economic efficiency = 7.7%

Element 3.2

1 (a) esterification
(b) acid-base
(c) redox
(d) esterification

(e) redox
(f) precipitation
(g) precipitation
(h) esterification
(i) redox
(j) acid-base
(k) redox

2 Because it involves the loss of oxygen (reduction) from the metal oxide.

3 acid + base → salt + water

4 See pages 152–3

5 (a) 5.44 g
(b) 8.8 g
(c) 61.8%
(d) £35.27

Element 3.3

1 (a) timer, amplifier, logic gate
(b) LDR, thermistor, switch
(c) motor, meter, heater, LED, buzzer, lamp
(d) switch, relay
(e) logic gate
(f) LED, lamp
(g) thermistor
(h) buzzer
(i) LDR

2 (i) To move people and objects (milk float).
(ii) To allow communication over long distances (telephone).
(iii) To monitor situations and warn of danger (smoke alarm).
(iv) To make measurements.
(v) To control processes automatically.

3 Power supply, input devices, processor, output devices. See Figure 3.3.3, page 163.

4 Thermistor as an input device. Heater and LEDs (as indicators) as the output devices.

Element 4.1

1 To see how well someone is: recovering from injury; learning a new skill; strengthening their muscles; improving their posture.

2 Reduce chance of backache/prevent loss of voice.

3 Load carried; fitness of the body; mental condition.

4 Stamina = endurance/ability to keep going without gasping for breath; strength = muscle power.

5 Speed; strength; stamina; reaction time; recovery rate.

6 Familiarity with task; fatigue; increased skill.

Element 4.2

1 To control a production process; to control energy transfer; to ensure safety.

2 (a) Effect of concentration of reactants on rate:
- increase in concentration causes an increase in rate
- decrease in concentration causes a decrease in rate.

(b) Effect of temperature on rate:
- increase in temperature causes an increase in rate
- decrease in temperature causes an decrease in rate.

3 (a) Effect of concentration of reactants on rate:
- increase in concentration causes an increase in rate
- decrease in concentration causes a decrease in rate.

(b) Effect of surface area of a solid reactant on rate:
- increase in surface area causes an increase in rate
- decrease in surface area causes a decrease in rate.

(c) Effect of temperature on rate:
- increase in temperature causes an increase in rate
- decrease in temperature causes an decrease in rate.

4 Catalysts are vital to many industrial processes, making them economically viable. Catalysts are particularly useful in industry when without them acceptable rates can only be achieved by very high temperatures or pressures. Both of these make big energy demands and so are expensive. Suitable catalysts allow lower temperatures and pressures to be used.

5 For a reaction to occur, particles (atoms, ions or molecules) of reactant must collide with one another. The more often particles collide, the faster the reaction.
Note: Not all collisions lead to reaction. Those which do are called *effective* collisions. Particles must have sufficient energy to undergo an effective collision. This means they must have sufficient energy (more than the activation energy) for the chemical bonds to break.

Element 4.3 answers

1 The performance of a mechanical device can be assessed by considering the following: the size and direction of the output force; the speed of the output relative to the input (the velocity ratio); the sensitivity of the device (its mechanical advantage); it power; its efficiency.

2 Crowbar

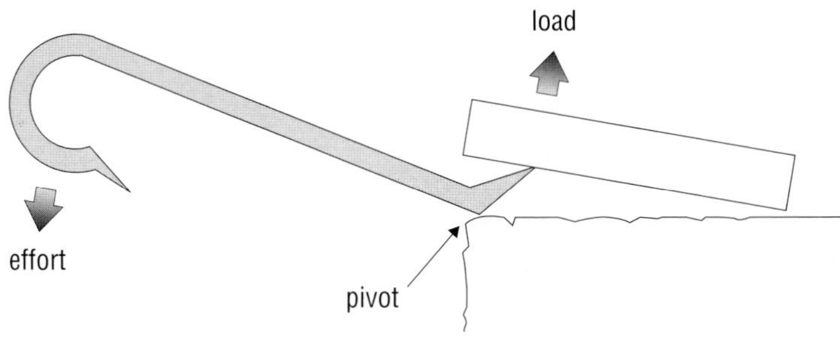

(a) Removing lids, breaking open cases. See illustration A1.
(b) Strength, length of handle, position of pivot.
(c) Make it long, strong and light, with the pivot very close to the sharp end.

Scissors

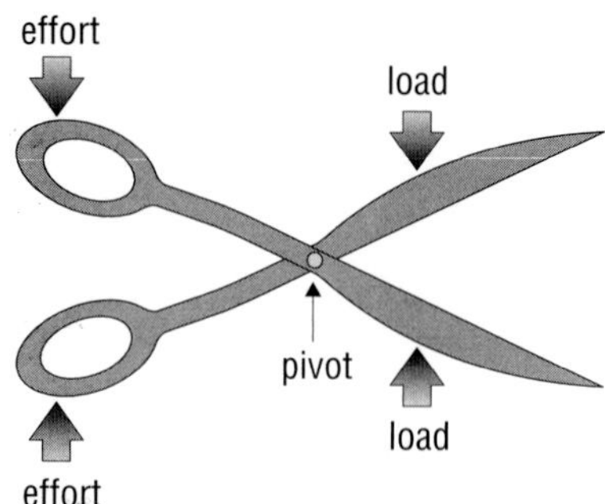

(a) Cutting paper and cloth. See illustration A2.
(b) Friction at the pivot, length of handle, sharpness of blades and position of material being cut.
(c) Have long handles, lubricate the pivot, sharpen the blades and have the material close to the pivot.

Wheelbarrow

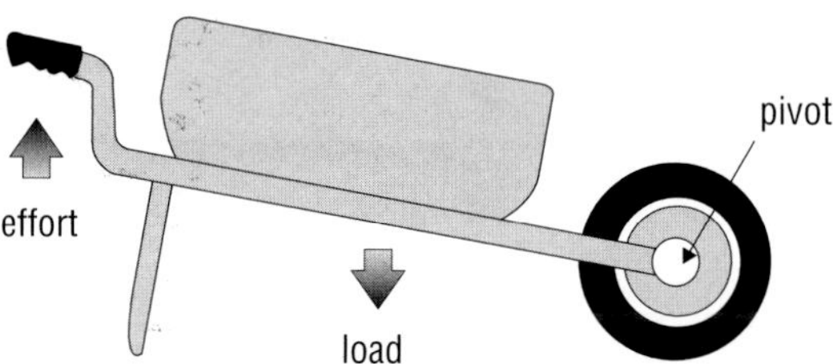

(a) Transport heavy loads from one place to another over rough ground. See illustration A3.
(b) Length of handles, placing of load, friction at the wheel axle, weight and strength of barrow itself.
(c) Make the barrow long, light and strong. Place the load directly over the axle. Lubricate the wheel and axle.

3 See illustration A4.

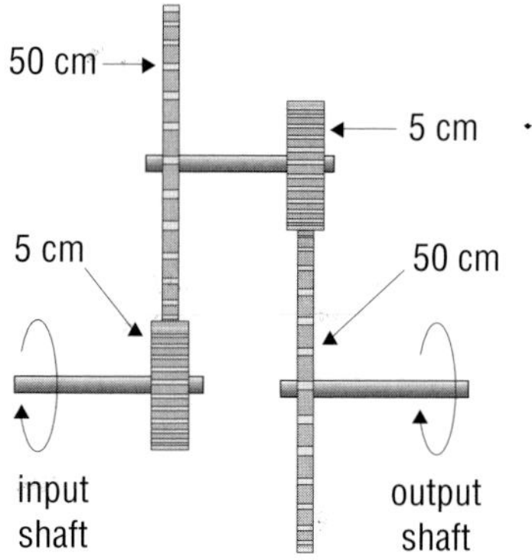

4 Gears can transmit much larger forces than belts without danger of breaking or slipping.

5 The back wheel must be able to move up and down relative to the rest of the motorbike. So, a flexible transmission system must be used, such as a belt or chain. A chain will not slip on a sprocket wheel, so will be able to transmit much larger forces than a belt. Performance can be optimised by lubricating the chain.

6 Slide projector: projects an image of a film transparency onto a large screen.
Magnifying glass: produces a magnified image when placed between the eye and an object.
Microscope: creates magnified images of very small objects.
Video camera: records a sequence of images on magnetic tape.
Telescope: forms magnified images of distant objects.

7 The position, size and sharpness of an image can be used to assess its quality.

8 The power of the lens, how far away the object is and the aperture of the lens.

9 See Figure 4.3.24 (page 232).

Index